Motivations, Tools and Theories of Pre-Modern Science

by

MARK GRAUBARD

Natural Science Program
University of Minnesota
Minneapolis

Burgess Publishing Company
426 South Sixth Street • Minneapolis, Minn. 55415

Printed in the United States of America
Library of Congress Catalog Card Number 67-13091

Why This Book? For Whom Is It Intended?

Modern science has grown rich, diversified and dramatic in substance and scope. Its impact on human affairs has been strong and pervasive and its rate of progress has been proceeding of late on a scale that baffles even most of the workers in its fields. Little wonder that any textbook in science which the contemporary college student is using, deals almost exclusively with the most recent findings in its specialty, and includes only that work of the past which led directly to the latest achievements. The result is that science is presented in our best educational institutions as the end result of a process, with little attention to the actual struggle and search for scientific knowledge which man has pursued since his earliest history.

This, in a way, is unscientific since science is a continuous process with its "truth" as a mere resting place, a temporary springboard on which strength is gathered for further effort. By handing out final wisdom, as textbooks do, they tend willy nilly to strengthen the authoritarian method which assumes that truth is like a kernel in a hard-shelled nut, which must be cracked and peeled to reveal the hidden delicacy. It is a specious analogy but historically hard to defend. Scientific truths vary with knowledge and insight, and seldom fit into an unvarying mold. Scientific truth is as fluid and continuous as is the search for it. It is an exciting and enduring challenge, with the best of the moment occupying the seat of honor. The occupants change, the office remains.

It is the aim of the present volume to remedy this situation. It seeks to acquaint the student of science, whether he intends to specialize in it or not, with the anatomy of scientific growth and evolution. It hopes to show how our antecedent cultures grappled with problems much as we do today. Science lives by the work and ideas of gifted minds, and these have always been available, with unavoidable fluctuations. The terrain on which they operated differed, the tools, goals and outlooks differed, but the pursuit with its challenges, successes and frustrations was the same at all times.

It is hoped that this book will aid the science student shed or modify many hitherto held notions about the nature of the scientific method, induction-deduction, Aristotelianism, progress and reaction, and similar cliches he seems to gather, as it were, from the cultural atmosphere he breathes. The material is vast and the sample here presented is small. It is the author's hope that it is a much needed introduction to a neglected subject.

ACKNOWLEDGEMENTS

1. Figures 4.3, 4.4, 4.6, 4.7, 4.8 and 4.9 from R. A. Parker, *The Calendars of Ancient Egypt* by kind permission of the Oriental Institute of the University of Chicago.
2. Figures 6.2, 6.4, 6.5, 6.15, 6.16, 6.17, 6.18, 6.19 from C. Singer *et al.*, Editors, *A History of Technology* by kind permission of Clarendon Press, Oxford, England.
3. Figure 6.7 from A. Neuburger, *The Technical Arts of the Ancients* by kind permission of Methuen & Co. Ltd., London.
4. Figure 6.8 from R. J. Forbes, *Studies in Ancient Technology* by kind permission of E. J. Brill, Publishers, Leiden, Holland.
5. Figure 8.3 from A. Pannekoek, *History of Astronomy* by kind permission of John Wiley & Sons, New York.
6. Figures 9.6, 9.7 from Derek J. Price, *The Equatorie of the Planetis* by kind permission of Cambridge University Press, Cambridge, England.
7. Figures 6.20, 6.21, 6.22, 6.23 from R. C. Thompson, *A Roman Reformer and Inventor* by kind permission of the Bodleian Library, Oxford, England.

Contents

I The Lure of the Sky in Antiquity

1. Awareness of the Heavens

The science one learns in textbooks will necessarily convey a somewhat distorted image of the manner in which man came by his mighty edifice of organized, communicable and verifiable knowledge of the world about him. A textbook necessarily selects tested achievements, which lead to further experimentation and discoveries crowned as a rule with an attractive and fruitful theory and, more often than not, some practical applications. What remains unseen are the struggles by hundreds of gifted men endowed with curiosity, patience and skill who labored as assiduously as any of the recognized contributors to scientific progress, but whose efforts either led nowhere or flowed into channels that were lost in the cemetery of history, unmarked and unrecorded. For every successful solution of a problem, there are often dozens of brilliant minds that had grappled with it throughout the centuries with uncertain results. Some knew that the answer had eluded them completely, others died in the belief that they had not perhaps answered it fully but in some way helped to loose the mystery. Still others were certain to the last that they had fully conquered the unknown and laid it bare for all to marvel at, and only the blind and obdurate failed to recognize their achievement.

The efforts of this latter group, without which the achievements of a Copernicus, Kepler, Galileo, Newton, Lavoisier, Mendeleyev, Rutherford, or Einstein would have been impossible, go unrecorded in our textbooks. The study of science resembles in many ways the now outmoded study of history in which only the deeds of rulers, the dramatic events of wars and defeats, or, in our own times, the eras of depressions and affluence are singled out, without the hopes and aches of the daily life of most people, or the thoughts of those few men of vision whose voices go unheeded in societies that honor chivalry or fasting, as did the Middle Ages, or that worship material and unlimited individual rights as does our own era.

To fully understand the nature of science, its glories and setbacks, its various rates of progress and its often puzzling periods of quiescence, it is essential to examine, however briefly, some phases of its history so as to get an intimate view of its actual workings. Since the conspicuous characteristics of modern science are its broad array of powerful tools, such as the cosmotron or electron microscope, and the fantastic theories that can peer into the atomic nucleus or the outer reaches of space, we have chosen to examine the nature and history of these two aspects of science in antiquity. The tools of science were far different two or three thousand years ago than they are today and so were the theories. But the very fact that both were in existence then, fully recognized, admired, debated and tested, is of significance. The way these tools and theories came into being, the use they were put to, the light in which they were viewed by men of learning and the non-scholarly, by the rulers as well as the lowly, the manner in which they were questioned, replaced or abandoned, will shed light on the role of science within the behavior web of man in a changing society.

Without knowledge of this process, the student is likely to gain the wrong impression of the nature of science and its mode of growth. By seeing only the finished products he is likely to assume, as indeed many authors of textbooks facilitate his doing so, that scientific inventiveness and thought come upon him suddenly with the inception of the modern era. It is presumed by many writers that the ancients were held in the merciless grip of stark superstition until liberated by the coming of the method of science. Frequently one encounters the notion that because necessity is the mother of invention, man was unconcerned with the world about him until forced to become involved by one form of practical pressure or another. Also, that until he discovered modern scientific logic, he did not know presumably the difference between fact and fancy. Until he was taught by one pioneering genius or another to question authority, defy religious leaders who craftily sought to oppress his mind, and his secular leaders who sought to direct his loyalties, he presumably did not know how to doubt, question, challenge or reject conventional views.

The clarifications of these and many other modern assumptions, will be found in the historical facts themselves. The reason that many of these beliefs may justly be classified as modern superstitions, is largely due to the fact that most contemporary scientists have until recently been little concerned with the past because of the strangeness of outmoded conceptions. In addition, the unimaginable rate of progress of modern science has turned the eyes and minds of scientists to the present and above all to the future and sharply away from the past. The total upshot of these attitudes has been a rather broad neglect of past science and a failure to understand its true aims, methods and motivations. It is the object of this book to supplement whatever scientific study the student is pursuing with historical materials that would sharpen his comprehension of the nature of the scientific quest, its challenges, pitfalls and victories.

Strange though it may seem, man's earliest sciences were mathematics, the study of abstracted properties of numbers and shapes, and astronomy, the study of the movements of the remote objects seen in the heavens. Equally strange is it that our very latest sciences are those dealing with man and society, the behavioral and social sciences, as yet far from strictly amenable to the stringent methodologies of the exact sciences. Among the sciences of man may be cited human biology, genetics, psychology, psychiatry, epidemiology, public health and statistics; among the social are anthropology, political theory, economics and sociology. As organized subjects these are little more than a century or two old.

The early emergence of mathematics, sophisticated though it may appear to us, may be due to the fact that of all the scientific pursuits it is less dependent upon the external world, upon actual experiences and knowledge of events and properties, and more on mental powers of abstraction and what may roughly be styled mathematical ability. The process seems to require few assumptions chained to reality and subject to modification by experience. Given the abstraction of numbers, of the concepts of a point, line, and plane, the mathematically creative mind can proceed to construct vast logical systems which hold together with beautiful coherence and lead to many attractive and valuable conclusions.

Not so in the other sciences, for example, astronomy. Here, imaginative assumptions are not sufficient for the construction of a large edifice of theorems, consequences and corollaries. Also, new facts may be added by constant observation, and well-established theories may, therefore, have to be radically changed or wholly rejected. Fertile minds may invent new theories which some may regard as more attractive or more serviceable than the prevailing ones. Finally, new instruments may in time become available and bring to light phenomena which had previously been completely hidden from view. In mathematics, whatever new ideas emerge to modify fundamental concepts, occur rather slowly, and are cumulative rather than replacing.

The beginnings of any science lie in man's becoming aware of the respective aspect of nature. Millions of people see trees, yet remain unaware of the fact that all broad-leafed trees, or deciduous, have flowers; millions see the moon in the daytime but are unable to recall her exact shape or position in the sky; everybody sees leaves but is unaware of their shape or exact time or mode of emergence. No sooner does mankind become aware of a problem than, given time, it will accumulate considerable knowledge in that field. One can see how this works in our common experience. Take the case of a youngster who becomes aware of the diversity of rocks in the world, or of trees, or of butterflies. He will commence collecting samples and within a few years acquire considerable knowledge. In his natural course of growth he will associate with others sharing the same interests and thus expand his horizons. He may join a club and even subscribe to a national magazine and continue his growth in expertness. Science has grown everywhere in precisely this manner, which is the course of the very process of growth.

Ancient astronomy was well qualified to become man's first natural science. Early in history primitive man everywhere became deeply aware of the intense drama of the steady flow of intriguing celestial phenomena. He had no comfortable home to lure him away night after night from the stars changing their stations with the year's seasons, the waning and waxing moon, the wanderings of the mysterious planets, eclipses, or comets. In the daytime too, the heavens were closely watched when neither drab nor monotonous. The sun, that fountain of warmth and light, the father of the seasons, shifted daily his position and presided over the seasons of the year. He never rose in the same place two days in a row, nor did he set by rote. He climbed upward after reaching the lowest point in the southern sky on the day of the winter solstice, the shortest day of the year, until he reached the highest point on June 22. That day marked the summer solstice, the longest day of the year. These and other events captivated primitive man's fancy and elicited from him at first not a desire for accurate, objective measurements and descriptions, but a sense of awe and wonder, of poetic romance and worship. Some aspects of this basically emotional, hence irrational and superstitious attitude of man to his celestial environment, is discernible in all past cultures, primitive as well as highly developed. But while in most cultures the lore that surrounded the heavens was vague and amorphous, it erupted into full bloom in the burgeoning civilization of Sumer and Babylon and became the very hub of their religions. This meant that the celestial drama evolved into the central theme of these nations' conceptions of the universe, the sky's effect on man, and man's relation to its component elements. The stars and planets became objects of worship, symbols of indistinct but deeply-felt emotional entities which performed a significant role in soothing man's fears and hopes, invigorating his spirits and brightening his days.

2. Initial Response

A millenium or two before the Babylonian sages (including Sumerian, Mesopotamian, etc.) ventured to formulate their speculations on the influence of celestial phenomena upon human fates and compose the earliest astrological theories, poets, priests and prophets were busily incorporating celestial events into their lore. The very heavenly bodies soon became deities demanding worship and prayer. The earliest recorded literature of Babylonia's clay tablets, *The Epic of Creation,* "undoubtedly written in the period of the First Babylonian Dynasty 2225-1926 B.C.," is full of religious-celestial references. Tablet 5, says their discoverer and translator, is "an astronomical poem of the movements of the planets in the ecliptic, the motions of the moon, and the positions of the signs of the zodiac as constructed by Marduk.... The book concludes with a song of praise by the gods concerning the firmament made by Marduk.... The Epic of Creation is also a solar myth and intimately connected with the spring sun, whose return from the region of darkness was celebrated by a long festival at the beginning of the year." (S. Langdon, *The Babylonian Epic of Creation.* Oxford University Press, 1923, p. 15-16).

While celebrating the New Year with ritual and prayer, the high priest chanted:

> "The Star-Jupiter who brings prophesies to all
> Is my Lord. My Lord be at peace.
> The Star-Mercury allows rain to fall;
> The Star-Saturn, the star of Law and Justice;
> The Star-Mars, stormy god of fire;
> Sirius, who stirs the waters of the sea;
> The Star-Venus, brightest among the stars
> The Dog-Star who conquers the mighty.

(Heinrich Zimmern. *Das Babylonische Neyarfest.* Leipzig, 1926, p. 10). Clearly the stars were objects of worship.

In addition, the celestial bodies were represented by specific animals who thus also assumed the status of gods and were held sacred. "The sun was an ox, the moon was a steer, and the planets were sheep." (A. H. Sayce. *Lectures on the Origin and Growth of Religion.* London, 1909, p. 401). Venus was addressed by the priests in such phrases as the following:

"Goddess great and divine.
Should the king advance into his land
You will truly bedeck for him the Eastern sky...
My Lady, by your bridal jewel enveloped aglow by his embrace!
What Enlil on thee bestowed, you pour with generous hand upon the hills...
My Lady, up in heaven, on earth below, you have largely achieved your heart's desire."

(P. Maurus Witzel. *Perlen Sumerischer Poesie.* Fulda. 1925-1930, p. 149). And the poem proceeds to recount that all beasts and cattle, all four-legged creatures under the sky, the fish of the flowing streams and the birds of the air

"Wait upon my Lady in her bedchamber
All that is alive and inhabits the land bends the knee before her.
The lady whom they name their caring mother
My Lady gratifies all creatures in her land
My Lady is wondrous to behold up there in the heavens."

Offerings are brought to her temple, intoxicating liquors of exceeding power, basins overflowing with honey and butter. In time Venus becomes the goddess of vegetation and also of war. She is also the goddess of fate.

Poetic license and the power of fancy function so, that once a romantic road is opened up, the creative spirit will continue to advance upon it. Thus we find the myth of Tammuz, "The faithful son" associated with the image of Venus. Tammuz appears in history "certainly before 3000 B.C. as a figure already established in the Sumerian pantheon. The cult evidently originated much earlier." (S. Langdon. *Tammuz and Ishtar.* Oxford, 1914, p. 3). Like many religious myths of antiquity, the story of Tammuz also deals with the annual renewal of life, with the harmonizing rhythm of events in the heavens and events on earth. Tammuz is "the son of a virgin mother whom the shadows of the nether world each year claimed as a divine sacrifice for man and beast and vegetation." The myth deals with the regular recurrence of the seasons, the cycle of growth and death. There was wailing each year in midsummer for the disappearance of Tammuz in a month named after the god, and apparently around the time of the summer solstice when the sun begins to appear lower in the sky at noon and the length of daylight diminishes.

But this important event is not recorded through accurate observation, nor is it recounted in communicable prose. Here is the way the Babylonian poets or priests speak of it:

"Tammuz the Lord slumbers; in woe they sigh much.
The sacred consort of the heavenly queen, the lord slumbers, in woe they sigh much.
My king, thou art, thou who was hurried away--
Cruelly wast thou hurried away."

The reference is to the summer solstice, June 22, the longest day of the year, the day the sun reaches its highest point in the sky at noon, in the northern hemisphere. From that day on, for the next six months, the sun will daily sink lower in the sky, and the days will get shorter. The sun is thus losing out and all life dependent upon him must also lose.

"The wailing is for the plants, the first laments 'They grow not.'
The wailing is for the barley, the ears grow not.
For the habitations and the flocks it is; they produce not."

But with the coming of the spring the sun stages a comeback. "The Babylonians regarded the resurrected god as one who restores animal and plant life, and as one who bestows health of body and old age." (*Ibid,* p. 38).

It is easy enough for us today or for the Babylonians in subsequent years to measure the sun's positions daily; to note exactly the date of its lowest position in the sky, at noon, namely, circa December 22, and its return tour; to establish the exact moments of the equinoxes and thus arrive at a fairly accurate calendar. Two thousand years later the Babylonian astronomers did it as a matter of course in the same objective, matter-of-fact manner in which we calculate traffic density at certain intersections. But not so the early observers. They were poets, priests, awe-struck, fear-ridden watchers of the sky in whom each observed event was inextricably linked with an intense emotional or poetic response. Thus, the very same celestial phenomena were seen differently, interpreted differently, and functioned differently in the human conscience during the early poetic-religious era than in the later more scientific period.

The poetic-religious approach will take some celestial event as its starting point, embed it in impressive embellishments, enrich it with romance, and spice it with drama here and wisdom there. This celestial event will be exploited for some social, ethical or moral lesson, if possible, and occasionally it will be transformed into a myth of significant literary-philosophical stature. Such was the case with the Tammuz myth whose central theme is the gradual decline of the sun's elevation after having reached his pinnacle on the day of the summer solstice. The poetic-romantic-religious approach demanded the introduction of a novel element in this case little related to reality and wholly a child of fancy.

The sinking, weakening sun became a lost child, a kidnapped divine son, held imprisoned in the darkness of Hades by an evil force, or god, while his anxious mother wandered hopefully in search of him. But the resurrection of a captured god is not easily attained, and clearly the sacrifice of some live and precious being was indicated, either a noble beast or a worthy man. "The idea that a divine man must be delivered up into death to satisfy the powers of Hades and to ensure the return of life after the season of drought and decay, is apparently innate in primitive religion." (*Ibid.,* p. 27).

The anxious mother was Venus, called Ishtar by the Babylonians. She was a constant though variable companion of the sun, appearing as morning star or evening star as she revolved about him. She was pictured as a kind mother in search of her lost son, or a distraught sister wandering in search of a lost brother.

"O heroic Ishtar, creatress of people
She that passes before the cattle, who loves the shepherd
She is the shepherdess of all lands...
She is adorned with the light of days and months
She is merciful
She brings light to the afflicted, makes rich the downcast,
Divinity of begetting, divinity of procreation thou art."

We see here the logic of symbolization at work. The poetic-religious approach requires only a good start, some event or relationship culled from the world of reality which then needs only serve as platform for the gifted, as springboard for the creative imagination. The religious-minded poet will develop that initial theme into a grand religious story, employing the sentiments of awe, prayer and worship to gratify those unique inner needs which manifest themselves in all human cultures. Frequently poets and priests appear who spice their creative themes with socio-ethical incidents or conceptions which in time become part of the myth. In some cultures these elements assume pivotal significance, in others they play minor roles.

In Babylonia the myth of the captured and resurrected sun developed the image of Venus (Ishtar) into a kind and self-sacrificing mother, a virgin queen, a goddess of the harvests, the keeper of the stars in the heavens and the shepherdess of cattle on earth. In time, wandering Venus found her way into the gloomy underworld where her son had been dragged on the day of the summer solstice. Note that this fable bears strong resemblance to the Greek myth of Demeter and Proserpine. In addition, this incipient situation, lent itself richly to auxiliary literary themes such as abduction, imprisonment, adventures in the course of the search, the conflict between light and darkness, hunger, anguish and supplication, resurrection, generation, growth and harvest, joy and gratitude. All these find their way into the drama in proper poetry and with fullest license. On occasion, Venus is even portrayed as the benefactress in battles or a willful and inconstant lover.

Early in the creation of this myth, constructed primarily around the rising and declining sun and secondarily entailing his guard and companion, Venus, there appeared the tendency to assign omens to practically all celestial events. To this date many people seem to exhibit an uncontrollable desire for reading meanings, signs and warnings into a diversity of occurrences. One might say it is part and parcel of human nature. The wish to read meanings or forebodings into eclipses, comets, shooting stars, fallen trees, black cats, monstrous births, dreams, coincidences and the like, is a most widespread feature of the human psyche and seems to be the legitimate offspring of two thoroughly human sentiments, hope and fear. Even in our own culture, most people not trained to resist terror, will show a twinge of alarm at the sight of an eclipse or at the sound of a creaking door or wailing wind on a stormy night, especially when these events find them in a depressed mood or uncongenial circumstances. Almost anyone having to cross a cemetery alone on a dark, gloomy night with only a howling wind for a companion, will experience fear at the sudden sound of a distant towerclock striking the midnight hour.

Tense expectation greatly accentuates the response to omens. Anyone awaiting a letter or a decision that can mean definite turning points in one's career, will automatically become an excellent subject for the study of the omen-seeking drive, or omen anxiety. This is particularly noticeable in children. Without being urged and without being taught, one tends to regard some phenomena not al all associated with the major event, or perhaps resembling it indistinctly, as indications of either a happy outcome or a fearsome one. When one awaits an important letter, the sight of a postman passing by without stopping may be taken as a bad omen, even though the person involved may know that the postman is off duty. Only with well-directed training may one learn to check this tendency. However, in times of danger, as in war, it may break through despite well-established restraints.

3. Myth Lore and Omen Anxiety

It is not difficult to see the sourcesprings of this omen-anxiety. Hope being an innate feature of universal human behavior, it is natural that in situations of tension, occurrences reminiscent of the event which is the cause of the anxiety, provoke a hopeful reponse, which is what we mean by a good omen. Conversely, any phenomenon suggesting a negative outcome can readily serve as a fear-provoking stimulus, hence a bad omen. In the course of time, man's love of generalization and symbolization will standardize impressive events or even ordinary ones into a system of omens or forebodings. Poets will write about them, troubadours will sing the poems, actors will dramatize them and folklore will speedily incorporate them into its thinking patterns and expressions.

If this theory is at all acceptable, then we shall have little difficulty in understanding primitive man's love of omens of various kinds, the more mysterious and impressive, the better. Cattle, which to begin with were domesticated to serve primarily as sacrifice to the gods, were widely exploited for omens. It apparently did not take long for primitive man to discover that he need not be a mere observer of omens but could also arrange for them to appear at will. In this way he obtained an answer to an anxiety that disturbed his peace or resolved a gnawing dilemma that demanded specific action on his part. Life was full of dangers and challenges, and decisions were not easy to come by. Anything that helped with guidance and advice was welcome, provided it came from sources endowed with authority and holiness.

Divination or the practice of peering into the future so as to know the will of the gods, the path of fate, the proper course for men to follow, thus came into being. The language of divination consisted of meanings or omens which the wise, the learned and the benighted understood and knew how to interpret. When a cow was sacrificed, her multilobed liver was carefully examined to read in the shape and arrangement of the lobes the message of the gods concerning some enterprise, or forewarnings of things to come. Fire and smoke, clouds and lightning, flights of birds, changes in the wind, the movements of animals, the messages hidden in numbers and forms and similar phenomena were variously employed in this mysterious and sacred art of foreseeing the future so as to face it in the most advantageous manner.

That the ever changing events in the sky be employed as omens was inevitable in view of man's emotion-laden attitude toward celestial doings in general. It was impossible for early man, in his state of boundless insecurity and bewilderment, to respond to an eclipse or comet in any other way than terror. His outlook upon nature was necessarily anthropocentric or ego-directed. In the absence of knowledge of the outside world, or even of speculative theorizing about it, the only available responses of the mind were the innate ones of fear and hope, hence of omen-anxiety.

Long before the Babylonians completed the construction of their entire religious edifice around the theme of celestial worship, they already employed the movements of the planets as omens. Clay tablets discovered in King Ashurbannipal's library (668-626 B. C.) and studied and decoded by many scholars, reveal the kind of omenology practiced two thousand years or so previously. "When the Moon appears on the first of the month of Kislew, the king of Akhad, wherever he goes, will ravage the land. There will be an overthrowing of fortresses and downfall of garrisons... When at the Moon's appearance a north wind blows, during that month a flood will come... When a halo surrounds the Moon and Jupiter stands within it, there will be an invasion of the forces of Aharru... When the Moon and Sun are seen with one another on the sixteenth day, king to king will send hostility. The king will be besieged in his palace for the space of a month... When the Moon occults Jupiter that year a king will die... When Mercury is visible in the month of Kislew, there will be robbers in the land...When an eclipse happens and a north wind blows, the gods will have mercy on the land... When a foetus has eight legs and two tails, the prince of the kingdom will seize power." (R. Campbell Thompson. *The Reports of the Magicians and Astrologers of Nineveh and Babylon,* Vol. II. London 1900).

Clearly, awareness of the sky brought in its trail the twin offspring of worship and the employment of omens. In the course of time, the former gave rise to the complex structure of the Babylonian religion of the sky, with its deification of the seven visible planets which contributed their names to our days of the week. The latter led to the complex system of astrology which did not reach its full development as a science, meaning merely as an organized body of symbols, rules, correlations, meanings and modes of prediction, until it diffused into Greece around the fifth or fourth centuries B. C.

The Babylonian and later Chaldean religion of the sky entailed worship of the seven planets, the sun and moon and the five true planets visible to the naked eye--Mercury, Venus, Mars, Jupiter and Saturn. It promulgated the building of respective temples for each of the seven deities presided over by priests, no doubt, seriously dedicated to their honored assignments. It was therefore only reasonable that the priest of the temple of Venus study carefully the motions of that planet and become intimately acquainted with her orbits and changes in color and brightness. Such priests also had to submit reports to their kings on the meanings of the daily planetary positions. The tablets cited above contained omens not only from the positions of the planets but also from atmospheric phenomena, the position of the moon's horns (tusks), eclipses, occultation, (the covering up of stars by the moon's passage between them and the earth) halos, the risings and settings of stars near the sun, and the curious motions of the planets observed against the background of the stars. These tablets contained no technical terminology, no figures, and little accuracy.

Nevertheless, the very contact of priests with the phenomena of the heavens carried within it the seeds of the possibility of science. Sooner or later some priest or associate would appear who had a penchant for accurate data or for mathematical formulation. Simple instruments were built and accurate observations recorded. Most significant was the fact that since the priest was dedicated to his job and permanently attached to his temple and, as a rule, stood in serious devotion to his god or goddess represented by the planet, he was most favorably situated to take continuous observations of the positions of his respective celestial body. The Babylonian observations religiously gathered for many centuries, constituted, the core of the data used by the two great theoretical system-builders of astronomy, Ptolemy and Copernicus.

While an exact science of astronomy was emerging from the originally poetic-religious lore and its foetus of star-worship, crude beginnings could be discerned of what later became astrology. This web of postulates and speculation which today is known to be devoid of any validity, emerged in quite a logical manner from the primitive omenology. Strangely enough, just as scientific astronomy was generated in the womb of Babylonian religious lore but reached its fruition in Greece, so astrology did not reach maturity until its beginnings reached Greece and there grew and ripened. The early Babylonians had attained considerable mathematical skill by the year 2000 B.C. or so, and therefore did not find it impossible to develop a certain amount of quantitative astronomical thinking. Constellations were mapped out, the path of the sun as seen against the stars, hence against the constellations of the Zodiac, was outlined. The annual changes of the sun's motions were noted; the moon was most carefully observed, especially with respect to the times of the first monthly appearance of the new crescent in the western horizon, and the shifting positions of the five planets against the background of stars were also well traced. A lunar month and a workable calendar were rendered feasible, and by the time of King Ashurbannipal had been in long use. A strictly mathematical and coherent theory of planetary motions waited for its final elaboration until the coming of Ptolemy, around the second century A. D.

Babylonian beginnings of mere omen lore were quite crude. Although omens of the kind here cited were deduced day by day from a large variety of celestial, atmospheric and earthly events, they never crystallized into what might be called an organized science. This event did begin to take place, however, in Greece, around the second century B. C. and reached its pinnacle a few centuries later, first in Greece then in Rome. Also, the Bablyonian priests read omens or made prognostications only for the rulers, and the influences dealt with were believed to affect their private fates as well as the fates of the nation. Greek astrology, developing as it did in a culture which was far less autocratic and more democratic, applied astrological omens or forecasts to individual human beings, giving rise to horoscopes or forecasts of individual fates from the positions of the planets at birth. Greek astronomy, though based on a theory which was later supplanted, was a valid and rich mathematical edifice, while Greek astrology, speculative, symbolical and overly elaborate from the very start, bulging with heavy remnants of emotional omenology, gave rise to no worthy successor but was in time completely brushed aside with the advance of modern science.

In summary, we may say that our vast science of celestial phenomena began with man's becoming aware of the heavens and the movements of the heavenly bodies. He was not particularly motivated either by necessity or utilitarian advantages. On the contrary, his initial incentive was the lure of the sky. The awe-inspiring, fearsome, mystifying, poetry-eliciting impact made by such an external force can lead to organized religion as well as to organized science with its inevitable birth of theories. The impact can be rich in poetic vision and fable full of literary embellishments, of beauty of thought and phrase, of drama, heroic deeds, moods, passions and sentiments. Since the material deals with a concrete aspect of nature, it is also possible that in the course of time some maverick of the priestly tribe begin to see nature realistically, factually and quantitatively. When this happened in Babylon, the science of astronomy was founded. Perhaps because the religious or mystical-poetic elements were too powerful; perhaps because the glory of Babylon was too short-lived, the scientific offshoot did not attain its full efflorescence there, but only after reaching Greece.

Man's innate response to the celestial drama entailed the hope-anxiety complex of omenology. From earliest times, priests who soon became specialized as the exclusive keepers and watchers of a particular celestial god, began sending daily reports to the king of the happenings involving their divine object in the sky. These reports contained as well the particular messages they deciphered from their mysterious interpretations of the special conduct or location of their god-planet. Originally these dire or benign portents concerned only the fates of the rulers, their close members of their family, or the well-being of the nation as a whole.

With these beginnings the art or science of omens spread to Greece, where like its scientific twin sister, astronomy, it was welcome and became in time transformed into an imaginative, intricate, but well-organized pseudo-science, known as astrology. Unlike the Babylonian omen-messages, Greek astrology developed symbols for the prognostication of personal fates and vicissitudes from the positions of the stars and planets at birth. It became personal and catered to the tension-laden curiosity of each individual about his own fate. Curiously enough, the man who wrote the greatest, most scientific and elaborate synthesis of the geometry and astronomy of antiquity, was also the author of what later became the most authoritative textbook on astrology. His name was Claudius Ptolemy. His book on astronomy was called *The Almagest* and his book on astrology the *Tetrabiblos*, or *The Four Books*. He was, besides, the author of the most authoritative ancient and medieval book called *Geography* which was being reissued with suitable additions even long after the voyages of discovery and explorations.

II The Making of a Calendar

1. The Periodicity of Time

It was part of the religious response to the ever-impressive celestial drama to pay poetic homage to its divine actors and do that in the form of prayers, ritual performances, and sacrifices. Particularly in Babylonia, where the planets were raised to the level of divinities, did it become customary to have special holidays dedicated to the various planets, above all, the sun, moon and Venus. The recommencement of a lunar cycle, namely, the beginning of a lunar month, and the recommencement of a solar cycle, hence the New Year, were the occasions for special festivities not only in Babylon but in other cultures as well.

Careful observations came into being, although their methodical gathering no doubt had to wait until some individual appeared on the scene who was sufficiently gifted to devise some instrument for the purpose. Moreover, such an instrument would have to utilize the available geometry, however elementary, for recording the many celestial positions. That such men did appear, is apparent from the data they left behind, although their names and precise times are still obscure. Thus, a mathematical text recorded on a baked clay tablet in Sumeria-Babylonia from the times of King Hammurabi, hence around 1800 B. C., conveys considerable information about the kind of data arranged by then in an orderly manner. Such mathematical tables tell us much of the kind of scientific activity that must have prevailed centuries prior to the date of those clay tablets. Modern museums have in their possession at least 500,000 tablets of which some are mathematical school texts, such as multiplication tables or tables of fractions, while others are problem texts dealing with sophisticated queries to which solutions are to be formed.

Babylonian tablet texts dating from early and late periods of the first millenium B. C., record quite accurate positions of sun and moon and refer to their specific locations at certain times of the year within the zodiacal constellations. The numbers are given in terms of degrees, minutes and seconds, thus indicating accurate observations, to say nothing of some mathematical language and operations. We know that the art of writing was already practiced in Mesopotamia and probably Egypt as well around 3000 B. C., and that number signs were expressed in terms of a base of sixty, as ours are in terms of a base of ten. We find a sequence of numbers 0, 31, 25; 1, 2, 50; 1, 5, 40. They show that their authors had made the great discovery of the importance of place value, which is employed in our ouwn arithmetic. In our numbers the place of a digit designates from right to left, units, tens, hundreds, thousands and so forth in multiples of ten. In the Babylonian system of the three places above separated by commas, the one to the right represents units, the next left or middle number stands for sixties and the one to the left of that, 60x60. The number 1, 2, 50, is equivalent to 50+2x60+1x60x60 or 50+120+3600 = 3770. Similarly in our system the number, 563 = 3+6x10+5x10x10. It will readily be seen that the above Babylonian number represents a scale which we ourselves still use in our geometry when we employ degrees, the number 1, 2, 50 representing 1°, 2', 50", or 1 degree, 2 minutes and 50 seconds. It should be noted that just as we use both number systems, the decimal (10) and the sexagesimal (60), so did the Babylonians make use of both these systems, although they seem to have employed the sexagesimal more frequently.

While complete mathematical details of astronomical observations and theory were not fully worked out in Babylonia until a little before 500 B.C., much mathematics, geometry and observation were pursued in that culture area for probably more than two thousand years prior to that date. For example, the sun's orbital belt in the heavens comprised thirty-six decans (segments of ten degrees each) or twelve constellations, against which the sun can be seen by an observer on earth. This constitutes the so-called belt of the zodiac which had been known as far back as the year 3000 B.C. or thereabouts. But such knowledge in those early days was vague and was employed more in a poetic-religious sense than in strictly mathematical terms.

The first practical outcome of even crude familiarity with this belt can be a calendar. And man came by fairly functional celestial calendars early in his history, apparently even before the year 3000 B.C.

Workable calendars could well be devised before measuring instruments were invented. After all, birds know the seasons by instinct. Early flowers respond to the coming of spring in their own fashion, while man, whenever he lived close to the bosom of nature, could readily tell the succession of the year by the birds and the flowers alone. Primitive man lived, as most people do today, by and for the present. If his knowledge of time and the seasons sufficed for his religious holidays and his immediate needs of hunting, fishing or plowing, he was fully satisfied and could live with that system for many centuries. One is therefore little surprised to find that the early Roman calendar which like most primitive calendars was a lunar one, hence based on the cycles of the moon around the earth, began in March, reckoned as the first month, which meant that it began with the coming of spring, and terminated in December, or the last (tenth) month. Winter simply did not count because it was an interim or perhaps insignificant period, a period of waiting for the next spring. The months of January and February were added much later to make twelve, completing the year which had to be linked to the solar cycle if it were to recommence in the spring. This reform was introduced by Numa, who reigned at Rome around 700 B.C. He added the month of January at the beginning of the year, before March. He added February at the end of the year, after December. In 452 B.C. this order was changed to the present one. But since the months were lunar and contained 29 and 30 days alternately, the calendar was still askew. A process known as intercalation was then resorted to, meaning, the act of adding extra days so as to compensate for the shortage inevitably brought about by a year of twelve lunar months. Unfortunately, Rome failed to devise a regular scheme for such intercalations but left it to the religious authorities to do that on a year to year basis. This practice led to much corruption as when some years were prolonged to give elected officials more time to strengthen their positions or to rid themselves of opponents and the like. It was not until the time of Julius Caesar, 45 B.C., that the calendar was fully reformed to yield the so-called Julian calendar. The actual reforms must be postponed till after we discuss the instruments employed, since they involved some degree of quantitative sophistication.

The earliest Babylonian calendar was also strictly lunar, and in no way made to harmonize or synchronize with the sun's cycle. The modern calendar of the Moslem faith is a good example of such a system of time reckoning. Each month has twenty-nine and a half days and extends from the day of the first visible crescent in the west to the next crescent. The ancient Jews also used this calendar, except that they adjusted it to the seasons, which imply the solar cycle. Their mode of intercalation involved the addition of a thirteenth month and a few days every third year. Clearly, a strictly lunar year of 12 months will only have $29\frac{1}{2} \times 12 = 354$ days, and will be $11\frac{1}{4}$ days short of the solar year. By adding 33 and 3/4 days to the year, harmonious adjustment to the solar cycle is obtained. An adequate, workable lunar calendar can be achieved by observation with the unaided eye, in spite of the fact that first seen crescent moons appear in the western sky in a diversity of positions resulting in difficulties of detection.

Even the sun and stars can serve as signs for a functional calendar, sufficient for immediate needs even without benefit of any instruments. The very opening lines of Hesiod's "Days" cites the farmer's two main activities of ploughing and sowing as determined by the rising and setting of the Pleiades. The Star Arcturus, "rising in his radiance at even-tide" just 60 days after the winter solstice, the shortest day of the year, was a safer sign of the coming of spring than the "twittering swallow." The Dog Star, or Sirius, was a symbol of summer. According to Vergil, farmers know the "twelve constellations of the world" through which the sun wanders the year round, so that they "may foretell the storms in the doubtful sky, the day of harvest and the time of sowing." Hesiod gives other markers as well: The cry of the migrating cranes shows the time of plowing and sowing, and vines should be pruned before the appearance of the swallow. Thus a variety of cyclical events in the heavens or on earth can serve in practice as a pretense for the making of a calendar.

In this citation we may discern two methods for the determination of a year, either of which can be established with the unaided eye. There is only one time in the year in which a star, after being for a while unseen because it is near the sun, makes its reappearance in the east just prior to sunrise. Thus the sun entered Aries, the Ram, at the time of Ptolemy on March 21 and Taurus, the bull, containing the Pleiades, on April 21 or thereabouts. A constellation which houses the sun cannot, of course, be seen, except perhaps during an eclipse. But as the sun continues to shift daily his position against the stars, or in our terms today, as the earth continues to revolve in its orbit, the Pleiades will soon be seen rising in the East just a few minutes before dawn. This is called its heliacal rising. As the sun moves away, eastward or leftward in the sky about one degree per day, the Pleiades will be seen to rise earlier and earlier. Only one year later will the Pleiades again make their first predawn debut after a period of invisibility. Since the sun enters the constellation Taurus, the Bull, around April 21, we can see why Hesiod gave May as the period of the heliacal rising of the Pleiades.

The second method of designing a calendar without benefit of instruments referred to by Hesiod, is by observing the motions of the sun. At every latitude on earth the sun's position at noon can roughly be seen to increase its height, or elevation, from the shortest day of the year to the longest, and then reverse its direction for the next six months. Without measurement this would be a crude system indeed and is far from being as accurate as from the heliacal rising or setting of a star.

In ancient Egypt, the earliest calendar was strictly agricultural. It consisted of three seasons of four months each: one, of the river's inundation which fertilized the valley with mud and silt; a second, of four months of planting and cultivation, and a third, the season of harvest. Since the inundation occurs regularly around the beginning of the summer season, which is also the time of the heliacal rising of Sirius, the dog-star, the brightest star in the northern sky somehow linked the agricultural year to an astronomical event. But Egypt, like the other Eastern cultures, also had a lunar calendar as well.

There is much evidence that the basic motivation behind the calendar was the need to know the exact dates for the ritual celebrations of various holidays. The divisions of the year in Egypt may seem to us motivated wholly by agricultural needs. In reality the division was done merely in accordance with the only natural periodicity that the environment imprinted firmly on the mind. Day and night are such divisions, and so are the seasons. Moreover, the very performances of ordinary tasks were viewed as religious acts, as will be seen from the Decree of Canopus (238 B. C.) mentioned below.

Calendars for practical agricultural purposes have little need for the kind of accuracy obtainable only with refined instruments. Surely, the farmer needs no precise knowledge of the exact moment of the vernal equinox for plowing, or for performing any of his various tasks. If the rhythm of weather and climate do not guide him in his activities, he is no farmer. True, a man with a penchant for mechanical and observational activities might conceivably appear even on a farm, where without the stimulation of a purpose, the applications of his contributions would be slow. There did exist, however, within the culture, a potent stimulus for the intensification of curiosity, the search for instruments, and the gathering of exact data on the motions of the sky and its starry objects. That motivating force was the religious aura in which the sky and the planets were held, and the universally felt need for worship and celebration of the planetary gods and their positions in the heavens at specific times.

It is reasonable to assume from all the available data and from the spirit of the culture, that usable measuring devices emerged out of the love the priests bore their planetary gods and the desire they had to follow their mysterious and sacred movements among the stars. The ancients had great regard for accuracy in matters concerning ritual and sacrifice, even to the degree of executing priests for accidentally reciting false texts or for performing services at the wrong time, or even for a slip of the tongue. Such errors were regarded as highly offensive to the gods, and only the death of the guilty ones could assuage their anger. This kind of attitude of life and death earnestness about the positions and movements of feared and beloved gods, was most conducive to the gathering of data and the honoring of accuracy in measurement. Since all the planets were divine, each was followed with meticulous care. Particularly watched were the sun and moon.

2. Measuring the Periodicity

One of the earliest instruments was the gnomon. This is merely a vertical rod standing on level ground upon which the sun can cast a shadow when he shines (Figure 2.1). The Egyptians built their gnomons in the form of obelisks which are verticals with four planes on the column and four triangular planes at the apex (Figure 2.2). A vertical employed in thus casting the sun's shadow was called a gnomon, meaning one that knows, or a way of knowing. These gnomons were universally held in high regard and were incorporated into standard temple paraphernalia, whether the particular religion centered around celestial events or not. At times, a culture would hold as sacred the ground upon which a gnomon stood. In Egypt, the city of Heliopolis, devoted to sun worship, swarmed with obelisks, which structures came to be used as well for monuments to kings and gods.

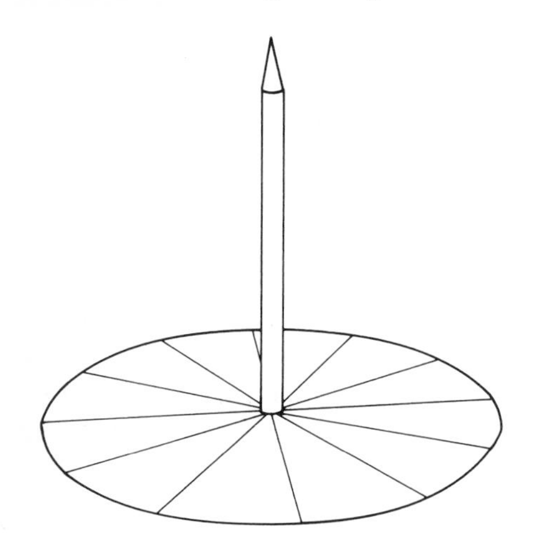

Figure 2.1

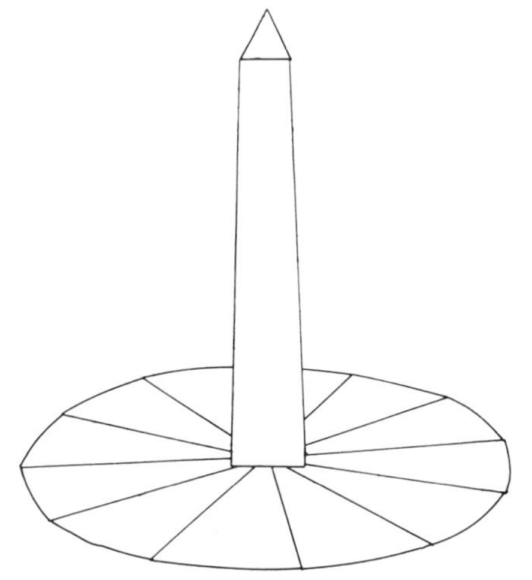

Figure 2.2

That a gnomon can deliver much information can readily be established. On a plane without obstructions it can easily mark the spot on the horizon where the sun rises and where it sets. Bisecting the arc thus formed and joining that point to the gnomon, will form a fairly good local meridian line, meaning an imaginary line joining true north and south. This is readily attained by drawing a convenient circle around the gnomon and regarding it as a model of a horizon. A line can then be drawn to join the gnomon with the points of sunrise and sunset. These two lines will intersect the circle; the two respective points of intersection are then joined, and a perpendicular is drawn through the center of that line. This perpendicular has the gnomon on it and is identical with the local meridian.

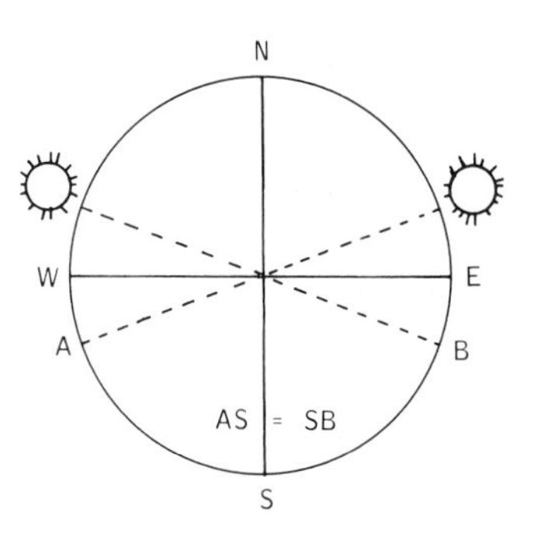

Figure 2.3

By forming a circle around the gnomon it was possible not only to observe the shifting locations of the points of sunrise and sunset from day to day, but to establish as well a system of hourly divisions for the morning and afternoon. Above all, however, the gnomon served to establish the moment of noon, the chief reference point for the day.

Clearly, when the sun is low in the eastern sky at dawn and for some time thereafter, the shadows cast by the gnomon will extend westward and will be long. As the sun moves southward, it also climbs higher in the sky until it reaches its highest point at noon and thereafter begins to descend toward the western sky. By late afternoon and evening it will again be casting long shadows of the gnomon that extend to the east, going off to infinity as the sun sinks below the horizon. Noon will be the turning point in the length of the gnomon's shadow, and be then at its shortest. This fact cannot, however, deliver the exact moment of noon, namely, 12:00. To do that the ancients resorted to another device, here represented.

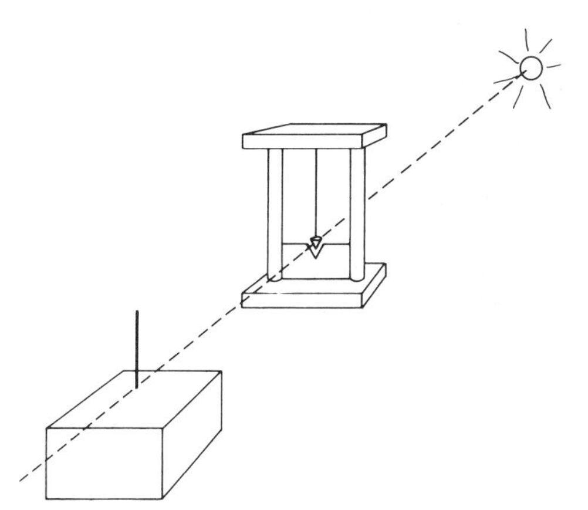

Figure 2.4

Two verticals are arranged in the court of a temple to designate the plane of the meridian, the line joining north and south, as precisely as can be established. This task was regarded by antiquity of prime importance, and crucial in the building of temples. One of these two verticals was obtained by placing a lintel stop across two columns erected a few feet from each other in an east-west plane and then suspending a plumbline from the lintel. To the north of this gatelike structure stood another vertical, the two making the meridian plane containing the plumbline.

These two verticals will let their shadows fall toward the west at dawn, and as the sun moves southward, both shadows will correspondingly be pointing to the north. They will move like the hands of a clock from sunrise to sunset. Because the sun is far from the earth, the shadows are always parallel to each other. The ancients, Pliny, Ptolemy and others, cited this fact as evidence of the vast distance from the earth at which the sun must be located. The long shadows of the two parallels at dawn get smaller and closer to each other as the sun moves southward. At one moment, however, the two shadows fuse into one continuous straight line along the local meridian. This is the moment of local noon, or the very brief time interval when the center of the sun's disk crosses the local meridian. After the passage of that fleeting moment, the shadows of the two verticals veer eastward and the distance between them gets larger though the lines remain forever parallel. In this manner, it was possible for every locality to have one exact moment during the day which served as a set marker for time reckoning, for events before and after that moment. This was the moment of local noon. Similarly, when the sun in its daily circular path around the earth crossed the lower half of the imaginary meridian circle, it was exactly midnight. The sky with all its stars mustered into constellations, was as well known as earthly maps, and the rate of travel of the sun against the stellar backdrop being also known, it was not too difficult to ascertain the precise moment of the sun's crossing the meridian circle below the horizon.

In his memorable book *On Architecture,* Vitruvius (first century B. C.) gives the following method of determining true north and south, hence the meridian. In a central square, he advises, smooth off ground by means of a level and set up on it a bronze gnomon, or shadow-hunter. At about the fifth hour of the forenoon mark the point of the tip of the shadow and with the base of the gnomon as center make a circle upon which this point should be located. Then watch the shadow during the afternoon and when its length becomes equal to the radius, which occurs when the gnomon's tip is again on the circle as it was in the forenoon, mark the point of intersection. From these two points draw arcs with the same compass to form intersection points, then connect these with the center. This line forms the meridian.

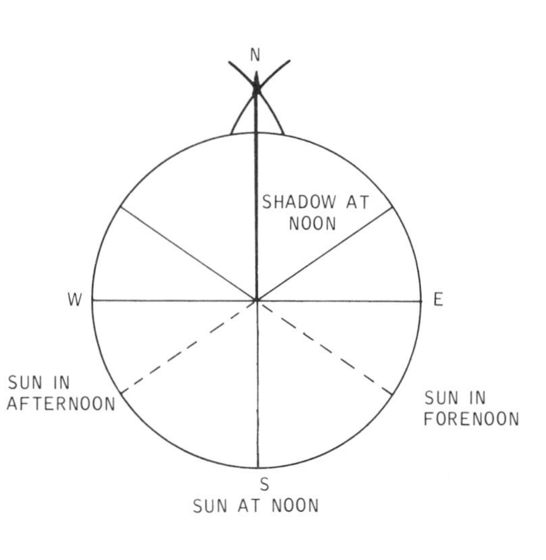

Figure 2.5

Roman surveyors more frequently used a method described by Hyginus. Set up a gnomon and describe a circle around its base of such a radius as to permit "its shadow to fall within its circumference part of the time." At sunrise the long shadow extends beyond the circle. Watch the shadow shorten as the sun climbs higher in the sky. Soon, "the tip arrives at the line of the circumference, which point is then marked. Likewise we will watch the shadow as its tip passes out of the circle (in the afternoon) and again mark that point in the circumference." Join these two points with a straight line and mark the middle of that line, which point is then joined to the center of the circle. This line is the meridian. Though this method can give absolutely correct results only at the time of the summer and winter solstices, it was nevertheless quite satisfactory. (Figure 2. 6)

The Egyptians exploited the principle of the two verticals in the line of the meridian somewhat differently to establish the moment of noon. The instrument was known to them as the "merkhet" or "the measuring instrument" and consisted of a strip of wood or any other hard matter that had a V-shaped slit cut out of it. This was placed in the plane of the meridian and the observer looked through its narrowest part at a plumbline also hung from a fixed scaffoldlike structure on the meridian. A star crossing the meridian was observed by eye, while the sun was watched by the shadows of the string in the crotch of the V. The instrument dates back to about 3000 B. C. and is shown in Figure 2. 7.

Simple as the gnomon is, much knowledge accumulated from its use. One might even assert that the accumulation of basic data for the making of

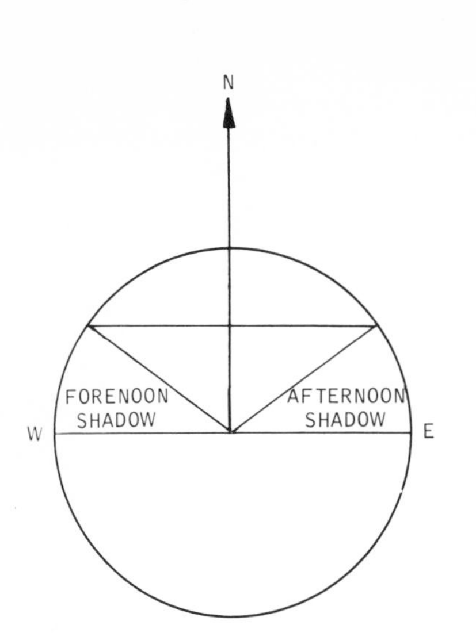

Figure 2.6

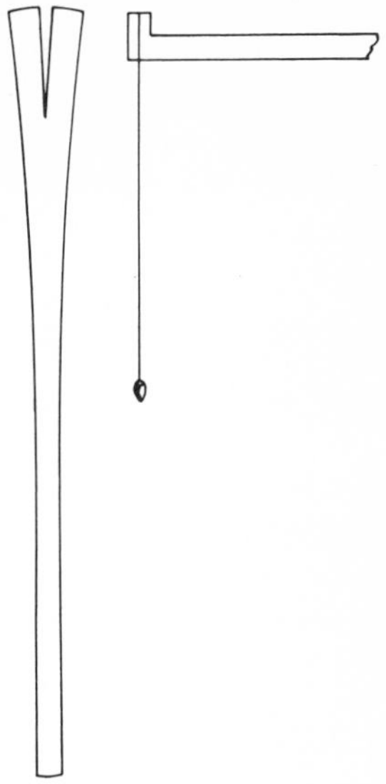

Figure 2.7

a calendar was virtually inevitable once the custom of taking daily oberva-tions became established. That occurred largely, as did most other activities of a scholarly kind such as the invention of the modern clock in the middle ages, primarily for religious reasons or for civic use. Since the gnomon stood in the temple court in Babylonia or as Vitruvius reports, "somewhere in the middle of the city," priests or officials cared for it and apparently took constant readings.

First, there was noted a definite relationship between the height of the gnomon, the length of the shadow on equinoxes and solstices, and the altitude of the locality. Equinoxes, or days in which day and night were equal, hence twelve hours each, were located six months apart and could be established with a fair degree of accuracy. An equinox, March 21 and September 22, was dis-tinguished by the fact that the sun rose true east and set true west, features which did not grace any other days. After the equinox of March 21 which heralded the arrival of spring, the noon shadow shortened, the sun stood higher in the sky, and rose further and further north of east until June 21 or so, which was the longest day, the summer solstice. Its noon shadow was shortest then, its point of sunrise furthest north, as was also its point of sunset. After that day the noon shadow got longer, both points of sunrise and sunset moved to-ward true east and west respectively, until the second equinox of the year, around September 22. On that day all calendrical features were the same as on March 21, and from that day onward, both points of sunrise and sunset moved to the south of east and south of west, respectively. The noonday shadow got longer and reached its greatest length on December 21. Similarly, on that day the sun rose at a point furthest south of east and set furthest south of west. Furthermore, angular deviations of sunrise and sunset from true east and west, were of the same approximate magnitude.

In this manner a periodicity in the conduct of the sun was noted, the full cycle of which constituted a year. It was not a very accurate method, in fact quite crude, but good enough for a workable calendar. It yielded the equinoxes and solstices, as well as the length of daylight and darkness for every day of the year. When this method is combined with observations of the heliacal rising of some conspicuous star, a fairly good calendar can be obtained.

Another form of gnomon was unearthed in some Babylonian excavations and is known as the Polos. (Figure 2. 8). It consists of a bowl, or a hollow hemisphere with a vertical needle fixed at its center, mounted on a base firmly placed on level ground. Because the vertical is at the bottom of the hollow, its shadow will fall on its rotunda and describe unique kinds of curves. In the winter the shadow will begin on the rim in the northwest, dip down a small amount to form a graph like a U, and then climb up again to the northeast. In the summer the shadow will begin on the rim to the southwest, climb down steeply at noon to its smallest distance from the vertical along the meridian, and then start moving up toward the southeast. At the equinoxes the morning shadow starts true west, wanders in an easterly direction northward to cross the meridian at noon, and climb up to the bowl's rim at true east.

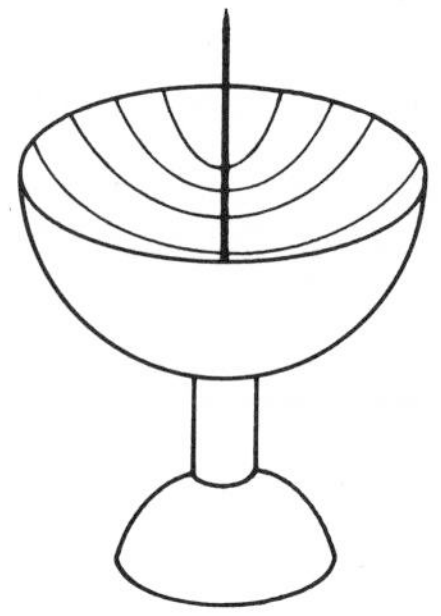

Figure 2.8

With time and the development of geometry, greater refinements in observation and thought began to take place. Since the origin of geometry as well as the origin of the earliest calendars are both lost in the obscurity of the Orient's ancient civilizations, it is difficult to trace the exact relationships between them. It is eminently reasonable to presume, however, that the two activities were closely related. Ever since geometry's inception the circle possessed 360 degrees, a number which could only be given to it by the fact that the early calendar chose that number as the most convenient one for the number of days in a year. Ancient Egypt had a number of calendars in operation. Besides the civil calendar of non-astronomical nature, already cited, it had a lunar calendar as well as a calendar based on the solar cycle in the heavens, revealed by the gnomon and the heliacal rising of Sirius.

3. The Basis for a Solar Calendar

The astronomical calendar began with the mapping out of 36 constellations in the belt of the zodiac, hence in the belt of stars against which the sun can be seen from the earth in its annual orbit. These constellations were known as decans because the sun lingered in each for approximately ten days. They were not given mythical or other symbolic names, nor did they enter into the lore with the glamor of the more famed zodiacal constellations, but were named instead by the most prominent stars which they contained. It was considerably later in history that three decans were merged into one zodiacal constellation of thirty degrees each, which were ceremoniously named and rendered romantic by suggestive symbols and myths. The division into decans was not abandoned, but as often happens in history, was diverted into other uses. The decans were used to designate the hours of the night. Since each decan was identified by a star, it served to indicate the last or lowest star visible in the east immediately prior to dawn. Since the sun moves eastward, or backward, daily one degree against the backdrop of stars, he traversed a decan in ten days, permitting a decan-star to appear higher in the sky just before dawn ten days after the sun's entry into its borders. After traversing one decan, the sun entered a new one to its left in the sky. The decan which houses the sun will be the last hour of the night since the sun will rise soon after that decan is seen in the east. In the course of a year, all the 36 decans will be run through by the sun. Also, during an equinox, half the sky will be seen at night and will contain 18 decans. Summer nights being shorter, they contained only 12 decans, which seems to have given rise to the division of the night into twelve hours.

Egypt was the first country to have a solar calendar. The Egyptians divided the month into three units of ten days each, three decans. The year contained twelve months of thirty days, a total of 360 days. Since at the end of this period the sun did not quite return to its initial position, it was known that the actual annual circuit of the sun took longer, namely, 365 days, or even 365 and a fraction, but the number 360 was retained for convenience. The five days were known as additional or epogomenal days.

Figure 2.9 shows a replica of a red sandstone slab found in an Egyptian tomb and dating back to about 2450 B.C. It has three rows of ten holes, a total of 30, which indicates its indubitable connection with the monthly calendar, the Egyptian month of 3 decans. The means of utilization of the calendar is also demonstrated. On the first of the month, the peg is placed in the first hole, on the second in the next, etc.

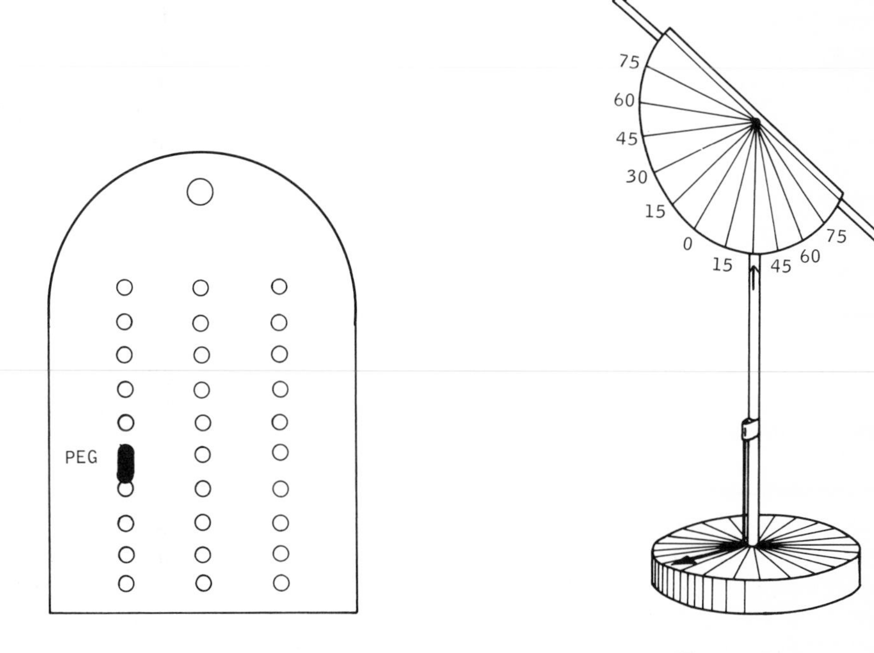

Figure 2.9

Figure 2.10

So far we have dealt with rather simple means of measuring the seasons and the year. The methods which may appear to us as crude no doubt required considerable thought, investigative courage and vision. But as has been pointed out, a scientific activity once begun, however humble its origin and initial techniques, inevitably advances, opens up new pathways, draws out new ideas and approaches, and bears new concepts. We have already seen how the sheer response to the heavenly wonders led to the study of the calendar, to the division of the sky into decans, to the month, and to a division of the night into twelve hours. By about 1300 B. C. the day too came to be divided into ten hours with a later addition of two more, one each for morning and evening twilight, respectively, which gave the full day a total of twenty four hours in use to this day.

Given the sense of wonder and awareness, curiosity will be set in motion. Knowledge will next accumulate no matter how mixed it will be with emotionalism, loose assumptions, irrationalism, superstition, and folly. With the march of events, time will take care of all these weaknesses and a free, rational science can and as a rule does emerge. Almost invariably emotionalism comes in time to be recognized as such, is checked however slowly, and quantitative methods emerge from a variety of stimuli and contributing causes.

With the development of geometry in ancient Babylonia and the notion of dividing a circle into 360 units, geometrical measurement came to be exploited for the purposes of astronomy. Instruments were devised for the more accurate measurement of celestial positions.

The simplest of instruments for finding angular distances of celestial bodies and the detection of changes in their position, was the celestial position-finder, or the simple astrolabe (Figure 2. 10). This consists of a horizontal beam pivoted at its center on a vertical beam. The vertical fits into a base and can be rotated in a full circle to the right and left. Note the graduated circle at the base placed horizontally and the graduated semicircle in the vertical plane.

To locate any celestial body, aim the sight on the horizontal rod at the north star or at the northern part of the meridian. This is the zero point from which all readings begin. The base of the instrument is to be securely placed in a set spot. Rotate the vertical beam whose pointer revolves along the horizontal circle to the right and then swing the horizontal beam until you have the object in view. Record the horizontal angle and then the vertical one.

With the aid of this instrument the position of any celestial body can be noted, and if measurements are taken with a fair degree of accuracy and persistence, a vast field of astronomical knowledge can be harvested.

The division of the circle into degrees was early applied to the plotting of the daily eastward motion of the moon and to the shifting of the sun's noon positions up and down the south meridian as it crossed it daily. Several instruments performing the same function were in use for this purpose and are cited in Ptolemy's *Almagest*.

First, there is the meridional armillary (Figure 2. 11). This consists of a graduated ring, normally of bronze, mounted on a pillar and held there firmly in the plane of the meridian. Within the fixed, graduated outer ring there is an inner one which has two small plates with tiny holes in them so situated that they can serve as sights through which to view a star, or through which to allow a ray of sunlight to fall upon a card held below the lower one so as not to view it with the eye. To obtain the image of the sun through both holes simultaneously, these must be in line with the sun's rays. Since the rings are in the plane of the meridian, a ray of sunlight can only go through these holes at the moment of noon, and then only when the two holes in the little plates on the inner ring are in line with the sun. The inner ring is rotated until this very situation prevails. It is provided with an arrowhead or pointer at the upper end so that the angular distance, either from true horizontal or vertical can be read. Thus, the meridional armillary (armilla = ring) merely serves to measure the angle of elevation of the sun above the horizon or from the zenith. Note that this same information can just as readily be obtained with the astrolobe.

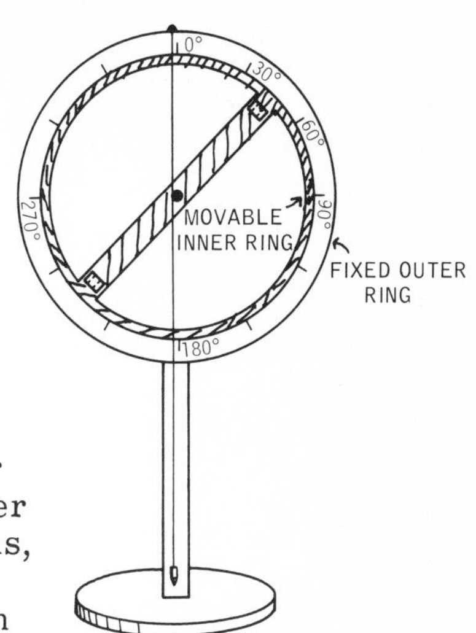

Figure 2.11

The outer circle is seen to be provided with a plumbline. This mode of setting up a true vertical whenever it might conceivably be useful is almost characteristic of antiquity. We encounter it again and again, as if the scholars of the time were in love with it, or as if they felt that by using it they were truly scientific. The fact is, that geometry being a powerful tool, knowledge of the true vertical whenever angles were measured, was both logical and necessary.

Directly after the meridional armillary, Ptolemy describes the "plinth," more often referred to as Ptolemy's quadrant. (Figure 2.12). This consisted of a flat, polished plane, placed upright in the plane of the meridian, and made of either wood or stone. Upon it, with a center at the upper southern point, was engraved a circle of which only one quarter was shown, hence the name quadrant. From the point which served as center, there protruded a rod, perpendicularly to the face of the quadrant, which served as gnomon. It lay horizontally pointing west. The base of the gnomon was attached to a rod that could be rotated along the polished face of the quadrant, like the radius of a circle, in the plane of the meridian. This motion is for the purpose of allowing the shadow of the projecting, horizontally placed gnomon, to fall upon it, that is, along its length. When that is obtained, the upper end of the rotating rod will point to the sun and the lower end will show the angle of elevation of the sun from the horizon, or its

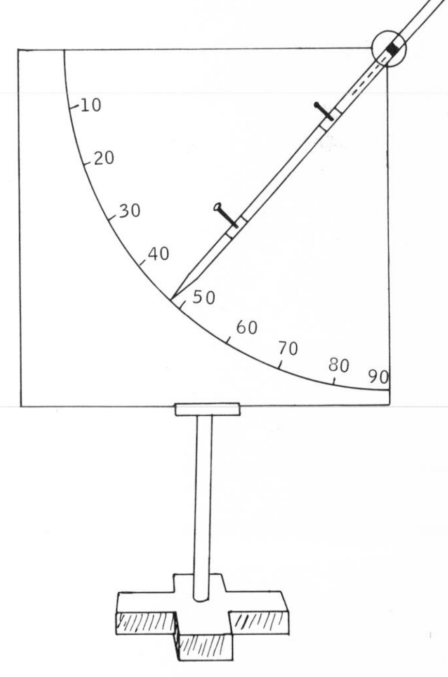

Figure 2.12

distance from the zenith. In the instrument here shown, the angles are written in so as to give the zenith distances. Their complements will be the altitudes, meaning height from the line of the horizon.

This instrument was employed to measure the height of the sun at noon in exactly the same way as the meridional armillary. It was merely another version of it.

Note that the movable radius has two sights upon it with which stars could be sighted. Since the entire block of the quadrant is firmly fixed in the plane of the meridian and as usual had a plumbline suspended from it to insure its true vertical position, the sights fixed to the rod when aimed at a star will aim at it only when that star happens to cross the meridian, and at no other time. This was called the *culmination* of that star, and constituted a fruitful concept employed in the mapping of the heavens, in the study of the planetary paths and the determination of the daily rotation of the sky independently of the sun. In our conception the latter point would mean the daily rotation of the earth as judged by the stars. Clearly, if you could measure the exact time it took from one culmination of a given star, say the Dog Star, Sirius, to the next, you know exactly the time it took the sky to perform one revolution about its celestial axis, or the time it took the earth to rotate once on its earthly axis. When we measure that circular turn from sunrise to sunrise, from sunset to sunset, or from noon to noon, we do so by relating the circuit to the motion of the sun. In the measurement of the sky's observed revolution by a star's culmination, we relate the event to the starry, or *sidereal,* sky. For this reason we say that this period measures the sidereal day.

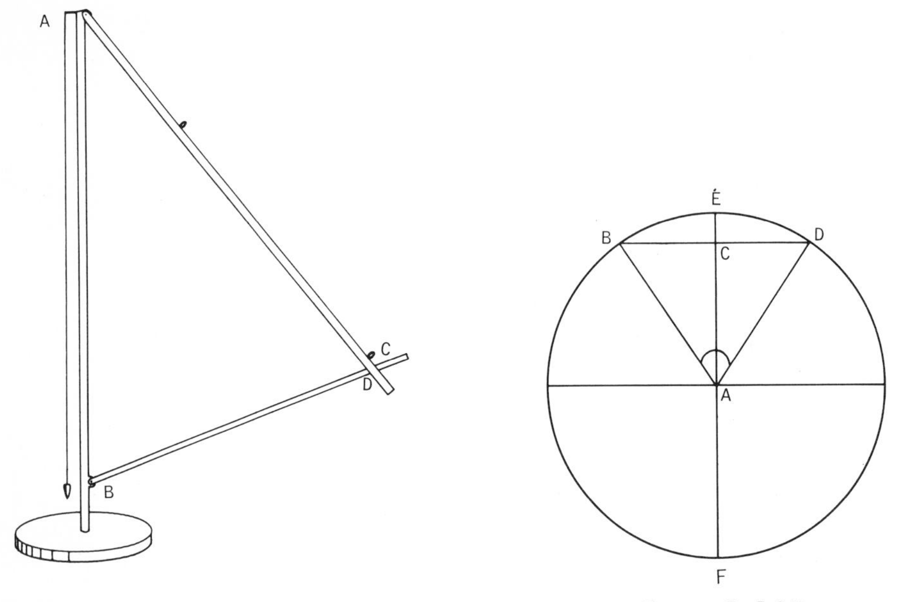

Figure 2.13A Figure 2.13B

The same function was performed by a third instrument described by Ptolemy and known as Ptolemy's Rulers, or the Parallactic Instrument. It was much used in the Middle Ages and Copernicus referred to it as the Triquetrum (Figure 2.13A). It was employed to measure the altitude or its complement, the zenith distance of stars, the moon, or the sun, preferably at their respective culmination time. The instrument consists of a vertical pole, AB, at the top of which is attached upon a hinge at A, a rod, AD, bearing two sights, and called *the alidade*. The sights were tiny holes in plates attached perpendicularly to the rod. At the bottom of the vertical pole, AB, was hinged another rod which engaged the AD rod, the alidade, in this fashion: the alidade had a slit into which the lower rod fitted at the point marked D, so as to move forward and backward in it.

A plumbline hung down from the alidade to indicate the vertical. For the detection of culmination, the instrument was firmly fixed in the plane of the meridian, and the star was observed as before. In Ptolemy's days the use of this instrument was somewhat clumsy; it was later simplified by the great Arab astronomer, Al-Battani (c. 858-929 A. D.). The rod BC was graduated and the rod AD was moved along its slit at D until the celestial object was in sight. The length of BD was then carefully read. Now, the instrument was so built that AD and AB were equal. Hence they could be regarded as radii of a circle with A as its center. Such being the case, BD would be the cord of the angle BAD.

It can be seen from Figure 2. 13B demonstrating cord BD that the ratio BC/BA = CD/DA because AC is perpendicular to BC and therefore bisects it. Thus BC = CD, and BA = DA, since both are radii. This being so, BC/BA = CD/DA = BD/EF, EF being the diameter. This is so because BD is twice BC or twice CD, and EF is twice the radius. In our case BD is the cord of corresponding arc of circle with AB = AD as radius. Thus by reading off the distance on rod BD in Figure 13A, the angle BAD can be known directly from a table in which the ratios of chord to diameter are worked out for all angles. This instrument can also be used to measure any angular distances of stars, hence their celestial positions, if it is so built that it need not always be in the plane of the meridian except when wanted.

Figure 2. 14 shows another instrument performing the same function and apparently favored in Alexandria and a few other cities. It consists of a ring or circle suspended from two fixed pivots in such a manner as to enable it to swing. The entire instrument is firmly placed in such a manner that the vertical diameter of the movable ring is in the plane of the meridian, with the line joining the pivots in the east-west plane. Toward noon this circle is swung so that the shadow of its upper arc falls directly upon the lower one, which must mean that the ring is then pointing toward the sun. The ring has a horizontal pointer attached tangentially to it at the top which indicates against a graduated semicircle the angle of elevation from the horizon, or the zenith distance of the sun on that day, respectively. A plumbline was suspended from the upper edge of the ring with its shadow falling upon its lowest tangential point properly marked, thus assuring the set position of the ring's pivots in the east-west plane.

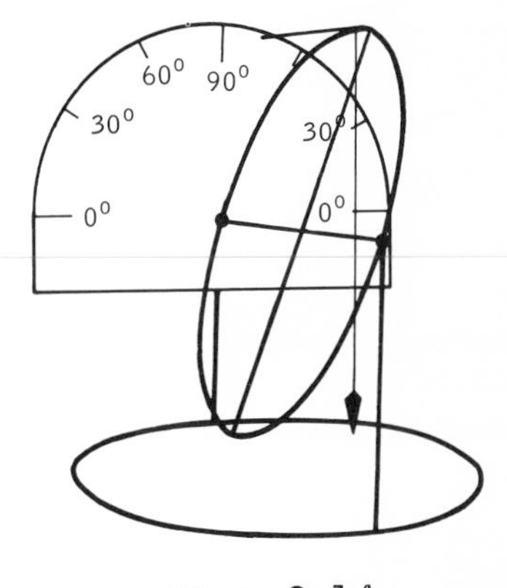

Figure 2.14

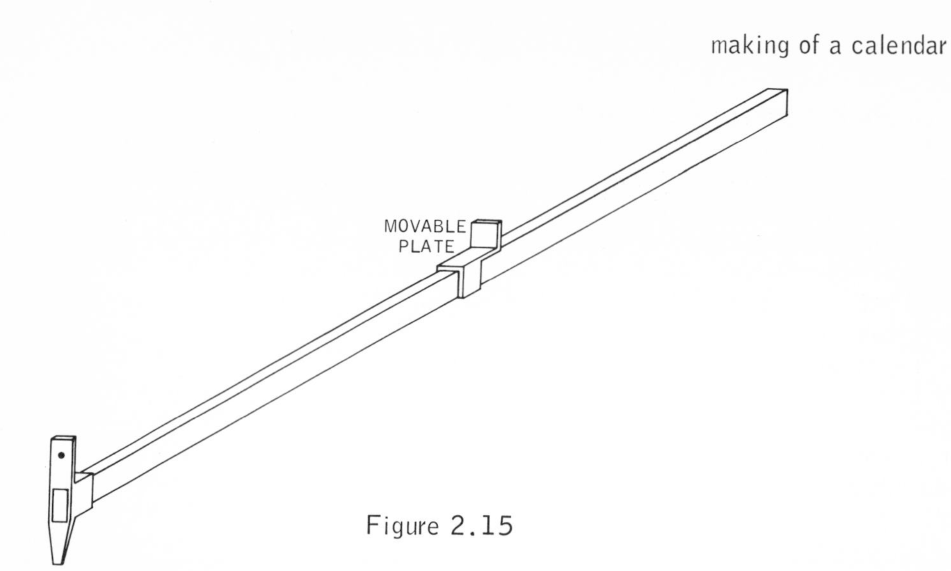

Figure 2.15

Ptolemy also records in his *Almagest* an instrument with which to measure the diameter of the sun, an exercise that could be readily carried out at dawn or sunset. It was called dioptra and was invented by Hipparchus. (Figure 2.15). It consisted of a graduated ruler which has a peephole in a plate fixed at one end perpendicularly to the ruler, and a movable plate also vertically placed but sliding in a groove running the ruler's entire length. The ruler was aimed at the sun at dawn or sunset with the eye looking through the hole in the fixed end plate and the movable plate pushed along back and forth until it was seen to cover the diameter of the sun exactly from edge to edge. Knowing the dimensions of the movable plate and its distance from the fixed one, one could readily calculate the angle subtended by the sun's diameter at the eye. It was also employed to find the diameter of the moon; both diameters were thus found to be of the same magnitude.

The instrument shown in Figure 2.16 is another one devised for the same purpose and based on the same principle. It has a horizontal base labeled with the cardinal directions and divided off into further compass points, or perhaps even degrees. It has also a vertical quadrant with sights through which the sun's ray can be made to fall, thus measuring on the vertical scale the angle of the sun's elevation. When fixed so that the vertical is in the plane of the meridian, the instrument acts fully like Ptolemy's quadrant. The advantage of this instrument is that the quadrant can be revolved upon its base so that other celestial bodies can be located, both with regard to their horizontal angle from north, their azimuth, as well as their altitude.

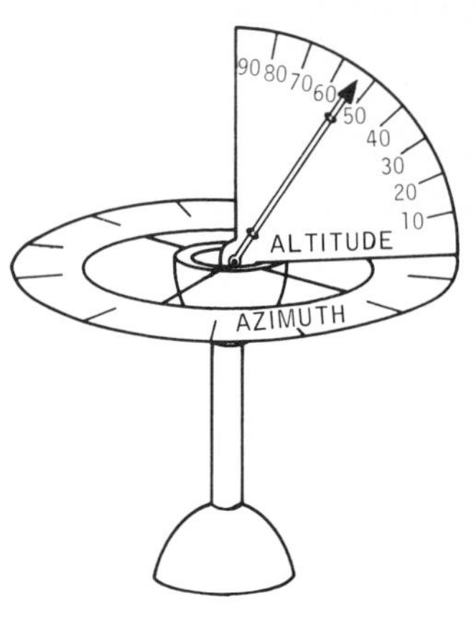

Figure 2.16

With the introduction of exact angular measurements, new floodgates were opened for further data, novel modes of attack, new speculations and verifications. With the coming of angular measurements, science gained a springboard from which great thrusts forward were possible, and were actually realized in time. Data, no matter how far from perfect in accuracy, began to accumulate and to tempt the imaginative and searching minds to great heights. And intriguing hypotheses did in fact follow in their track.

To begin with, angular measurements rendered possible fairly accurate determinations of the obliquity of the ecliptic, the solstices, and equinoxes. The term *ecliptic* refers to the actual linear path of the sun as mapped against the only background it has, that of the stellar sky. This line is necessarily located in the belt of the zodiac and is so named because it is the line in which all eclipses of sun and moon take place.

All of the graduated instruments cited, as well as the plane gnomons mentioned previously, indicated that, considering the data obtained of the sun at the noonhour only, that celestial body made an annual swing in the sky of 47° up and down along the meridian and back again, year in, year out. On December 21 the sun reaches its lowest point on the meridian at noon; at the equinoxes, it will invariably be about 23.5° above that point, and on June 21, it will be 47° above its lowest position on the winter solstice, and therefore 23.5° above that of the equinoxes (Figure 2.17). This will be true everywhere on earth where the sun is to be seen in all these three positions, as well as at the poles where it is seen only on a part of this path. Moreover, the path of the sun and moon could now be quantitatively plotted fairly accurately for the entire day and for the entire year, from the moment of their rising to the moment of their setting. The same celestial mapping could be done for the stars. Their exact positions could be readily plotted, their angular distances from other stars and their altitudes at culmination. A celestial globe and star charts could now be constructed, showing every star in its proper position. This could be far better prepared than terrestrial globes of which half the northern hemisphere and the entire southern one remained unknown. The foundations were laid for a calendar. Each one of the above four crucial positions of the sun, the two solstices and the two equinoxes, could be used, and was in fact so used, as the beginning of the year, since the year merely refers to the period of the sun's full cycle

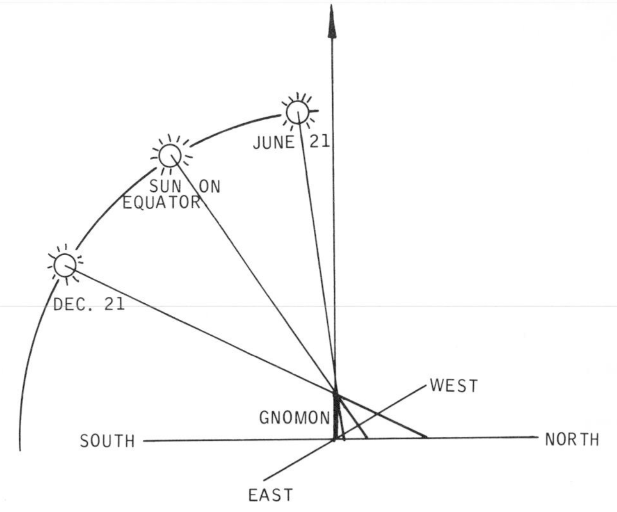

Figure 2.17

in the heavens, or as we would say, the time of a full revolution of the earth. Dates of holidays were well taken care of and society's needs were well enough served by the knowledge obtained.

But men of curiosity and thought continued their investigations, raised further questions and sought for answers. They began looking for some means of measuring duration, or time itself, and succeeded in evolving several excellent instruments for the attainment of that objective.

III The Measurement of Time Intervals

1. Simple Water Clocks

Some minds are forever stimulated to seek out new problems, raise new questions, discover hitherto unnoticed characteristics, or uncover new ways of examining one phase of nature or another. These acts of initiating new paths of investigation are rare events in history, and men who pioneer in these ventures are geniuses to whom mankind is forever indebted. But there exist also brilliant minds. A sufficient number of competent men follow through with the start given by the pathfinders and continue in their efforts until the initial paths widen out into broad avenues from which many bypaths radiate in a variety of often unforseen directions.

So it is today and so it was in antiquity. After the instruments previously discussed had been in use for various lengths of time, some inquisitive minds vitalized by the work performed and challenges encountered, hit upon new questions, concepts, and new modes of attack upon the intriguing drama of nature they saw enacted in the heavens. The questions raised and answers obtained can best be presented by the following quotation from an ancient writer, Sextus Empiricus, who lived around 200 A. D. Note that like all ancient authors, he speaks of his predecessors as "the ancients", even as we do today. "For in indicating the method of their approach they say that the ancients, after observing the rising of some particular bright star in the circle of the zodiac, proceeded next to fill with water a jar which had holes in it and then let the water flow into another receptacle placed underneath until the same star had arisen again; and as they conjectured that the revolution of the circle was from the same Sign to the same Sign, they next took the twelfth part of the water which had flowed through and calculated how long a time it took in flowing; for that, they said, was the length of time taken in covering the twelfth part of the circle, and the part of the circle covered bears to the whole circle the same ratio as the part of the water which has flowed bears to the whole of the water. From this proportion, that of the twelfth part, I mean, they marked off the final limit from some one conspicuous star observed at the time or from one of the more northerly or southerly stars which rise simultaneously. And they did the same in the case of the other twelfth portions." (*Against the Professors*. Loeb Classical Library. Book V. *Against the Astrologers*, pp. 24-26).

The author of the above citation happens to be a thoroughgoing skeptic and the object in writing his book was to show that all knowledge was nothing but vanity and pretense, based upon vacuity or self-deception. He labors accordingly at demolishing all learning, from rhetoric to geometry. No wonder that he finds fault with the above method of marking time by measuring the water that flows out of a reservoir. Says he further on: "For the scheme of the waterpots, mentioned above, is of no avail to rescue the Chaldeans, since owing to the flow of the water, and owing to the mixture of the air, the flow itself and the times parallel to the flow do not correspond. For as regards the motion of the water, it is likely that it is not the same at the beginning, when the flowing water is clear, and later on, when it is turbid and flows less easily; and as to the mixture of the air, it probably opposes the outflow, acting as a kind of block, when it is misty and rather dense, and gives it more aid when it is pellucid and of fine texture. The jar itself, too, will not leak equally when it is full and when it is half-empty or nearly emptied, but more rapidly at one time and more slowly at another, and at yet another time at a medium pace, whereas the celestial motion continues constantly at an even speed." (*Ibid*, pp. 75-77).

Sextus Empiricus describes here the most primitive water clock ever used and raises objections to its claim to accuracy which were certainly not valid in his day. The oldest water clock consisted of a container filled with water. It had an opening from which the water was allowed to run out steadily until it filled specified volumes, such as one, two or three cups, and so forth. (Figure 3.1). A cupful could well be regarded as a unit of time. But the people who hit upon the clever idea of measuring time intervals in this fashion, were apparently clever enough to observe that a water jug with a hole near its bottom will not yield a constant rate of outflow. When the jug is full the outflow will be rapid, as it gets empty the rate will slow down considerably. This inequality in flow is obviously due to the diminishing pressure, or head. To eliminate the inequality of flow, the height of the water in the reservoir must be kept constant, a feat easily accomplished by having either an overflow outlet or a valve. The ancients developed both controls. The sloping walls of the Egyptian water clock here demonstrated are in themselves sufficient evidence of awareness of the problem. The fall in pressure with outflow is somewhat compensated by this flower pot design. In reality, it does not remedy the situation but it indicates at least awareness of the problem and slight success in solving it. The inside of this conical structure is divided uniformly along a scale of equal heights marked by twelve horizontal circular lines on inside of walls, spaced according to a vertical measure of equal units. The volume of water flowing out during the first hour will be greater than the volume flowing out, say, the fifth or seventh hour, thus compensating in part for the greater pressure in the early hours when the container is full as compared to the flow later on when the container is less full. The pressure is weaker then, but the volume needed to designate an hour is also less.

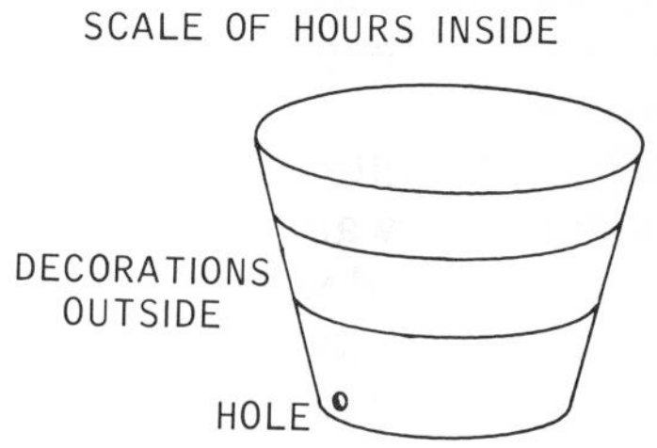

Figure 3.1

From the number of flowerpot containers found so far, it has been determined that different scales were in all probability employed in Egypt for different seasons or even months. The hours were uniform and amounted to one twelfth of the available sunlight, from sunup to sundown. More water therefore had to be put in the container on summer days than on winter days. This is indicated by the finding of different scales. Larger ones were used in summer months, shorter ones in winter. These water clocks were probably made for night use rather than daytime service, if one is to judge by their errors.

Water clocks of the above type are described as the outflow kind; there were also types which measured the inflow. All such devices went by the name of clepsydra, meaning water-thief, and by the number found one would deem them to have been quite popular. Besides measuring the hours of the day, they were also employed to measure the duration of a given event. The water outflow from the start of an event until its termination could easily be used as a measure of the duration of that particular event.

We know for certain that clepsydrae existed in Babylon and Egypt during the early part of the second millenium B. C., that they appeared in Greece roughly about the Age of Pericles and in Rome by the third century B. C. Plato makes Socrates wonder in his great dialogue *Theaetetus* how lawyers could establish truth by force of their rhetoric, in the absence of eyewitnesses, "while a little water is flowing in the clepsydra?" In Rome, too, clepsydrae were employed mainly in courthouses where lawyers for each side could speak for the durations of equal glassfuls. When interrupted, the speaker would complain that his antagonist "spoke into his water." Julius Caesar writes that he used the clepsydra to regulate the night watches of his centries in Britain.

As usual in antiquity, clepsydrae were seldom if ever used in private homes, but almost exclusively in temples and public places. They were beautifully decorated and often made so that gongs were rung by means of their operations, doors opened and figures appeared. The ringing of bells was effected by allowing balls to drop upon resounding pieces of metal. As a rule, a clepsydra was built in an impressive tower on a public square in the center of a town, and was guarded by a special official or by a priest. If the clepsydra had no automata to notify the townsfolk of the passage of time, a horn was sounded or a gong struck by a special attendant.

As already stated, the rate of outflow of liquid from a hole near the bottom of the container will depend upon the head of pressure, or height of column of water in the container. The more water in it, the heavier the weight of the upper water upon the layer level with the hole, and therefore the faster the flow. As the level falls with the passage of time, the pressure falls and the outflow is slower. It did not take long, we may surmise, for the inventors of those days to find this out. The great compiler of ancient inventions, Hero of Alexandria, living in the first century B. C., the author of several books containing many automata, cites in his famous work, *Pneumatica,* a valve employed to eliminate the inequality in pressure (Figure 3. 2).

The water passes through this valve as it comes into the container, the beaker, and flows out of it at a uniform rate. It comes in through the rubber tubing at A, runs down the inverted funnel into the beaker and out through the tube at the bottom left, B. Within the funnel there floats a wooden cone, C. If the flow is fast, the water rises in the beaker, and raises the cone, thus stopping the intake channel. But as the water constantly flows out, the level falls and the cone will sink, readmitting the water. Thus by the cone's bobbing up and down, the water level is under control, which means that the rate of outflow is kept constant.

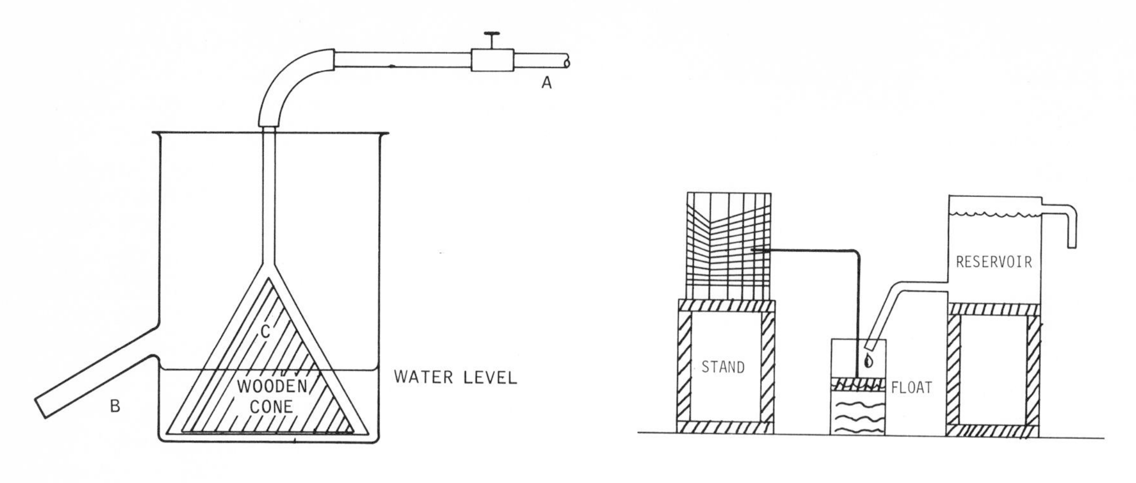

Figure 3.2

Figure 3.3

There are, of course, other ways of obtaining a steady flow. The simplest one is to bring the water from a mountain stream or from a reservoir into a tank which is always kept full to overflowing. The overflow is gathered and directed toward community use, while the tank is provided with a steady outflow. For efficiency's sake, a hole near the top of the tank would do, or a nozzle inserted near the top and made to carry the overflow into town, as shown in the illustrations.

The simplest water clock of Babylon is shown in Figure 3.3. To the left we have cylinder divided by the twelve signs of the zodiac into twelve months. These are the vertical strips marked off by vertical lines. In each month there are to be seen horizontal lines indicating the hours. The Babylonians, and after them all other peoples until only about five centuries ago, were mostly concerned with time during the period of daylight. In consequence, only the daylight span was divided into hours, twelve of them. And since the time interval from sunrise to sunset varies from day to day, it was so marked on the cylinder. The illustration shows the shortest day of the year, December 21, on the second vertical from the left, beginning the sign of Capricornus, then the three winter months to the right of it. These three months show increasing amounts of daylight, all divided into twelfths, or hours. The longer the day, the longer the hours.

On the right we have the water reservoir which obtains its water from a steady source of supply, say, from a mountain lake. On the right of this reservoir is the overflow outlet, obliging the water level to be constant at that top line. A controlled rate of outflow permits the water to flow at a constant rate into the glass jar in the center which contains a cork float. Into that cork is inserted a vertical rod which has a horizontal arm attached to it on top. That horizontal arm is provided with a figure of a man pointing to the hour lines. The flow of water into the glass jar raises the float and shows the time.

Note that the night hours are not indicated. Also, note that the cylinder had to be turned daily to bring under the pointer the daylight length for the given day. This could have been done by a slave, or more reliably by a priest dedicated to the service.

An interesting hypothesis has recently been advanced to explain why twelve was picked for the number of hours to the day. In early Sumer, around the middle of the third millenium B. C. the term *danna* was used to designate a unit of length. In the course of events the danna became a unit of time, specifically the period required for walking a danna. Thus, the day and night could be expressed in dannas. Since the day and night are equivalent to one revolution of the celestial vault, the sky's period of revolution also came to be measured in dannas. Because a day happened to have twelve walking dannas, the circumference of the sky was correspondingly divided into twelve dannas. And because normally the danna has thirty subdivisions, "the length of the main circle of the sky was divided into 12 x 30 or 360 parts. This is the origin of our 'degrees' and the custom of modern astronomy of measuring time in degrees." (Otto E. Neugebauer, in *Studies in the History of Science,* University of Pennsylvania Press. Philadelphia, 1941, p. 16). This need not necessarily exclude the generally appealing assumption that the number 360 derived from the number of days in a year. It may be that the day was divided into 12 dannas because twelve was an easily come by and popular number. But the fact that the danna was divided into 30 dubdivisions, and that the total number of each subdivisions per day was nearly the same as the number of days in a year, seems a strange coincidence. It has also been claimed that in Egypt the day was divided into twelve subdivisions because the sky, which completes a revolution per day, was divided into twelve subdivisions (E. von Basserman-Jordan. *Die Geschichte der Zeitmessung und der Uhren.* Berlin, 1920, p. 4). It is a fact, however, that the complete celestial revolution was taken to occur in twelve hours in Babylon, and each such hour was in reality two of our own hours.

The division of the day into twelve unequal hours seemed perfectly natural to the men of the ancient world, although it does not appear so at first to us. So long as the day differed in length, both according to the season and also at different latitudes, the ancients considered it logical to harmonize this diversity with unequal lengths of hours.

In Figure 3. 4, the dubious water clock attributed to Ctesibius (early second century B. C.) is represented. Here we encounter a new feature of the scientific mind of antiquity, namely, automatic action. It is difficult for contemporary Western man to picture the appeal of automation to primitive cultures and the awe and admiration which such mechanisms inspired. While witnessing an automaton's performance, the audience would feel itself transported into the overpowering presence of all the magic and mystery of the universe. Observers experience nothing different from what the dedicated, young modern enthusiast of science experiences at the sight of a cleverly designed cosmic ray detector, a film of solar flares or prominences, or artificial stimulation of a honey bee in a hive so as to make her perform preordained dance movements. These latter will, in turn, induce the worker bees present to leave the hive and pursue a particular flight. Both observers, the ancient and the contemproary, feel they are in the presence of the wonderful world of science, of marvelous human mastery over the forces of nature, but also of nature's fantastic and inexhaustible mystery and its endless challenge.

Men of antiquity who contrived and built automata were lauded by all. Thus Aulus Gellius writes (around 190 A. D.) in his *Attic Nights* of his great admiration for Archytas of Tarentum (c. 390 B. C.) who had designed an artificial pigeon which "as exhibited flew about well balanced in the air, and was set in motion by an inward air current." Aristotle also speaks of a Venus automaton, (*On the Soul* 1, 3 and *Politics* 1, 3) and several other ancient authors cite a crawling snail, a human robot, and a flying artificial eagle. Hero of Alexandria, cited above, author of such books as *Pneumatics, Mechanics, Mirrors, Dioptra,* etc., also wrote a book entitled *On Automata,* which he implies to be rather moderate in size and designed to serve the purpose of entertainment and curiosity. Some of these will be described below. That the Middle Ages revelled in automatic movements of birds, saints, knights, jousts, animals, musical instruments, symbolic figures and the like, is common knowledge. Some dramatic and typical representatives of this form of expression can still be seen today in the fascinating and elaborate automata preserved in many of the cathedrals and town halls of Europe.

In the clock of Ctesibius we note the following. As usual, an aqueduct supplies water to a reservoir which is provided with an overflow control, or any other valve, to maintain the water level constant inside it. The water flows out of this reservoir into the usual receiver, containing a float provided with an indicator. The indicator points to a raised cylinder upon which are marked the months and the days. The duration of sunlight of each day, sunrise to sunset, is marked off and is divided into twelfths, or hours. The usual result is obtained, twelve short hours for winter days and twelve long hours for summer days.

But there is one important addition. In the previous models the cylinder carrying the time scale had to be turned by hand from day to day, since the daily amounts of sunlight varied. In the picture shown here the date happens to be November 4. The rate of water inflow is uniform at all times, and only the distance traversed by the pointer varies with the seasons, as in the previous clock.

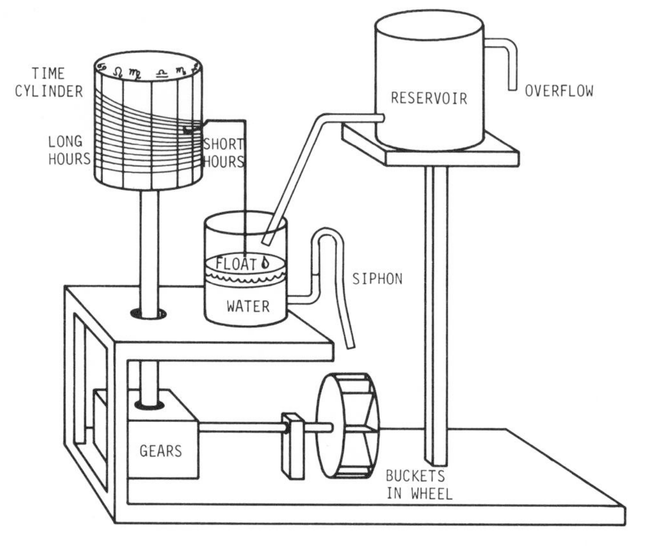

Figure 3.4

The receiving tank is provided with a siphon. As the day advances, more and more water flows into the receiver which makes the float rise but also raises the water level in the siphon. When the water in the receiving vessel reaches the level of the top of the siphon, the water in the siphon flows over into the down-tube, and the siphon goes into action emptying the receiver. The water siphoned off flows into a bucket in a wheel with a slanted bottom, simulating a compartment. As this compartment fills, it weighs down upon the wheel and causes it to rotate. The rotation of the water wheel is made, by means of gears, to rotate the cylinder carrying the time chart. The water from the turned over wheel compartment spills into a collecting vessel and can be directed to wherever it is desired. The rotation of the time cylinder does away with the need for having an attendant slave or priest turn it daily to the proper date with its unique quantity of daylight.

We have here a dramatic example of an automatic labor-saving device. It is truly a machine which does away with human labor, although it was almost certainly not constructed with that in mind. It was built out of a desire to construct something clever even as one writes peotry, tells stories, or invents mathematical puzzles. Like all other clever devices and automata, this one, too, was placed in temples as, at a later time, churches were adorned with paintings and sculpture. Works of science were produced for their cleverness and beauty. The creative scientist was interested in constructing them in the same manner and for the same reasons as the artist was interested in constructing his particular sculptures or paintings.

It should be noted that while the water in the receiver did not have to be emptied daily after sunset, and the time cylinder did not have to be turned, the siphon height had to be adjusted to the daily quantity of water which went into the receiver between the beginning of the flow at sunup and its close at sundown. In addition to the siphon's adjustment of height, the only attention this automaton required was the opening of the faucet at dawn and its closing at sunset. Faucets often consisted of conical stoppers placed within conical sockets, hence built on the principle of the valve demonstrated in Figure 3.2. They could also be constructed, like the ones in use today, with a hole horizontally through the stopper to link the inflow to the outflow tube thus controlling the flow of liquid by turning the faucet and thereby varying the exposed cross section of the faucet's channel.

Figures 3.5A and 3.5B represent a different type of water clock, in part the forerunner of our own timepieces, so far as the face of our clocks is concerned. The water supply is the same as before and the receiver and float operate on the same principles. The difference lies in the application of the rack and pinion arrangement to the rising float. The picture illustrates a copy of a model excavated in Rome which is, no doubt, a later production, perhaps of the beginning of the Christian era. It was apparently used to measure time intervals independently of the calendar, since no information is available about months or days.

Its basic mode of operation is simple enough. The circular face rests upon the receiver tank and the hand upon the face is linked to a gearwheel or pinion, supported back of it. To the supporting frame is also attached a tube through which moves a rod provided with teeth, constituting a rack, which is attached to a float at its base. As this float rises with the inflow of water, the rack, which engages the pinion, rotates it and thereby rotates the hand on the clock face. The inflow of water causes the hand to describe a circle and indicate the hours.

So far as we know, the system of twelve hours for each daylight interval, whatever the season, was in general use. The water clocks described prior to the one with rack and pinion were well served by having the time chart for the day so adjusted that a winter day required a smaller overall height, hence volume of water, than a summer day. This was achieved by simply having the twelve spacings climbed by the float's pointer, cover smaller distances in winter than in summer. To attain this arrangement one simply turned the cylinder carrying the time chart, each day one degree, approximately.

In the present clock this is not possible. The only arrangement that will yield twelve short hours for the winter stretch of daylight and twelve longer hours for the summer day is a respectively varying rate of inflow. Clearly, a rapid inflow in the wintertime will make the hand go around faster than a slower rate, thus corresponding to a shorter day required for the winter, with a longer, slower, flow for the summer, and intermediate rates for spring and fall. We shall soon see that the ancients developed precisely such compensating devices.

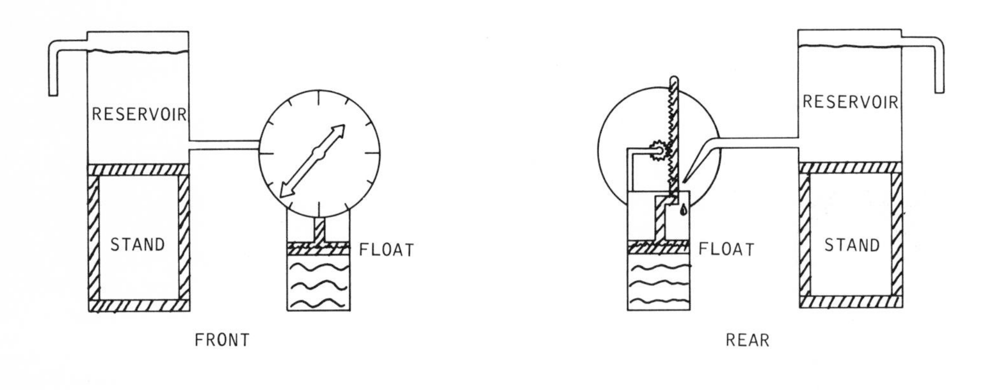

Figure 3.5A

Figure 3.5B

2. The Anaphoric Clock

A different use of the same principle is seen in Figures 3. 6A, B, C, D, and E, which demonstrate a clepsydra described by Vitruvius somewhat sketchy, revealing a high degree of sophistication. Many modern authors have attempted to elucidate the true nature of this particular clock, and the following is what seems to be a reasonable summary of their speculations.

As in all clepsydrae, water is conducted from aqueducts to a reservoir, where its level is maintained at a constant height. From this reservoir the water flows into the container, here the cylinder, which holds the float to which is attached a string, wound around an axle placed horizontally above, in an appropriate structure. The other, or free, end of the string has a weight attached to it that acts as counterweight to the float. The water flowing into the container raises the float, thus permitting the weight to sink and thereby causing the axle to rotate. To the end of the axle facing the viewer, there is attached a plate representing the heavens, and serving to simulate the movement of the heavenly vault with its stars and planets across the local sky in its daily rotation (Figure 3. 6A).

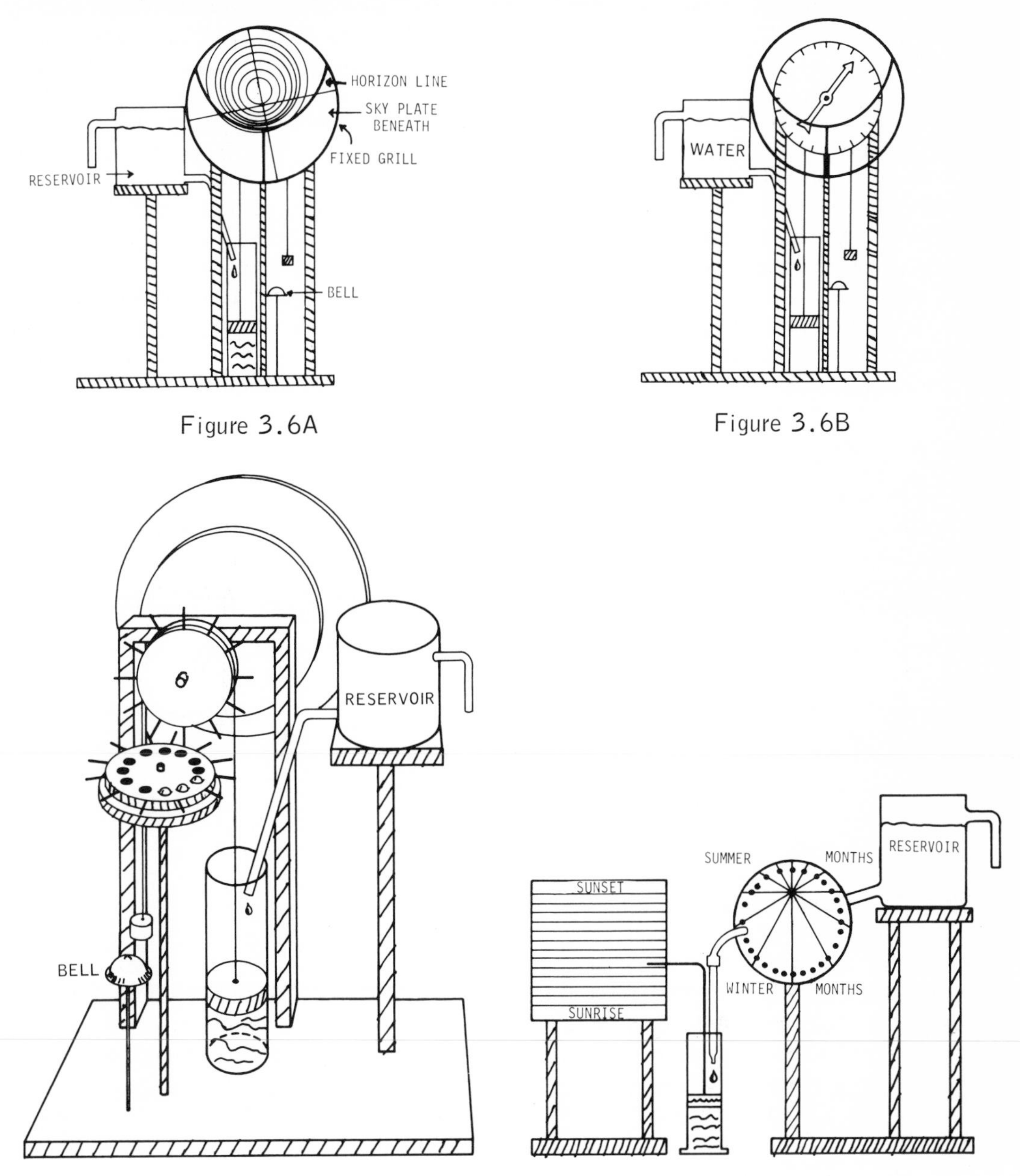

Figure 3.6A

Figure 3.6B

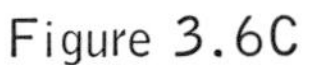
Figure 3.6C

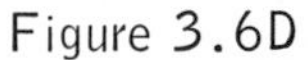
Figure 3.6D

In front of the plate representing the sky which rotates about the North Star as its center, there is a grill representing the particular horizon for the place of observation. This celestial map is constructed very much like our star charts in which one turns a plate containing the image of the sky, so that the circular cutout in the fixed plate above it displays the constellations visible locally at various hours of the night. Here in Figure 3. 6A we have a similar arrangement. The sky shown on the circular plate is in actuality represented as a projection of the vault of the heavens upon a horizontal plane below, with the North Star, Polaris, as the center of rotation, hence the center of the plate. The constellations of the zodiac will thus form an eccentric circle. It is eccentric because the plane in which we visualize its circle of twelve constellations lies at an angle of $23\frac{1}{2}°$ to the plane of the celestial equator, and any inclined circle is necessarily represented by an eccentric circle if projected upon a horizon which is a plane tangent to a point on a globe.

Note that the horizon line is the U-shaped line. Any constellation beneath this line is actually below the horizon and will be unseen at that particular locality. The sky model here represented was employed upon a clock excavated at the turn of the century in Central Europe. It was intended for the city of Juvarum in Austria, presumably for a latitude of about 48°N. The sky rotates clockwise as it does in reality for a viewer who faces south. (Should he face north, the sky is seen to rotate counterclockwise.) Here in the model, south is up, east to the left and west to the right of the sky-plate. The nature of the horizon grid is best seen in Figure 3. 6B, which also shows the hand over the clock face marked out to 24 hours. Such would be the scale if it were used for astronomical purposes rather than for the common telling of time. Observers of the sky, as we learned from Sextus Empiricus, employed water clocks to measure the sidereal day, the time between successive culminations of a given star. (The clock hand is added to show what this clock could do.)

The kind of waterclock here described was called anaphoric, which means rising in Greek, because its circular plate of the sky indicated not only the daily path of the sun but also the particular stars rising and setting upon a given horizon. Different latitudes saw different cuts of the celestial sphere above their horizons. Consider our terrestrial globe by viewing one on the table before you. Take a card and place it over, let us say, Chicago. This card is the horizon for that city. To the ancients the earth was a tiny sphere within an immense sphere of the sky. Before modern times, the latter was taken to be literally what it seemed, namely, a big, remote sphere holding the stars vaguely in its texture or on its surface. In consequence, any horizon will, if extended far enough in all directions, cut the celestial sphere so as to have its own unique segment, or half of it. The anaphoric clock served to make you see clearly on a horizontal plane the particular sky you will see on each local horizon in accordance with its latitude at any particular time, especially in the daytime. It did it by means of a horizontal projection of the dome of the sky above your horizon, hence at your latitude.

The horizontal projection of the sky constitutes a clever geometrical device which will be met with again in ancient science and deserves careful description. To project the dome of the sky upon a plane, imagine yourself far down at the south celestial pole looking northward. The way things will then appear is demonstrated in Figure 3. 7. The outer circle is the sky. Its points

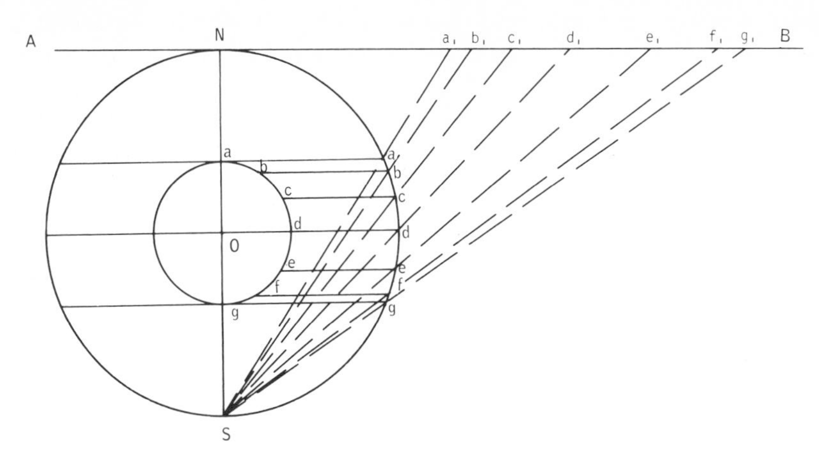

Figure 3.7

a, b, c mark the positions of the zodiacal constellations north of the equator d, and e, f, and g the positions of the constellations south of the equator. (A. G. Drachmann. *Ctesibius, Philon and Heron.* Copenhagen, 1948, p. 21-26).

The line ANB will show the constellations of the celestial sphere as you see them against space from your position, not on earth but at the South Pole of the vast sphere of the heavens. The symbols represent the zodiacal constellations which are assumed, as the observer must assume, to be placed in their natural positions inside the celestial sphere. This means that the circle of the zodiacal constellations must be extended to the more distant sphere of which the points N and S are the imagined poles. Hence their extensions to points a to g. These constellations extend roughly 24° above and 24° below the celestial equator, d, with Cancer the crab, a, nearest the north pole, and Capricornus the goat, g, nearest the south pole. One thus obtains an accurate scale for a plane projection, since all the arc segments between the zodiacal signs have measurable dimensions which correspond to respective distances on the line ANB. Thus angle ∡ or NOd, which is on the plane or in space, 90°, is now equivalent to angle ∡ or NSd_1, and is 45°, because in this presentation the angles are half the arc they subtend. Since g is the point of winter solstice, taken then as approximately 24° south of the equator, in the constellation Capricornus, the angle NSg = 45° + 24/2 = 57°. Similarly ∡ angle NSa_1 where a is Cancer, the summer solstice, yields a value of 45 - 12 = 33°. The arcs of the various segments of the sky subtended at the center O, are as the sines of their corresponding angles. Thus the arc 24° corresponds to sin 24° as measured from the center, O, and is half the cord ag, since a is 24° above the celestial equator and g 24° below it. Arc cd is half of the numerical value of sin 24°. Having obtained these values, one then employs the ratios of the projected relative distances to draw the correct map of a plane, or stereoscopic projection of the vault of the sky upon a flat surface.

To complete a sketch of the horizon one must know the latitude of the place where the clock is to be erected. One draws next an analemma, which is a geometric construction that designates the daily position of the sun for a given latitude.

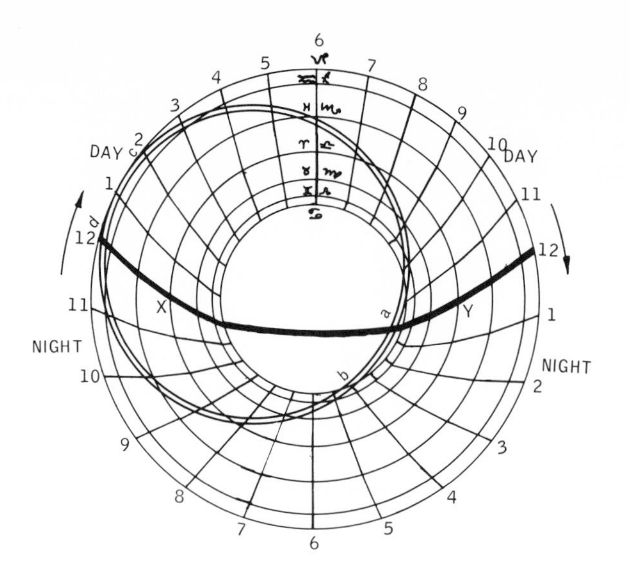

Figure 3.8

The analemma of a given location records the height of the sun at noon and the positions of sunrise and of sunset all year round. If one draws then a circle for the horizon, one can lay off on it the points of sunset and sunrise as located by their angular distances from the meridian every day of the year. This is what is represented in Figure 3.8, which contains both the projected sky and horizon of the latitude of Alexandria, given by Vitruvius as about 31°N. latitude.

The entire drawing represents a plane projection of the sky as seen by an imaginary viewer situated far down on the diagram, at the south celestial pole and looking northward. The scale is based on proportions obtained as described. Through each zodiacal constellation a circle is drawn, thus representing the month corresponding to the sun's stay in the respective constellation. The common center of the circles is the projected center of the revolution of the sky, hence the north pole of the heavens. The projected image of the belt of the zodiac is represented by the double lined excentric circle. That belt crosses all the twelve months represented by the concentric circles. The twelfth part of the year in which the sun is northernmost in the sky, zodiacal segment ab, is the time interval encompassing the thirty days about the summer solstice. Conversely, the zodiacal segment cd is the corresponding time interval of the winter solstice when the sun is furthest from the north pole, that is furthest south on the meridian at noon. [The fuller reasoning behind this kind of projection will be explained below.]

Radiating from the center are lines which divide at this latitude the intervals of day and night each month of the year into twelve parts each. The lines marked 12 on the left and on the right will, when joined across the center, mark the fixed horizon line on a separate grid. This joined line constitutes the horizon because the one on the left marks the points of sunrise for each monthly segment and the one on the right the points of sunset. Points marked X and Y, show the sunrise and sunset on the equinox days, the 21 of March and September. The sun can only be on the zodiacal circle which is indicated on a disc with the stars and planets, and which revolves in the back of the fixed grill of the horizon line with its division into hours, twelve and twelve. The disc of the sky was made to have 365 holes in the zodiacal double ring and a peg representing the sun was put in the proper hole each day when the clock was made ready. Thus on June 21 the sun would be midway in the zodiacal region ab (from Cancer to Leo) and would inscribe the Cancer ♋ circle, cutting the horizon line on the left early in the morning and setting on the right late in the evening as it follows the innermost circle. Conversely, when the sun is on zodiacal segment cd on December 21, it follows the outermost circle, emerges above the horizon line 12, late in the morning, and sets early. The proportions of arc above and below the horizon line tell the relative ratios of day and night for each monthly segment of the year, and thereby for each day. In this manner the anaphoric clock was a truly complex and sophisticated achievement of the first order.

This remarkable clock also performs a third function of lasting merit that we still use to this day. It serves as an alarm clock. How it operates can best be seen in Figure 3.6C. The pulley operated by the rising float and its counterweight had a gear arrangement which locked with a horizontal wheel as seen in Figure 3.6C. One revolution of the vertical pulley corresponded with one revolution of the horizontal wheel. The latter had holes in it and rotated above a plate fixed to its supporting column. Within the holes of the rotating wheel were balls of brass or wood, or stone pebbles. The fixed plate beneath this horizontal wheel had only one hole. Beneath this hole a metal belljar was situated. As the upper gear wheel rotated in time, one of its balls came to be located above the hole in the fixed lower plate so that the ball fell through it and struck the bell. Arrangements could be made to catch the bouncing balls for repeated use. The number of balls placed in the holes of the horizontal gear wheel depended upon how frequently one wished the bell to ring.

We see here two principles which are still in use today: the circular clock face and hand to indicate hours, and an adjustable alarm bell. The third, the ingenious invention of attaching the moving sky to a clock and obliging it to reveal all the celestial bodies in their shifting orbits each minute of the 24-hour period of day and night, was put aside by our civilization. This civilization is completely indifferent to celestial events except when they qualify for front page news, as in the case of solar eclipses, or even lunar ones.

The anaphoric clock had another device of great ingenuity which is demonstrated in Figure 3.6D. It happens to be the sole application of a new principle in which the scale of the usual twelve hourly divisions from sunup to sundown was kept constant, while the rate of flow of the water into the float-containing vessel was controlled so as to yield correct results. The manner in which this was achieved was as follows: The water from the tank to the float-containing vessel was made to fall through different heights. Since the pressure which determines the rate of fall of the water is controlled by the difference in levels of the top of the water volume to its level of outflow, the higher the outlet is placed, hence the nearer to the top, the slower the flow. Conversely, the lower the outlet, that is, the further from the upper level of the water column it is placed, the faster the rate of outflow. And the faster the flow, the shorter the time in which the marker based on the float will cover the span of the twelve hours indicated in Figure 3.6D. This principle is cleverly exploited by obliging the water to flow into the float vessel through an opening lodged at the proper height of the sun in the zodiac on a given day. This meant that the circle of the zodiac was also provided with 365 outlets or faucets, one for each day. The outlets for Sagittarius-Capricornus, the last days of Fall and first of Winter, were arranged to be low on the disk so that the difference in water levels was largest then. This yielded twelve short hours on the scale. Conversely, when the sun was in Gemini-Cancer, the period of the longest days, the reverse was true. The faucets were high on the zodiacal belt so that the difference in water column, the pressure, was weakest and the water flowed slowly and yielded twelve long hours. The intermediate months had their outlets between these two extremes yielding appropriate lengths for the hourly divisions of their respective daylights.

One more clock need be mentioned, namely, that of Plato which is referred to by Atheneus (*Deipnosophists* 4, 174), and was interpreted by H. Diels in his *Antike Technik* (1920, p. 198). It is an alarm clock operating a whistle. It consists of three vessels (Figure 3.9). The first is a clepsydra that is filled with as much water as is needed for the desired time interval. The water is permitted to flow from it into the second vessel (II) which is provided with a siphon. As this vessel fills up, the curve of the siphon is closed by the rising water and vessel II is then emptied. The siphon extends into the closed but empty vessel III, from which the driven out air is made to flow through an aperture so as to produce a shrill whistle.

In conclusion we should be reminded of the great service performed by the still well-known hour-glass which, however, did not come into its own until the Middle Ages and is claimed to be of Arabic origin. There can be little doubt that it is a more convenient instrument for telling time intervals than any of the water clocks described, which list probably exhausts the major available models. It is less messy than water, requires no supply line, can be carried on voyages in wagons or on boats, and is easy to pack. It has the disadvantage of requiring continuous attention. While the water clocks demanded to be emptied every evening and had to be started at every sunrise, the hour glass, whether filled with sand or dry seeds, had to be turned at intervals, which depended upon their dimensions and grain employed.

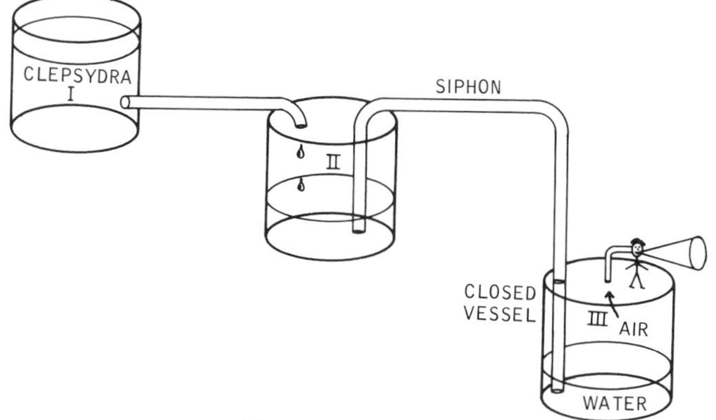

Figure 3.9

The following quotation throws some light on its use by a famous navigator: (*Admiral of the Ocean Sea* by Samuel Eliot Morison. 2 Vols. Vol 1, pp. 160-161. Time Edition).

"In Columbus' day, and until the late sixteenth century, the only ship's clock available was the *ampoletta* or relos de arena (sand clock), a half-hour glass containing enough sand to run from the upper to the lower section in exactly thirty minutes. Made in Venice, these glasses were so fragile that a large number of spares were carried--Magellan had eighteen on his flagship. It was the duty of a gromet or ship's boy in each watch to mind the ampoletta and reverse it promptly when the sand ran out. A very rough sea might retard the running of the sand, or the gromet might go to sleep; Columbus on one occasion expresses in his Journal the fear that the boys were slack about it. As a ship gains time sailing east and loses it sailing west, even the most modern ship's clock has to be corrected daily by wireless. The only way Columbus could do this with his hour-glass clock was to erect a pin or gnomon on the center of his compass card, and watch for the exact moment of noon when the sun's shadow touched the fleur-de-lis that marked the north, and then turn the glass. But that could hardly be counted on to give him true noon nearer than 15 or 20 minutes, and he did not do it very often, for it is evident from some of his log entries that his 'ship's time' was as much as half an hour slow by the sun."

All kinds of morals may be drawn from this sketch and its message. Certain it is that until the coming of the mechanical clock and the use of the escapement, man had to measure his time in ways which seem crude to us but which were essentially adequate enough not only for great progress in astronomy and navigation, but also for practical, domestic, social and political purposes.

IV The Calendars of Antiquity and Our Own Times

1. Lunar and Lunisolar Calendars

Calendars, like most complex patterns of a culture, such as religion, language, government, or customs, are never suddenly and purposefully conceived and brought full-grown into being. Neither men of genius nor appointed committees, neither annointed prophets nor men of boundless dedication, produce a complete, functional calendar, formally presented to the people for their use and enjoyment. Social institutions or innovations seldom come into being in this manner. They evolve as a rule from some small, indirect, or incidental beginnings, and grow by assimilating a facet here or by appropriating a segment there, occasionally adding a distinctly novel element to the growing practice. What one sees at any particular time of a social pattern is in all likelihood a mosaic of an evolutionary past in which many, at times even unrelated, elements fused to compose the final product. Our contemporary calendar is such an outgrowth.

Time seems to be an innately built-in concept in the psyche of man. Development, growth, maturation and aging are biological functions of which men can hardly remain unaware. Events in time are part and parcel of an animal's existence, since in practice all organismal functions are cyclical, specifically, eating, sleeping, work, rest, mating, birth, and more. By being aware of these events, man automatically becomes conscious of the passage of time. Season follows season, each associated with somewhat different events. Sufficiently impressive as some of them invariably are, a scheme of time-reckoning is automatically imposed upon the human mind and a calendar comes willy-nilly into being. The cyclic recurrences of winter and summer, of wars or floods, of flights of birds, of heat and cold, of short days and long ones, of budding time and harvest time, of foaling, egg laying and the like, suggest and even force some scheme of time-keeping upon the individual and his society. Such recognition, as a rule, finds a place within the web of the culture.

There is, moreover, that everlasting, pervading sky with its unending panorama of change, dramatic, and inspiring. Its rhythm more than any other harmonic beat of nature came to be the most popular, convenient foundation for a calendar, forming a natural set of markers for the passage of time. The moon, mysterious and ubiquitous, a goddess as well as a practical, immediate force on earth, affects men and women, plants and animals, rivers and winds, wombs and passions. This intriguing planet that never stands still and never remains the same even two nights in a row, quite naturally imposed its life cycle as a universal unit of time measurement, a keystone of the calendar. It gave rise to the term month and was watched and honored in practically all civilizations.

The evolving cultures of antiquity almost generally began with a lunar calendar. We find lunar calendars in early Babylon, Egypt, Greece and Rome, and also in most primitive cultures. The moon not only varies its shape but also its orbit. The sun too, even more tellingly, as we saw, varies rhythmically on a year to year basis with regard to its elevation in the heavens at noon, its point of sunrise and sunset, and against the background of the stars. Both these celestial bodies were therefore used as guides to the passage of time, as foundations for a calendar. In the Moslem calendar, the moon is used exclusively as index; in the modern, universal, or Christian calendar, the sun is the sole key to time-reckoning; in some ancient cultures and most prominently in the Biblical, or Hebrew, calendar, a combination of the two was employed. These constitute the three calendars in service today--the lunar, the solar, and the lunisolar.

Let us consider the lunar calendar first. It was historically the oldest and was used by virtually all nations whose evolution reached the point of utilization of a time-reckoning scheme beyond the cycle of day and night. This latter unit is primary. No human being and surely no group of any size can help noting the day and employing it as a unit of time. The month may theoretically be considered a more sophisticated unit, but in practice it was as universal as the day and night period. With primitive man's exaggerated awareness of the heavens and his emotional involvement in all its doings, neither the bewitching evening crescent of the western sky, nor the placid, seemingly lost and useless crescent of the pre-dawn morning, facing its tusks in the opposite direction, nor the moon's waxing to fullness and subsequent waning, repeated in endless succession, could possibly escape his notice. The moon's cycle, its lunation, came to be used universally as the second and longer unit of time-reckoning, the moonth, or as we say today, the month. The lunation, the period designating a full cycle of the moon, thus came to be the natural unit of time in pre-historic and pre-agricultural eras.

We saw that the Egyptians were the first to note periodic celestial cycles involving mainly the sun and stars, and that the Babylonians initiated knowledge of celestial cycles involving the planets. The latter were never employed as a unit of time measurement while, as we saw, rising and setting stars were. The Egyptian year was founded upon the first heliacal rising of Sothis, their name for Sirius, the dog-star, which in reality designated a circular revolution of the sun around the vault of the heavens.

Because of the seasons, the year was a natural unit of time measurement, since except for limited regions of the globe, its presence is felt by everyone. There is either summer or winter, or seasons of rain and drought; there is the time of growth and ripening of fruit. No more than the phases of the moon can such periodicity be overlooked. In Egypt, the conspicuous seasonal phenomenon was the flooding of the Nile. In spite of the fact that its specific time of onset varies from year to year, flooding occurs within sufficiently narrow limits to attract attention.

To a large degree, the history of the true calendar is an attempt at harmonizing these two conspicuous cyclical phenomena of nature--the moon's periodic rhythm, and the seasonal periodicity expressed in the cyclical behavior of the sun. Most, if not all, early societies that we are acquainted with, are aware of these two potential methods of constructing a calendar, as well as of a third one which is merely an aspect of the solar periodicity, namely, the changing configurations of the stars in the heavens.

Continuous time-reckoning involving the moon as basis of the monthly unit of measurement, makes its appearance in almost all human societies, regardless of stage of advancement. Most human cultures make use of the moon's revolution around the earth and employ it as a basic division of time, even as they do the night and day period. The month is employed even by cultures which cannot count well enough to record the number of days in it. Similarly, some primitive society may be aware of an annual interval from snow to snow or flood to flood without counting the intervening days.

The first appearances of the crescent moon and, at times, the full moon, were frequent subjects of joyous worship in many primitive and early cultures. To count the flow of time, notches were often made in a stick or knots in a rope. The month thus became the unit for continuous reckoning in history, and was frequently given identification by distinctive names within the yearly cycle and was also associated with some outstanding seasonal event. For convenience the customary number of twelve months to the seasonal year was occasionally increased by one to make thirteen, so as to keep the months and seasons in line. Wherever the calendar did undergo any further elaboration, it remained as a rule in the hands of the priest whose function was primarily ecclesiastical and ritualistic. All life was ordered in primitive societies along religious rites; one might put it conversely and say that religious ritual and regulations constituted the formal aspects of the life of the people.

Occasionally, months were named after stars because these become identifiable landmarks of the seasons, since the times of their rising and setting were linked to the sun. Chief among the constellations that have served to designate a month associated with it, was the constellation of the Pleiades. This fact of tying the lunar month to the seasons, necessarily brought in its trail another phenomenon that soon became widespread. The phenomenon of intercalation, or the cutom of adding a month, a lunation, to the counting of years so as to keep the series in harmony with the solar seasons. The lunar month having only $29\frac{1}{2}$ days will yield a year of $(29\frac{1}{2} \times 12) = 354$ days. Twelve lunations will thus be a little over 11 days short of a common (non-leap) year. To keep the lunar months in line with the seasons, an extra month, called an intercalary month, has to be added every three years, plus three more days.

But while most calendars of primitive cultures were synchronized luni-solar schemes, there evolved in history a calendar which is completely lunar. It is still in existence today, and is honored by close to a half billion people. Such a calendar is the one used by the Mohammedans. The old Arabian names of months refer to seasons and to festivals. Since even before the coming of Mohammed pilgrimages were made to Mecca for religious and trade reasons, it transpired that some months were named in reference to the famed Mecca fairs, just as the names of other months contained references to rains or the foaling of camels. The Meccan fairs necessarily depended upon the seasons, both because of facility in travel and the products sold. The months for the fair therefore had to have a fixed position in the solar year. Although the evidence is somewhat indirect, it seems safe to conclude that the pre-Mohammedan Arabs had the usual intercalary month every third year. The Arab calendar was not in those years an organized scholarly scheme, as it was in advanced cultures. A special priest was in charge of declaring leap years and adding the thirteenth month regarded as holy in consequence.

The prophet Mohammed prohibited this monthly intercalation and declared mandatory upon his followers a pure or straight lunar year of twelve months, six of 29 days and six of 30, thus yielding a year of 354 days. Such a calendar is completely independent of the seasons, and in the course of time any month of a given name will wander through all the four seasons. The sacred month of Ramadan, which commemorates the Hegira or Mohammed's escape from Mecca by a fast from sunup to sundown each day, may fall in the short days of winter as well as in summer when the days are long and the sacrifice greater. Also, Moslems who reach the age of about $33\frac{1}{2}$ years by their count, will only be $32\frac{1}{2}$ years by the solar calendar. The reasons for Mohammed's prohibition of intercalation in the relevant passage of the Koran (9:36ff.) are not too clearly discernable. "The nasî is in truth an addition to unbelief in which the unbelievers go astray," meaning by nasî the process of intercalation, it is presumed. Martin P. Nilsson in his book, *Primitive Time-Reckoning,* gives a credible explanation for the prophet's prohibition. Before the time of Mohammed, the Arabs were certainly far from being in a cultured or even civilized state. Their calendar was not planned for long range service, and the intercalation every third year was purely empirical. This meant that an official, a priest, was appointed to handle the matter, since the month at the end of every third year was regarded as sacred. "The intercalation therefore involved a transference of the sanctity of the month following the feast of pilgrims to the next but one after the feast." (p. 257)

There being no ordered calendar cycle, the priest in charge merely announced to the pilgrims his decision to have an additional month and they broadcast the news to all communities. "However, the entrusting of such power over the calendar to one individual lends itself too easily to abuses with a view to ends which have nothing to do with the calendar. The stock example is afforded by the Roman pontifices (judges) at the end of the Republic. It is therefore nothing to wonder at, that the calendar should have been disorganized during Mohammed's stay in Mecca." (p. 258)

Mohammed sought to eliminate the abuses introduced by the bribery and corruption of the official in charge; by freely shifting the intercalary month, he disturbed the traditional dependence of the month of pilgrimage upon the time of year. He therefore abolished intercalation altogether and gave the world what is probably the first organized and rationalized strictly lunar calendar with no reference at all to seasons. A student of evolution unaware of the origin of the lunar calendar, might be led to consider it as most primitive and prior to intercalation, which only goes to show how devious the actual mode of social evolution can be.

The Mohammedan era begins with the day after the prophet's flight from Mecca to Medina, its day one, which fell on Friday, July 16, 622 A.D. Its calendar is also partitioned into cycles of 19 common years of 354 days, and 11 intercalary years having an extra day at the year's end, hence of 355 days.

The object of this intercalation is to have as accurate a lunar month as possible. The year thus gets to be 354-11/30 days long, and the month 29-191/360 days, which comes within 2.8 seconds of the exact astronomical mean lunation, an error of one day in 2,400 years.

The earliest known organized or fixed calendars were lunisolar because, as already stated, man was keenly aware of both lunar and solar cycles. By an organized calendar is meant one that is critically considered and arranged in a planned manner, either for permanence or for some period of reasonable length. There is no definite evidence that such calendars were in use in Babylonia and Egypt before two thousand years prior to the Christian era. Much observation of the heavens occurred in those lands and much lore about the stars and planets arose there. Both countries made use of effective calendars probably as far back as three millenia B.C. Such calendars were wholly lunar, or if lunisolar, they received their intercalary months on an empirical basis from year to year. Around 1800 B.C., Hammurabi, King of Babylon, wrote to his minister: "The year is out of place. Have the next month recorded under the name of Ululu II. Payment of taxes at Babylon, instead of ending on the 25th day of Tanitu, shall end on the 25th day of Ululu II." Thus, the adjustment was accomplished and life proceeded unhampered for individuals and the community.

As luck would have it, these two countries from which so many authentic records have come down to us, are the most controversial with regard to specific knowledge of their astronomy and mathematics as well as their exact uses of calendars. As recently as 1952, one of the greatest authorities in the field expressed himself in the following terms about Babylonian astronomy: "There is scarcely another chapter in the history of science where an equally deep gap exists between the generally accepted description of a period and the results which have slowly emerged from a detailed investigation of the source material." (O. Neugebauer, *The Exact Sciences in Antiquity*. Harper Torchbook, 1962. p. 97). True, the author is concerned exclusively with strictly mathematical procedures and is after statements or approaches made, as he says, "on a purely rational basis," in the belief that locating and naming "of conspicuous stars or constellations does not constitute an astronomical science." This limits the search to the final stages of calendrical knowledge. But even if one were willing to enlarge the scope of the definition of science, there would still be little agreement among the scholars, because the evidence is generally inconclusive. Certain it is, however, that by the end of the preparatory period lasting from about 1800 to about 400 B.C., Babylonian culture had recognized the band of the zodiac with its twelve constellations of 30 degrees each, had a fixed lunisolar calendar, possessed knowledge of the periodic motions of the planets, and, of course, the motions of the sun, the equinoxes, solstices, and the periods of daylight and darkness at different latitudes.

It also seems certain that it was not until a little after 400 B.C. that intercalations became standardized. Prior to that date, orders were issued by the Babylonian king to his administrative officials or by the priests of Esagila, the great temple in Babylon, that there would be an intercalary month during that year, identified as year 10 or 15 of the reign of the given king. Intercalation could be made in two places of the calendar: A month could be added either after the sixth or after the twelfth month. The message designated which one it was to be, indicating that the calendar was still empirical, ordered as the need arose rather than by a formula for automatic intercalations in the same manner as we have leap years.

The year 747 B.C., occurring in the reign of Nabonassar, marks the beginning of an era in which "Babylonian astronomers began to recognize, as the result of centuries of observation of the heavens, that 235 lunar months have always exactly the same number of days as nineteen solar years. This meant that seven lunar months must be intercalated each nineteen year period." (R. A. Parker and W. H. Dubberstein. *Babylonian Chronology.* Brown University Press, 1956. p. 1). Intercalation became standardized a little after that year, with the extra month inserted at first mostly after the sixth month, but later more regularly after the twelfth.

In addition to the strictly lunar count of time there was the lunisolar year, the year employed to this day by orthordox Jewry, in which a strictly lunar month is the basic unit of time while an extra month is added regularly every three years to keep all twelve months tied to the seasons. The cycle of lunar months is harmonized with each cycle of the sun. As the Jewish calendar testifies, this is a serviceable arrangement that can perform all the tasks a calendar is expected to do, while each individual common year is merely an artificial unit of twelve lunar cycles. Through the inclusion of two common years in a package of three years of 37 lunations with three extra days, the arbitrary common year of twelve lunar months is harmonized with the natural solar year. In such a calendar, all feasts, holidays, and rituals, which were initially products of man's interaction with nature, remain lunar in their timing. Only the strictly solar holy days or those holidays based upon positions of stars, whose visibility, rising and setting, depends essentially on the sun, were not lunar in origin, and there were not many of these.

In Egypt and later in Babylonia, a strictly solar calendar evolved in the course of time, side by side with the older lunar one. By a strictly solar year, we mean a year consisting of 12 months of 30 days each, months which were not tied to the moon in any way, just as our months today are in no way so connected. In addition, the year had five free or loose days unattached to a month, added at the end of the year to make a total of 365 days. These additional five days were intercalary days. Such a calendar evolved in Egypt and in Babylonia after many centuries in which the strictly lunar month had been employed.

This solar calendar was, in effect, a civil calendar, meaning a year adjusted to the seasons and in use generally throughout the nation for social, economic and administrative purposes. It consisted of 365 days and was tied to the sun's apparent circuit in the heavens by employing the heliacal rising of the dogstar, Sothis, our Sirius. It is possible to arrive at this number of days by simply obtaining the average of several of the three lunar year cycles of 354, 354, 384 days, which in itself gives 364 days. In a longer run than three years, the wish to keep the linear cycle abreast of the seasons would oblige the administrative authorities to add an extra day now and then so as to synchronize the two scales. The average of a larger number of cycles could yield 365 days per year. The keepers of the calendar were probably aided in their task by their choice of the rising of Sothis as the beginning of the new year. The evidence shows that such a first civil year was introduced around the year 2937 B.C. There were two significant features to this newly evolved year. First, in honor of tradition, the lunar features of the year remained in force, since no new calendar per se ever introduces new customs or abolishes old ones. Next, since the year has in reality $365\frac{1}{4}$ days instead of 365, the official year's beginning will not be simultaneous with the heliacal rising of Sothis for long, but will fall behind it one day every four years. Since the major events of the calendar were rooted in the lunar tradition and lunar month, with proper intercalations retained for ritual and religious purposes, the shift of the New Year's day away from the heliacal rising of Sothis was hardly taken seriously for some time. There is even some evidence that the Egyptians had also evolved a year which had twelve lunar months and eleven intercalary days. (Richard A Parker, *The Calendars of Ancient Egypt*. University of Chicago Press, 1950).

A purely solar calendar serves as the civil calendar of today. The moon is paid no attention whatever and follows its lone satellite orbit, unwatched and unrecorded, utterly disregarded by the calendar. Our calendar year rests on the sun's path in the zodiac, the solstices and equinoxes, and runs approximately from winter solstice to winter solstice, though not quite, since January 1 comes about ten days after the winter solstice.

On the other hand, the Christian religious calendar is still a lunisolar one, like its parent, the Jewish calendar, because the moon must be taken into account in the determination of Easter. This introduces quite a number of complexities into the calendar, and has produced disturbances that led to the abandonment of the older Julian calendar named after Julius Caesar, its founder. They finally led to its replacement by the present calendar, the Gregorian, so named after Pope Gregory XIII who introduced it in 1582 A.D. But before considering these matters, we must examine some basic phenomena still valid today, though discovered and taken into account by the ancients.

2. The Elements of a Calendar

Let us consider the elements of which a calendar is composed. First, there is the twenty four hour day, which refers to one rotation of the earth around its axis. But a rotation of a sphere on its axis has to be measured against some outer mark. For us on earth this can be done in two ways. Since the earth is infinitely far from the stars, the times elapsing between two meridional crossings of any star will be identical. By a meridional crossing is meant the act of sighting a given star exactly on the meridian, hence true south at midnight. The interval between two such crossings designates one full rotation of the globe. This is called a sidereal (starry) day and has been found to be perfectly constant for several millenia. However, our actual day is the solar day which is the interval between successive passages of the sun across the meridian, hence the period from noon to noon (or midnight to midnight). This is a solar day, which is necessarily a little longer than the sidereal day because the sun moves eastward, or backwards, one degree every day, which is the same as saying that the earth moves a corresponding amount in the opposite direction. It therefore takes a little longer to bring a given point on earth

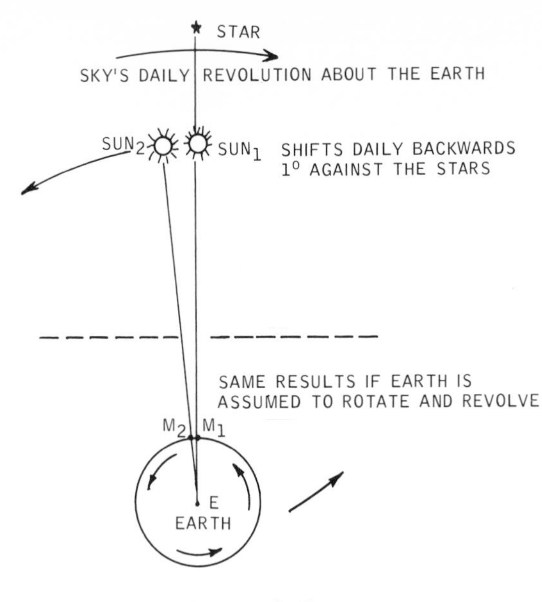

Figure 4.1

opposite the shifting sun. In Figure 4.1 when the sky makes one complete revolution in a clockwise direction, or in terms of our present scheme, when M_1 on earth rotates 360 degrees to be again in line EM_1-Star, the duration is about four minutes shorter than the solar day, measured from noon to noon, since the sun has within the 24-hour period shifted its position about one degree and is now opposite M_2. Thus for the sun to be again on the meridian along the line EM_2-Sun, the sky has to revolve the extra distance M_1 M_2. This distance is about 1° and takes approximately 4 minutes in time. 360/24 hrs. = 15° per hour. A shift of one degree is therefore 60 min./15°, hence 4 minutes in time per degree. The ancients used water clocks to measure the exact length of the sidereal day. The same result is obtained if one assumes the earth to rotate and to shift in its orbit 1° approximately per day around the sun.

The solar day does not happen to be a constant quantity. The ancients knew that as well, since they watched the sun's daily eastward motion of 1° against the stars, and saw that it varied in a regular fashion. We know today that this apparent irregularity is caused by two phenomena. To begin with, the earth's speed in its orbit is not uniform, as is clearly seen from Kepler's Second Law. In the summertime, the earth moves slowly in its ellipse, since it is far from the sun. The period of June 22 to September 22 is longer by about six days than is the period of winter, December 21 to March 21. There is next the fact that the plane of the ecliptic, or the sun's path, lies at an angle of $23\frac{1}{2}°$ to the plane of the equator. Going by appearances we will say that the sun moves up the ecliptic or down it, so that the apparent shift is not always equal. For the sake of simplicity and uniformity, the concept of a mean solar day was introduced to yield an accurate average. Hence, we speak of the solar day as the distance covered daily by an imaginary, moving sun.

Moreover, the day can be and has been variously defined in history. The "natural day" is from sunup to sundown. The ancient Jews marked their day from sunset to sunset. The Romans counted their day variously, but at the time of Christ had it begin at 6:00 a. m., so that Christ's death, occurring on the ninth hour, took place at 3:00 p. m. The ancient Jews and others divided the night into three watches, the Greeks and Romans into four. Modern times commence the civil or common day at midnight, astronomers commence theirs at noon.

Another component of our calendar is the week. It must be regarded as an artificial unit rather than a natural one, unlike the day, the month, and the year which represent natural events. The week was made for social convenience, either as the interval between market days, or for religious reasons. The Romans had an artificial unit which they called the nundine, consisting of eight day packages, the eighth being the market-day. The Jewish or biblical week consists of seven days, the last being a day of rest. The planetary week rests upon the fact that the ancients knew the seven planets seen with the unaided eye. They counted the sun and moon as planets, and of course, not the earth.

There is no conclusive explanation of the origin of the week, but it is certain that two institutions, or customs, contributed to its existence. The first is the biblical story of creation entailing seven days named by number, the sabbath serving as the seventh day, or the day of rest. Second, the planetary week in which hours were named after the seven planets, and the days came to be named after the midnight hour of each day. This form of the week originated in the Roman Empire at the time when the Jewish influence was strongly felt, especially around the time of the beginning of the Christian Era, and simultaneously when the influence of Chaldean astrology was spreading throughout the Roman culture sphere.

Somehow the Jewish sabbath became in the outlook of astrology the day of Saturn, a day of inaction, a day of rest, and perhaps a day of bad luck, since Saturn was the planet of gloom and misfortune. Already in his Roman History, Dio Cassius (around 230 A. D.) assumed the fusion of the two types of week to be well established. The seemingly correct explanation is given by him of the origin of the planetary names of the days of the week. Says Dio Cassius: "Reckon the hours of the day and night; assign the first to Saturn, the second to Jupiter, the third to Mars, the fourth to the Sun, the fifth to Venus, the sixth to Mercury, and the seventh to the Moon in the order accepted by the Egyptians. Repeat this process and when you have gone through the 24 hours you will find that the first hour of the second day belongs to the sun. Again repeat the process throughout the second day or Sun's day, and you will assign the first hour of the third day to the Moon. Go through the other days in the same way, and each day will obtain the deity with which it is connected." In other words, given 24 hours to the day, with Saturn as the deity assigned to the first hour, then Saturn will also be the deity of the eighth, fifteenth, and twenty-second hour. The proper order of the planets being Saturn, Jupiter, Mars, Sun, Venus, Mercury, Moon, the 23rd hour will belong to Jupiter, the 24th to Mars and the first of the next day to the Sun. If the deity of the first hour becomes the deity of the day, then after *Saturn's day* the *Sun's day* must follow, then the *Moon's day,* then *Jupiter's day,* next *Venus' day,* and finally

Saturday again, which is precisely the sequence of our week. In French, we have Lundi, Mardi, Mercredi, Jeudi, and Vendredi, named after the planets. In English, the Teutonic names have been inserted: Tiu, the Teutonic Mars in Tuesday, Woden, the Teutonic Mercury, in Wednesday, Thor, the Teutonic Jupiter in Thursday, and Friga, the Teutonic Venus, in Friday. Sunday, the Christian day of gathering for prayer, also evolved out of the process of interaction of the pagan planetary order of the days with the Jewish week of biblical origin.

Quite different is the nature of the month, which is a distinct astronomical event, the period of a lunation. As we have seen, the month has served since earliest times as a universal unit of reckoning. However, in countries which blossomed forth scientifically and culturally, there evolved a keen desire to be more accurate about the determination of the month's exact beginning and ending. For strictly religious reasons this became a matter of prime importance in pagan Babylonia as well as in monotheistic Israel. The Babylonians' concern is understandable, since celestial worship was part of their faith. The Jewish concern is more difficult to understand, especially in its intensive elaboration. As one scholar says of it: "The determination of the month's origin was in Jewish custom associated with so much painstaking and complex minutiae during the Roman era, that one cannot help the impression that the orthodox Jew had no other concern in life besides his fastdays and calendar ritual." (Wilhelm Kubitschek, *Grundriss der Antiken Zeitrechnung*. München: 1928. p. 124) Since the Jews celebrated the first of the month as a holiday, it was important for them to know when to celebrate: Religious observances being of prime importance, it became a matter of life and death to know precisely which day was holy to God, otherwise the law would be broken and guilt before God accrued. The month began with the first sighting of the young crescent east of the setting sun. This is not always an easy matter, and if the young crescent is visible for a few minutes only, it may readily be missed. The ancient Hebrews recognized the testimony of two witnesses for the supreme council of rabbis so as to declare the day holy. Fires were then lit on the nearest hill in Judea. When seen by observers on other hills where wood had been stored in readiness, fires were lit there as well, until the entire tribe knew that the holy day of the first of the month was to be observed at that moment. For many centuries there was no regular calendar organized into a scheme for advanced knowledge. Only in 358 A. D. (under Rabbi Hillel II) was a cycle of 19 years put into effect with specific dates for monthly origins and specific years for intercalations.

The reasons for the variations in the appearance of the lunar crescent are as follows. During new moon (moon unseen), the sun and moon are in line with the earth, on the same side, hence, as seen from earth, at the same point on the ecliptic. We say then that the sun and moon are in conjunction. If the earth did not revolve around the sun but remained stationary in space, the moon would make its orbit around it in 27.3 days. Because of the earth's annual revolution, the earth shifts in its orbit around the sun during the moon's cycle around it of 27.3 days, about 30°, from A to B in Figure 4.2. We must bear in mind that our month is measured from new moon to new moon, hence from solar conjunction to solar conjunction. In B, we note that to complete a month, the moon at C, although it has completed a full revolution around the earth, must move over to the left to be in line with the sun, and yield a new monthly start, the next new moon. This will complete a full month, a synodic month, or a month by the sun from new moon to new moon. As before, when we explained the measuring of a sidereal day, similarly here we may also refer to a sidereal month, which is a lunar revolution measured by the stars. If we view the moon at C against a given star, a month will always be marked by the moon's return to C against the same star, hence along a line parallel to the previous Earth-C line in A, the star being so far away as to show no difference in direction of sight, hence no parallox. The synodic month (moon at C then back to C_1, against Sun) is 29.5 days long, approximately.

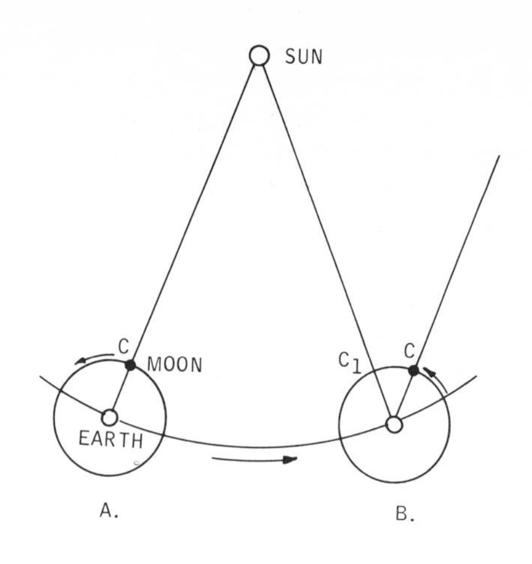

Figure 4.2

The synodic month actually averages 29.53059 days. Since the moon's orbit is an ellipse, it will have a perigee (the nearest point) when it is nearest earth (221,463 miles) and an apogee when furthest (252,710 miles). This is demonstrated in Figure 4.3 from which we can also see that when the earth is at aphelion, furthest from sun, in A, the moon will be in conjunction at its perigee. Since the moon's orbit remains the same in space, it must follow that when the earth is at perihelion, nearest sun, hence on opposite side of ellipse, the moon will then be at apogee. In A, the synodic month is short because the moon has a short distance from C to C_1 on line Earth-Sun and travels fast there, being nearer earth. In B when moon is at apogee this same distance, C to C_1 on line of E-S, is greater, the moon travels slowly, and the synodic month is longer.

The time that elapses between the moon's conjunction and its first visibility as a crescent is a variable quantity. In Babylon, latitude 32.5 degrees North, it varies from a minimum of $16\frac{1}{2}$ hours to a maximum of 42 hours. Three factors influence this phenomenon. First comes the moon's distance from the earth. In Figure 4.4 A we see the moon circling the earth at apogee, when in 24 hours it makes a smaller arc than in the diagram below, 4.4 B, when it is at perigee and moves faster. In the latter case its crescent will, for this reason, be seen sooner after invisibility than in the former.

There is next the time of year. Consider the western horizon on March 21, the vernal equinox. Bear in mind that the ecliptic, or path of sun, is at angle of $23\frac{1}{2}$ degrees to the celestial equator. Figure 4.5 shows the path of the sun for the year along the zodiacal constellations, assuming, of course, a stationary earth. In the beginning of spring, on March 21, at new moon, both sun and moon are together on the equator. (Figure 4.6 A). The day after, the sun has moved one degree to the left along the ecliptic and above the equator to position S_1. (Figure 4.6 B). The moon moves faster eastward against the stars and has shifted leftward in the sky, a little over 12 degrees.

As the two bodies move along with the sky in their daily westward motion, the sun sets and finds itself in position S_2 and the moon follows in M_2. The vertical distance between them is considerable under these conditions, and the crescent moon is therefore easily seen for a relatively long time above the western horizon. In the Fall, at the autumnal equinox, the situation is different, as can be seen in Figure 4. 7, and 4. 5. The sun and moon are again together at conjunction, as seen in A, while one day later the sun has moved one degree to the left and is on the ecliptic below the equator this time, moving toward the winter constellations. After sunset, the sun is at S_2 and the moon 12 degrees to the left of it at M_2. The vertical distance between these two bodies which determines the crescent moon's visibility above the horizon after the sun sets, is in this instance very small, as seen in Figure 4. 7 B.

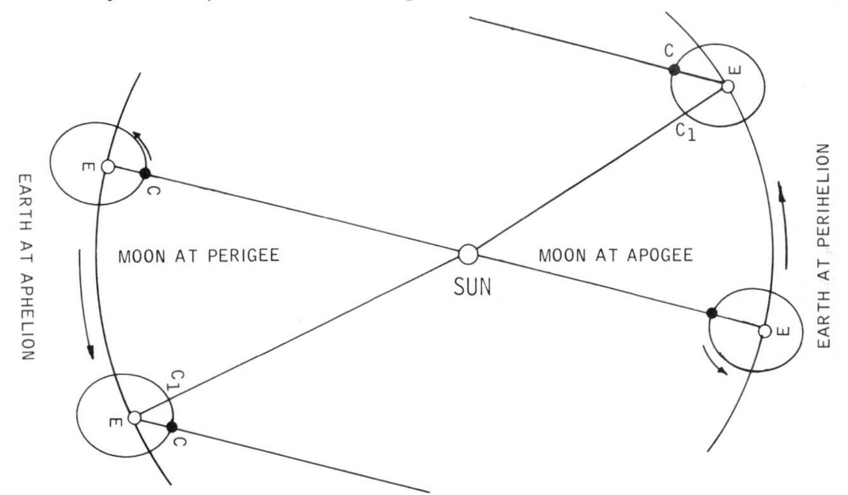

A. EARTH ON ONE SIDE OF SUN. B. EARTH ON OPPOSITE SIDE.
MOON'S ELLIPTICAL ORBIT IS UNCHANGED IN SPACE.

Figure 4.3

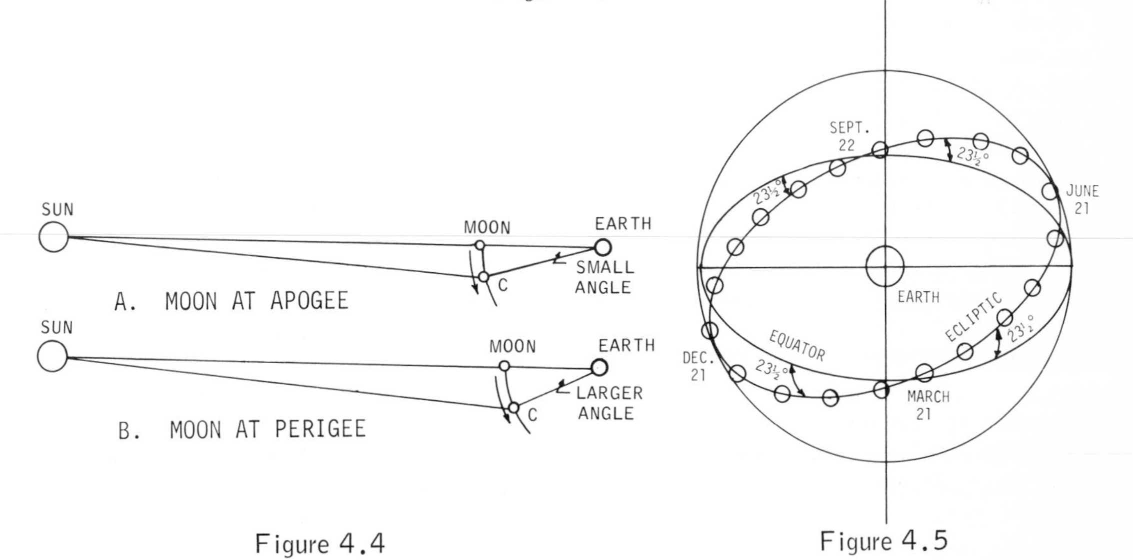

Figure 4.4

Figure 4.5

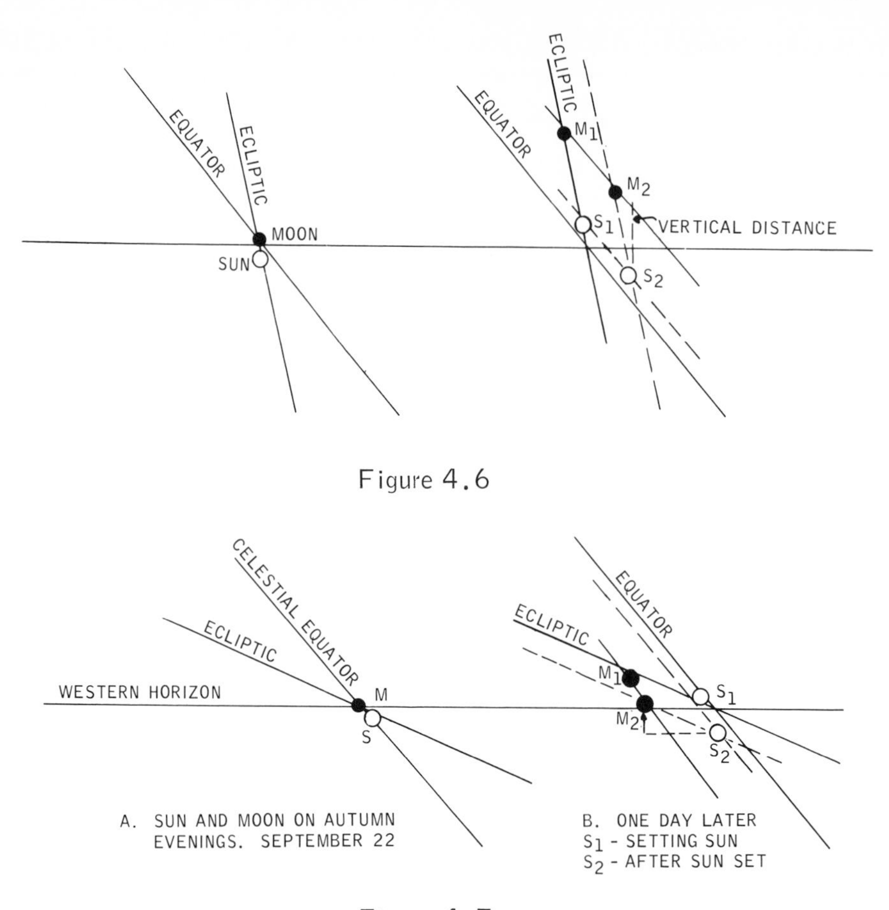

Figure 4.7

There is finally the effect of the moon's latitude. The orbit of the moon is inclined to that of the earth's, at an angle of a little over 5 degrees. This means that from observation points on earth, the moon can be seen at its furthest, five degrees north and five degrees south of the ecliptic. The latter is essentially the projection line of the plane of the earth's orbit around the sun as seen against the sky. Hence, in the two instances considered, in March and September, the moon may be either on or near the ecliptic, and furthest, 5 degrees above it, or 5 degrees below it. These positions will manifest themselves in differences in visibility, as seen in Figure 4. 8. Again we see that in March, regardless whether the moon is north or south of the ecliptic, the angle of the ecliptic in the sky is such that the crescent moon will be seen longer on the western horizon than in September. Figure 4. 8 merely reproduces the situation demonstrated in the preceding two figures to show the effect of the moon's latitude under respective conditions.

Moreover, the latitude of the observer also makes a difference in crescent visibility, sine the higher north one goes, the lower in the sky lies the celestial equator. This need not concern us, since the ancient world was more or less within a narrow belt of latitude. More relevant is another factor. The fact is that the time from conjunction to conjunction can vary and yield different lengths of synodic months, the actual average length of which is 29 days, 12 hours, 44 minutes and 2.8 seconds. The average time of the moon's sidereal revolution is 27 days, 7 hours, 43 minutes, 11.5 seconds. The variation can yield at times two 30-day or two 29 day months in succession, respectively. In addition, even the interval between conjunction and full moon can vary, as can be seen from Figure 4.9.

Since, as was stated previously, the orbit of the moon in its plane of revolution remains unchanged in space, the arc from conjunction to full moon, as seen in A and B, can vary, depending on the position of the earth in its orbit around the sun. This period varies in fact from 13.73 days to 15.80 days.

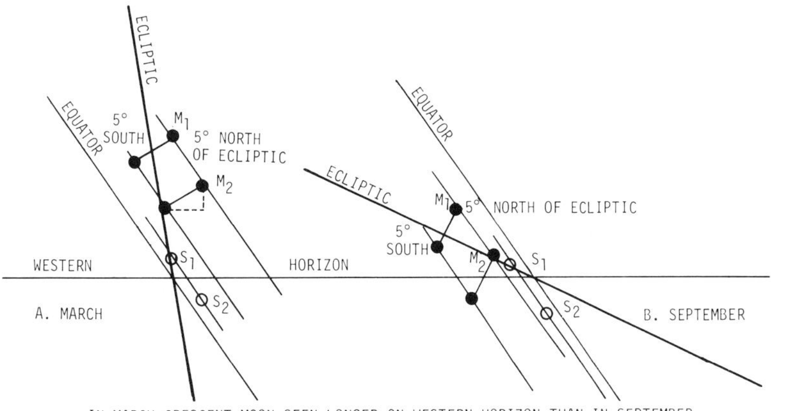

Figure 4.8

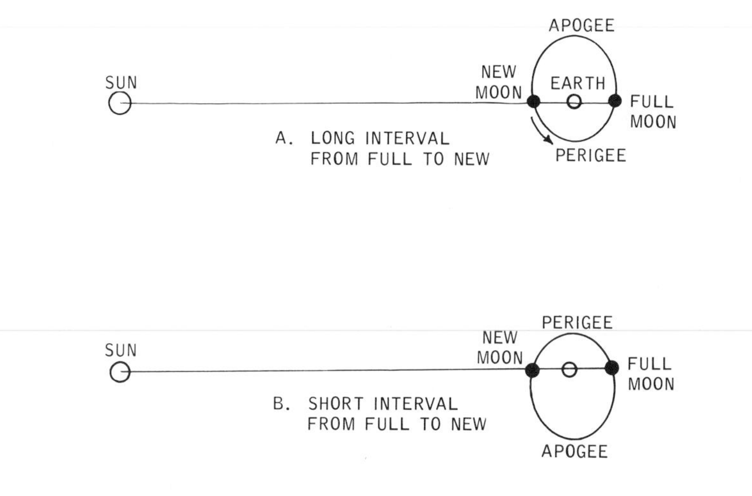

Figure 4.9

Confronted with these numerous phenomena, the ancients lacked the theoretical conceptions for their complete understanding and coordination. They were obliged to adopt the empirical method of determining the beginning of each month on its own evidence and of intercalating when necessary, so as to keep their lunar reckonings in line with the sun. The former procedure presented little difficulty, the latter gave room to much calculation and to several schemes. The main object was to find a segment of time in which the number of lunar months and solar years were whole integers, so that it could form the basis for a convenient repeatable time scale. Such a scale would synchronize the solar and lunar cycles and yield a condominium, or concominion, both meaning harmony between them.

The earliest account of this long-lasting search that we know of, was written by Geminus, the author of an introductory work on astronomy, composed between the years 73 and 67 B. C. This work is now lost but some of its contents are left to us in the form of a translated and reworked account by Manilius.

Says Geminus:

"The Egyptian calendar was based on the very opposite principle from the Greek one. The Egyptians did not count the years by the sun, nor the months and days by the moon, but followed their own principle. They wished their sacrifices to fall in different seasons of the year rather than be fixed to any particular period, so that summer festivals should fall in different seasons with the march of many years. Their year consisted of twelve months of 30 days, to which five additional days were added at the end. They did not include the additional quarter day of which they were aware, so as to permit their holidays to shift against the seasons. Their calendar thus fell back one day in four years. In 120 years, the backsliding amounted to 30 days, or one month.

The Greeks, on the other hand, kept the year on a solar basis, hence adjusted to the sun, but the month on a lunar. The Egyptian did not force each year to adhere fully to the solar scheme, but added occasional leap months on a year to year basis. Thus, neither were the years in full harmony with the sun nor were the days and months in running agreement with the moon. They therefore sought some unifying scheme that would harmonize the year with the months and supply a time unit which would contain a whole number of solar as well as lunar cycles, specifically of whole years, whole months, and whole days. The first such unit was the eight-year one, or octaeteris, which counted 99 months with the inclusion of three leap months, and contained 2922 days, $(360 \times 8) + (5 \times 8) + (\frac{1}{4} \times 8) = 2880 + 40 + 2 = 2922$ days. Or since the solar year had $365\frac{1}{4}$ days and the lunar year 354 $(29\frac{1}{2} \times 12)$, the solar had an excess of $11\frac{1}{4}$ days. They therefore searched for a number which, when multiplied by $11\frac{1}{4}$, would give a whole number for both days and months. The multiplier 8 will do the job, since $11\frac{1}{4} \times 8 = 90$, hence three months. Thus eight years will have $354 \times 8 = 2832$ days, which, by addition of 90 days, will yield 2922 or the same period as eight solar years. This means that eight true lunar years of 12 lunations each, to which three months are added (intercalated) to yield 99 lunations, are identical with eight solar years of $365\frac{1}{4}$ days. Thus, after eight years, all festivals will show a cyclical recurrence.

But it so happens that the lunar month is longer than $29\frac{1}{2}$ days by 1/33 day. Hence, 99 lunations have $(29\frac{1}{2} + 1/33) \times 99 = 2923\frac{1}{2}$ days, which means that the condominion is frustrated and every eight years the lunar cycle runs one day and a half ahead of the solar, or three days in 16 years.

These extra three days in 16 years served to displace the lunar cycle of the months. The addition of three days every 16 years resulted in an extra month of thirty days accumulating in excess every 160 years. To remedy this discomfit, the Egyptians resorted to withholding one of the three leap months normally added every eight years and applied it once every 160 years, hence to one cycle of eight years every 20 cycles. In this manner, the solar cycles were kept in phase with the lunar. [That is, they dropped one month of 30 days every 160 years.]

But no harmony was actually attained even then. As luck would have it, none of the basic periodic events in nature capable of serving as units of measure for time, are integers or even convenient mixed numbers. For example, the lunar month is not exactly 29½ days but 29-31/60 days, which renders it necessary to add four days every 16 years instead of 3. Also, the number of leap months per year has to be somewhat greater than the number of common months, and the moon year will be not 354 days but 354-1/3. The difference between a solar year of 365¼ and a lunar year of 354-1/3 will therefore be 10-11/12 days, which, when multiplied by 8 (years) yields 87-1/3 days and not the three months normally added. To rectify this situation, a cycle of 19 years is introduced, which demands the intercalation of seven months in order to harmonize the lunar with solar reckoning. In eight such 19-year cycles there will be 56 intercalated months, while in 19 cycles of eight-year periods, comprising in each case 152 years, there should be 57 such months.

The astronomers Euctemon, Philippas, and Callippos preferred the 19 year cycle, to which they assigned 6940 days or 235 months inclusive of the intercalated ones. (This would, according to their reckoning, assume a year of 365-5/19 days.) In the 235 months, they had 110 common (short) and 125 full months, which yield 6940 days, as required.

Unfortunately, even this scheme failed to give satisfactory synchronization. The solar year carefully measured is 365½ days, while the 19-year cycle yield 6940/19 = 365-5/19 days, which renders this number larger than the true length of the year by 1/76. To eliminate this source of error, the school of Callippos of Cyzicus introduced a new cycle, that of 76 years, which, as can be seen, is a four-fold 19-year cycle, hence one consisting of 235 x 4 = 940 months, of which 28 were intercalated, yielding a total of 27,759 days. This period has offered the best synchronization so far." (Wilhelm Kubitschek. *Grundriss der Antiken Zeitrechnung*. München, 1928. pp. 155-159.)

The 19-year cycle here described is better known as the Metonic cycle, after the Greek astronomer Meton, who introduced it around 432 B.C. into Greek chronometry. In this cycle, there were 12 years consisting of 12 lunar months of 29 and 30 days alternately, and seven years of 13 months as above, with the 13th month having 30 days in 6 years of the 7, and 29 in the seventh. Athens was delighted with Meton's invention, considering the cycle a truly great discovery. His name was inscribed in letters of gold on the Temple of Minerva, and the years were named by their numeral number of the 1 to 19 sequence, the era beginning on July 16, 433 B.C. The cycle was modified in 330 B.C. into the 76 year cycle of Calippos of Cyzicus, composed of four smaller cycles of 19 years each.

Normally, the Greeks described their historical years as the year since the victory of Coraebus in the Olympic games on the 17th of July, 776 B.C., the first year of that famous and enduring institution. Subsequent years were counted in cycles of four, the interval between Olympic games, which lasted until 394 A.D. when they were abolished by Theodosius.

The Metonic 19-year cycle left its imprint upon Christian culture as well as upon the Jewish faith. Both Christianity and Judaism adopted it and assigned a special number to each year within it. This ordinal position of the year within the package of 19, already honored by the Greeks, was called the *golden number*. The Christian golden number begins with year 0, rather than 1 A.D., so that to obtain the golden number for 1953, we have 1953/19 = 102, with a remainder of 15. The golden number of that year is therefore 15 + 1 = 16. The number 102, designating the number of full cycles completed since the year 0, is not taken into account and is disregarded. The Jewish golden number is two less than the Christian. In this connection, another calendrical term might be mentioned, namely the Dominical, or Sunday, Letter, which is of purely religious significance. If the first seven letters of the alphabet are assigned to the days of the week (from A to G, inclusive), then the ecclesiastical calendar whose days are thus marked, will indicate which days of the year are Sundays. If January First falls on a Wednesday, that day becomes A and Sunday is E, which will be the letter for every Sunday of that year. In leap years, the day of February 29 is given no letter, and in consequence, the letter of the first Sunday of the year will be the letter of every Sunday for a leap year as well. The object of this scheme is to know which dates of any month fall on Sundays. This knowledge is readily obtained if we asign to January 1, whatever day of the week it falls on, the letter A and continue to G. Whatever letter then falls on the first Sunday, will be the Dominical Letter for that year. Knowing this letter, one can then know readily, by matching with any current calendar, the day of the week any date of that year fell on. The reckoning is based on a cycle of 28 years (7x4) or "solar cycle."

Another term related to the 19-year cycle is the Epact, a term given to a figure deriving from the age of the moon on January first. The years are in consequence designated by Roman numerals from zero to XXIX, since January 1 can have any of the 30 daily positions of the moon during a full lunation. The term was introduced in 1582 by the Gregorian reform for the more accurate calculation of the moon's phases and as replacement of the old 19-year cycle.

In reality, the above statements are simplifications of more complex procedures. Jewish intercalations had more to it than the previously stated addition of an extra month every three years. Intercalations were made in terms of the 19-year cycle, an additional month being added the 3rd, 6th, 8th, 11th, 14th, 17th and 19th year. The number of days per year thus came to vary, being 353, 354 and 355 for a common year, and 383, 384 and 385 for a leap year. In addition, the Jewish calendar also honored a 28-year solar cycle for the following reasons. The tropical year of four seasons had $365\frac{1}{4}$ days, which is equivalent to 52 weeks and $1\frac{1}{4}$ days. The mean beginning of such a year reverts to the same hour of the same day of the week every 28 years, (7x4), starting a new *Great Solar Cycle,* the cycle that determines the Dominical Letter which is the Christian code for Sundays.

Jewish holidays were set by the lunar months but with the stipulation that certain holidays, such as, the Day of Atonement could not fall on a Friday or Sunday, and the seventh day of the Feast of Tabernacles, on Saturday. This introduced irregularities in the concordance between religious holidays and their astronomical counterparts which, as we shall see below, contributed to the problem of the calendrical determination of Easter.

3. Our Contemporary Calendar

The calendar in use by us today, the Gregorian, is a good example of the complex origins of any institution. It begins essentially with the old Egyptian solar calendar of 12 alternating months of 29 and 31 days and having five unattached intercalated days after the twelfth month, hence a year of 365 days. As could be seen from the text of Manilius, cited above, and from other sources, the sole object of the search for synchronization of lunar months with the solar cycle was the concern over religious holidays and ritual. As we shall see, this problem continued to be a source of concern and is such to this day, manifesting itself as the main cause of hesitancy in adopting new and admittedly simpler calendars.

The ancient Roman calendar consisted of a year of ten months, beginning with Martius (March) and ending with Decembris (December) and was in force from 738 B. C. to 713 B. C. In that year it was rectified to twelve lunar months, seven months of 29 days, four of 31, and February of 28 days, yielding a total of 355 days, with intercalation every two years. The year began on March 25, believed to correspond with the vernal equinox. In the year 451 B. C., the beginning of the year was shifted to January. Holidays for the year were announced by the high priest, the Pontifex Maximus, which apparently led to much petty manipulation and abuse to the calendar for the benefit of favorite office holders or contractors. The sequence of years in Roman history was reckoned with reference to the presumed date of the founding of Rome, 753 B. C., which is the starting point of Roman history. Roman dates were dated A. U. C., or *anno urbis conditae,* the year since the city's foundation.

When Julius Caesar assumed the office of Pontifex, he found the calendar completely out of harmony with the seasons and in disorder generally. After his conquest of Egypt, he commissioned the Alexandrian astronomer Sosigenes to reform it. Unlike his Greek predecessors, Sosigenes abandoned the centuries-long quest for synchronization, or condominion of solar and lunar years, and recommended a strictly solar year of 365. 25 days in line with the Egyptian scheme of a leap year every four years, introduced in that country in 238 B. C. under the official dictum known as the Decree of Canopus. The reform of Sosigenes was adopted in 45 B. C., after the field was cleared by having one year of 445 days, named the Year of Confusion, to indicate how much people dislike any tampering with the habitual timecount. In this manner our own calendar came into existence in which the lunar cycle ceased to play a role, the vernal equinox was placed on March 25, and the year was made to commence on January 1.

There was, however, some difficulty the following few years, because of the misinterpretation of the term fourth by the pontifices. They counted the leap year as one, then the next three years as two, three, and four, making the latter a leap year again, so that every third year by our reckoning was a leap year. This error was corrected by Augustus Caesar, and both the names of the months and respective number of days allotted to each, were finally established as we know them today.

With the introduction of Christianity, some new problems presented themselves. The Emperor Constantine, who became the first Christian ruler of Rome, convened the famour Council of Nicea in 325 A. D. which among other things formulated the Christian calendar. The vernal equinox having fallen that year on March 21, the Council decreed that Easter be celebrated on "the first Sunday upon or after the first full moon following the twenty-first day of March", the day of the vernal equinox that year. The reasons for this specification were the following. Jesus had come to Jerusalem to celebrate the Passover feast which took place that year on Thursday evening. He was imprisoned that night, crucified Friday morning, and was resurrected on Sunday. The Jewish Passover is celebrated on the night of the first full moon after the vernal equinox, so that the Sunday of the Resurrection should have been the Sunday thereafter, a sequence which seemed reasonable enough. But history invariably prefers devious ways.

To begin with, Sunday was originally neither a Jewish holiday nor even a Jewish name since that day was merely the First Day. It became a pagan feastday in Rome as the day of the sun which star had always represented an honored ancient deity. As late as 321 A. D. its observance was enjoined on all Roman subjects by a law authorized by the first Christian emperor, Constantine. Before that time Christians had declared it a day of gathering, rest and prayer. The Christians wanted to become separated from the Jews and to stop honoring their sabbath as they had done hitherto.

Much has been conjectured and written about the Jewish Passover. According to the Bible it combined for celebration the commemorative occasion of the Jews' exodus from Egypt with the sacrifice of a first born lamb without a blemish and the sprinkling of its blood upon the door for God to pass over, as he passed over Jewish homes similarly marked with blood in Egypt when He liquidated the first born Egyptians. Jews also ate unleavened bread for seven days and a sheaf of barley had to be offered on the fifteenth, the day after the feast. There were other features in addition to this holiday, but its occurrence on the day of the first full moon after the vernal equinox has in all likelihood a historic significance as a residue of pagan customs deriving from a combination of sun and moon worship. This suspicion is greatly strengthened by the fact that the feast of Tabernacles, the second major Jewish holiday, which also lasts seven days and combines harvest ceremonies and tokens of Exodus from Egypt with many other minor rituals and customs, also happens to fall on the first full moon after the autumnal equinox

The demands of some Jewish holidays previously cited, interfered with a regular date for Passover, because they necessitated juggling the calendar. As a result, discrepancies arose between the Passover and the vernal equinox. The early Christians celebrated all Jewish holidays since they were under the full Jewish influence of the Apostles. They lived as a Hebrew sect until the Gentile converts gained supremacy in numbers and Paul won out in his policy of rendering Christianity into an international faith rather than strictly a Jewish sect, one of the many at the time.

During the first two centuries of the Christian era, Eastern Christians who were under full Jewish influence, celebrated Easter on the same day as the Jewish Passover, on the fourteenth day of Nisan. In a way, they regarded the death of Jesus in the light of the Jewish sacrifice of the Paschal lamb. Their Easter was therefore not tied to any particular day of the week. Such Passover observers of Easter were called Quartodecimans, or celebrants of the 14th. Jews begin their day with sunset so that the night of the fourteenth is for them the fifteenth day of the month. But there were also sects who followed the Roman custom of starting the fifteenth with its morning. They celebrated on the fifteenth and were called Quintodecimans. But Jewish Christians in time lost their dominant position and became a minority in the faith they established, but no longer controlled. Late in the second century A. D. the persisting Quatrodecimans were excommunicated by Pope Victor, although the practice lingered on until the edict of the Council of Nicea 325 A. D. put a final end to the existing confusion in the celebration of Easter. At Rome, for example, the spring equinox had been fixed on March 25 and at Alexandria on March 21, correct by the Julian calendar at the time of the Council. Those who had celebrated Easter on the day of the Jewish Passover also ran into trouble with the vernal equinox because of the necessary manipulations of the Jewish calendar.

Even the post-Nicean Julian calendar could not escape built-in difficulties with regard to the determination of Easter which centered around the correct calendrical planning of the lunar cycles. The Metonic cycle of 19 solar years was not perfect and could contain either 6939 or 6940 days, depending on whether it had four or five leap years, both of which are possible with a period of 235 lunations. This situation yielded an average of 6939 3/4 days which is exactly 19 Julian years, the Metonic cycle. With the use of this cycle ecclesiastical computers hoped to calculate the dates of the new moon for all time -- a task which was soon discovered to be beset with obstacles. In 463 A. D., Pope Hilarius introduced a large cycle of 28 Metonic cycles thus containing 19 x 28, or 532 years. From this cycle a complete, repeatable set of Easter dates was calculated. The number 28 was derived as already described. It would seem that this scheme was not fully satisfactory because around 520 A. D. a Roman abbot named Dionysius Exiguus (the little Dionysius) submitted a report to the Pope whom he served as archivist, in which he introduced the Christian era, initiating it with the birth of Christ, the year 1. The previous year he named 1 B. C. and labeled it the year of the Incarnation, fixing March 25 as the date of Christ's conception and the true inception of the Christian era. This date remained as the New Year's day until 1582, when Pope Gregory XIII in his ordered reform of the calendar reverted to January 1, thus restoring the New Year's day of Julius Caesar. It is believed that Pope Gregory's reason for selecting January 1 as the year's origin was that it marked the Feast of the Circumcision since it was the eighth day after Christ's birth. The scheme of Dionysius was adopted in 532 but the irregularities continued. The Metonic cycle is imperfect because the actual motions of both sun and moon contain unavoidable, though small, irregularities. Given historical time, the small errors accumulate soon enough to compose a day.

Consider the prediction of lunar phases from the Metonic cycle of 19 years. Its average cycle of 235 lunations has in actuality (29. 530588 x 235) 6939. 68818 days. This means that every 307 years a new moon will occur one day earlier than the day assigned to it by the golden number reckoning of the year's position in the cycle. To compensate for this shift the epact was introduced with the calendar reform which by giving the particular phase of the moon on January 1, renders its course easily determinable for the entire year and the subsequent New Years of the cycle. Thus, the solar year being 11 days longer than the lunar (365-354), a new moon on January 1 of a given year, will mean that its phase is 11, 22, 3, 14, 25 etc. days later the subsequent years. Incidentally, the introduction of the epact changed the numbering system and minimized errors but did not eliminate the basic weakness in all calendrical calculations, namely, the small irregularities in the motions of the sun and moon. The determination of Easter is still the outcome of much complexity to this day.

The major difficulty with the determination of Easter derived from the fact that the Council of Nicea tied Easter not strictly to the vernal equinox but to March 21 which was the date of the vernal equinox for that year, 325 A. D. Disharmony was inevitable because the Julian calendar renders the year's length 365. 25 days, while in actuality it is 365. 2422 days, making it longer by 0. 0078 day. For this reason the astronomical equinox receded by that much from March 21 every year, and fell earlier. Conversely, since Easter was declared to be on the first Sunday after the first full moon after March 21, it was pushed further and further ahead from the actual celestial equinox which is defined as the moment the sun crosses the celestial equator. Thus, if point M on circle 1 represents the 21st of March, and V on circle 2 the vernal equinox, then these two points may be assumed to have been in line in the year 325. Since the calendar year was longer than the actual equinoctial year by 365.25 - 365.2422, it follows that the following year, point M will be ahead of V, at M_1, next at M_2, etc. And since Easter was decreed as the first Sunday after March 21 on the assumption that March 21 and the equinox will always be togehter, the Easter date is always ahead of the M-point, hence getting further and further away from E, the true equinoctial full moon, as seen on circle 3. In a century, the March 21 date moved ahead of V by 0.78 day, or one day in 128 years, hence almost 10 days in the 1257 years intervening between 325 A.D. and 1582 A.D. In the year 1545, the Council of Trent authorized the Pope to proceed with calendar reform which Pope Gregory XIII finally rendered effective in 1582. The changes were worked out by the astronomer Aloysius Lilius and the mathematician Christopher Clavius. The Papal Bull of that year decreed that following Thursday, October 4, 1582, should come Friday, October 15, 1582. The vernal equinox was put permanently on March 21. To prevent further inequalities, three leap years were dropped every 400 years, the century years not divisible by 400. This arrangement brings the Gregorian year to a value of 365.2425 days, still 0.0003 of a day longer than the average tropical year. But since this would amount to an error of one day in 3323 years, nothing has been done about it as yet.

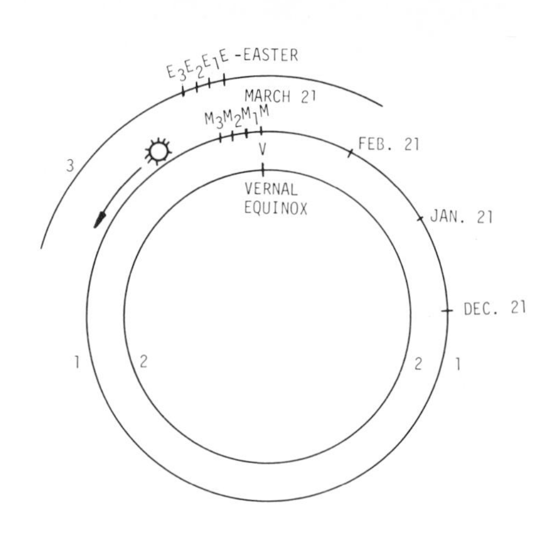

Figure 4.10

That our present calendar contains many residues of a variety of past customs is fully apparent. It is also easy to see that it has many inequalities. Thus, the number of days per quarter, days per month, days per year, workdays per month and other features, are irregularities that negate the purpose of a calendrical time scheme. As a result, several suggestions for calendar reforms have been offered, none of which has as yet managed to overcome the resistance of tradition and inertia.

Besides, the Gregorian calendar is still inexact with regard to a perfectly regular determination of Easter, based on the requirement that the vernal equinox occur always on March 21. In reality, the vernal equinox can be as much as two days earlier than March 21 so that a full moon may occur after the actual equinox but before March 21. Only by common consent is Easter determined by the calendar equinox so that in actuality it may occur on a rare occasion after the second full moon after the vernal equinox. The Greek

Orthodox Easter may at times coincide with the date of the other churches, but can fall as much as five weeks later. This is due to the fact that the Orthodox church calculates Easter by the actual movements of the moon rather than by the ecclesiastical system of calculations which rests upon several simplifying assumptions. Moreover, "The tables which are based on the 19-year cycle, fix the full moon for a definite calendar date for the whole world, whereas the true full moon occurs at a definite instant which may not be on the same calendar date all over the world." (Singer, Charles *et al (ed.) History of Technology,* Oxford University Press, 1958, 5 vols. vol. III p. 579) Man's search for a perfect calendar is at best still in an unfinished condition.

V Ancient Instruments for Fancy's Sake

1. The Social Status of Ancient Science

A well-known student of the evolution of human types writes as follows about the development of cultures: "The agricultural cycle, the setting of days for markets, the prediction of wind and weather for those planning travel by land or by water, all produced the need for a calendar. Standards of length, volume, and weight were also needed for the evaluation of both staples and precious commodities. From the effort of producing standards of time and space, and from the mathematical techniques of measuring and relating them, science arose.

"Early science was chiefly concerned with the study of the causes of variations in the climate, such as frosts and droughts, floods and rainfall, which affected agriculture. In Egypt, farmers needed to know exactly when the Nile would rise in order to be able to plant their crops at the right moment, just as in a tropical forest, where no change in seasons is apparent, rice-planters must know when to expect the arrival of the rains. Because the events that became the subject matter of early science were also the causes of disturbances to people, and because priests exist principally to allay such disturbances, the pursuit of science became an attribute of the priests. Their ability to predict natural events made it appear to the uneducated that they could also control these awesome happenings, and this enhanced their power." (Carleton S. Coon. *The Story of Man.* New York: 1962, p. 224)

These notions of the origin of science and its relation to the priesthood seem to be generally accepted within the scholarly community of our times. Our knowledge of ancient and primitive science is not refined enough to fully decide upon the accuracy of this statement although what we have already learned is sufficient to indicate that there are other phases to both science and the role of the priesthood than are cited here. In fact, the entire origin of science and role of the priesthood can be differently conceived. Since the subject is imperfectly known and the issue at stake is merely a matter of speculation, the subject hardly deserves to be further discussed.

The following may, nevertheless, justly be added. So far as our evidence has indicated, people were religious because religion was one of their ways of responding to the phenomena of nature; people were curious, because such was another of their ways of responding to the phenomena of nature; and priests filled the job of scholars, guardians, and servants of the findings of both these responses of man, because they found themselves in a role in which that was the natural thing for them to do. In other words, people did things because they were human and human beings do things for a variety of reasons. Often, even the same motivating force such as the sense of wonder, the need of the moment, the desire for excitement or play, or self defense, will elicit different responses in different individuals. History may subsequently find different combinations of these responses imprinted upon the established web or behavior patterns in different cultures.

It will be of special interest to learn how famous and learned scholars of antiquity saw the role played by science in their days. Let us first consider Vitruvius, author of a work called *On Architecture,* who lived during the first century before Christ, and helped in the rebuilding of Rome under Augustus Caesar. Says he: "1. Famous sportsmen who win victories at Olympia, Corinth, and Nemea have been assigned such great distinctions by the ancestors of the Greeks that they not only receive praise publicly at the games, as they stand with palm and crown, but also when they go back victorious to their own people they ride triumphant with their four-horse chariots into their native cities, and enjoy a pension for life from the state. When I observe this, I am surprised that similar or even greater distinctions are not assigned to those authors who confer infinite benefits on mankind throughout the ages. For this is the more worthy of enactment, in that while sportsmen make their own bodies stronger, authors not only cultivate their own perceptions, but by the information in their books prepare the minds of all to acquire knowledge and thus to stimulate their talents.

"2. For in what respect could Milo of Croton advantage mankind because he was unconquered, or others who won victories in the same kind, except that in their lifetime they enjoyed distinction among their fellow-citizens? But the daily teachings of Pythagoras, Democritus, Plato, Aristotle, and other thinkers, elaborated as they were by unbroken application, furnish ever-fresh and flowering harvests, not only to their fellow-citizens but also to all mankind. Those who from tender years are satisfied thence with abundance of knowledge, acquire the best habits of thought, institute civilized manners, equal rights, laws without which no state can be secure. 3. Since, therefore, such boons have been conferred on individuals and communities by wise writers, not only do I think that palms and crowns should be awarded to them, but that triumphs also should be decreed and that they should be canonized in the mansions of the gods."

Vitruvius then proceeds to enumerate "several conceptions of a few thinkers which have helped the furnishing of human life" and the names of whose authors deserve endless honors. First should come Plato, who taught us how to find the length of a side of a square obtained from doubling the area of a given square. Next should come Pythagoras because he "demonstrated how to make a set-square without the help of a craftsman," in other words, for his Pythagorean theorem. Then should come Archimedes for his "many and various wonderful discoveries," of which Vitruvius singles out this method of detecting the admixture of silver in the presumable golden crown of Hiero and therefore "the fraud of the contractor." He then cites other scientists and mathematicians whom he likens together with the great in literature to the gods whom mankind will eternally honor and worship. Among those cited are inventors of theorems and designers of instruments both of which please the mind. "The imaginations of these men were directed throughout not only to the improvement of conduct, but to the service of mankind." And by service he means the act of giving pleasure and stimulation to the mind.

Vitruvius discusses the works of Ctesibius, "who also discovered the nature of wind-pressure and the principles of pneumatics," and "was marked out by his talent and great industry, and had the name of being especially fond of mechanical contrivances." He designed hydraulic machines and "described the use of water-power in making automata and many other curiosities, and among them the construction of water-clocks." No practically useful inventions, either as labor-saving devices or as novel services, are conspicuously mentioned in the text. The only inventions that could be described as practical, meaning by it, rendering service rather than appealing to the mind, are the pulley for lifting great weights, the water wheel and the water-screw, both used for raising water to a higher level. All of these, however, had been in widespread use for some time.

We shall discuss later some of the machines described by Vitruvius. At this point, we are concerned mainly with his conceptions of science, the scientist, and of his place in society. We may consider another writer of broad cultural interests and examine his attitude. Plutarch, the author of *The Lives of the Noble Grecians and Romans,* was almost a contemporary of Vitruvius, and at his peak activity half or three-quarters of a century after him. He, too, had wide familiarity with the literature, philosophy, politics and science of his times. In his essay, *Marcellus,* Plutarch relates that "Marcellus, with sixty galleys, each with five rows of oars, furnished with all sorts of arms and missiles, and a huge bridge of planks laid upon eight ships chained together, upon which was carried the engine to cast stones and darts" attacked Syracuse. But all of these "were, it would seem, but trifles for Archimedes and his machines.

"These machines he had designed and contrived, not as matters of any importance, but as mere amusements in geometry; in compliance with King Hiero's desire and request, some little time before, that he should reduce to practice some part of his admirable speculation in science, and by accommodating the theoretic truth to sensation and ordinary use, bring it more within the appreciation of the people in general. Eudoxus and Archytas had been the first originators of the far-famed and highly-prized act of mechanics, which they employed as an elegant illustration of geometrical truths, and as a means of sustaining experimentally, to the satisfaction of the senses, conclusions too intricate for proof by words and diagrams. As, for example, to solve the problem, so often required in constructing geometrical figures, given the two extremes, to find the two mean lines of a proportion, both these mathematicians had recourse to the aid of instruments, adapting to their purpose certain curves and sections of lines. But what with Plato's indignation at it, and his invectives against it as the mere corruption and annihilation of the one good of geometry, which was thus shamefully turning its back upon the unembodied objects of pure intelligence to recur to sensation, and to ask help (not to be obtained without base supervisions and deprivation) from matter; so it was that mechanics came to be separated from geometry, and, repudiated and neglected by philosophers, took its place as an unliterary art."

Archimedes then went to work for his city of Syracuse and its king, Hiero, "whose friend and near relation he was." Archimedes demonstrated how he could by means of a pulley move a large ship loaded with freight and men out of the dry dock "in a straight line as smoothly and evenly as if she had been in the sea." As a result, the king "prevailed upon Archimedes to make him engines accommodated to all the purposes, offensive and defensive, of a siege." Archimedes built a variety of machines which were laid aside for a time of emergency. When Marcellus laid siege to the city, they were put to use. Archimedes brought forth machines that shot out " all sorts of missile weapons, and immense masses of stone that came down with incredible noise and violence... huge poles thrust out from the walls over the ships sunk some by the great weights which they let down from on high upon them; others they lifted up into the air by an iron hand or beak like a crane's beak and, when they had drawn them up by the prow, and set them on end upon the poop, they plunged them to the bottom of the sea;.... A ship was frequently lifted up to a great height in the air (a dreadful thing to behold) and was rolled to and fro, and kept swinging until the mariners were all thrown out, when at length it was dashed against the rocks, or let fall." Also, immense rocks were catapulted out of besieged Syracuse to smash Roman ships and ply endless damage. But Marcellus would not abandon the siege. "What, said he, must we give up fighting with this geometrical Briareus" and kept up the war and the siege. Finally by slyness and trickery he managed to get his men into an unguarded tower and took the city, and by sheer old luck Archimedes got killed in the process. The city was pillaged and plundered, which pained Marcellus deeply, "But nothing afflicted Marcellus so much as the death of Archimedes," who, lost in thought "intent upon working out some problem by a diagram," failed to heed a soldier's order to follow him to Marcellus, "which declining to do before he had worked out his problem to a demonstration, the soldier, enraged, drew his sword and ran him through.... His death was very afflicting to Marcellus... he sought for his kindred and honoured them with signal favors."

What kind of man was this famous scientist? Writes Plutarch: "Archimedes possessed so high a spirit, so profound a soul, and such treasures of scientific knowledge, that though these inventions had now obtained him the renown of more than human sagacity, he yet would not deign to leave behind him any commentary or writing on such subjects; but repudiating as sordid and ignoble the whole trade of engineering, and every sort of art that lends itself to mere use and profit, he placed his whole affection and ambition in those purer speculations where there can be no reference to the vulgar needs of life; studies, the superiority of which to all others is unquestioned, and in which the only doubt can be whether the beauty and grandeur of the subjects examined, of the precision and cogency of the methods and means of proof, most deserve our admiration. It is not possible to find in all geometry more difficult and intricate questions, or more simple and lucid explanations. Some ascribe this to his natural genius; while others think that incredible effort and toil produced these, to all appearances, easy and unlaboured results. No amount of investigation of yours would succeed in attaining the proof, and yet, once seen, you immediately believe you would have discovered it; by so smooth and so vapid a path he leads you to the conclusion required. And thus it ceases to be incredible that (as is commonly told of him) the charm of his familiar and domestic Siren made him forget his food and neglect his person to that degree that when he was occasionally carried by absolute violence to bathe or have his body anointed, he used to trace geometrical figures in the ashes of the fire, and diagrams in the oil on his body, being in a state of entire preoccupation, and, in the truest sense divine possession with his love and delight in science. His discoveries were numerous and admirable; but he is said to have requested his friends and relations that, when he was dead, they would place over his tomb a sphere containing a cylinder, inscribing it with the ratio which the containing solid bears to the contained."

It is indeed remarkable how thoroughly contemporary most, if not all, of Plutarch's sketch of a scientist, must appear to us today. There is the unlimited admiration for the theoretician, the unveiled contempt for the practical man concerned with "mere use and profit," and even some hint of rebuke for those who are after publicity and renown through publication. Not in harmony with current trends, but in the true spirit of the past, group loyalty was still honored in those days, and Archimedes took off time to devise machines for national defense which in time his city made good use of. The relation between pure and applied science, the nature of genius, the truth or fiction behind the layman's image of the scientist, these and other topics here touched upon, are still with us in about the same unsettled condition in which Plutarch found them in his day.

We encounter here quite a different picture from the one presented by many historians, namely, that science arose in response to practical needs. Like so many other misrepresentations of truth, this one, too, has a kernel of applicability, but a kernel hidden by numerous layers of obscure composition and relevance. The fact is that to the thoughtful minds of both the times of Plutarch, first century A. D., and of Plato, fifth century B. C., true science meant logical, mathematical reasoning maintained by ingenuity and demonstration. Application to practical needs required urging and was considered degrading to the nobility of the pursuit. At best, applications were conceived of mainly for military purposes and not for practical human needs or the alleviation of human labor.

The ancients were nonetheless fully aware of the value of such practical possibilities. Vitruvius, for example, in discussing the particular machine which he defines as "a continuous material system having special fitness for the moving of weights," points out that "all machinery is generated by Nature, and the revolution of the universe guides and controls... Since then our fathers had observed this to be so, they took precedents from Nature; imitating them, and led on by what is divine, they developed the comforts of life by their inventions. And so, they rendered some things more convenient, by machines and their revolutions, and other things by handy implements. Thus, what they perceived useful in practice they caused to be advanced by their methods, step by step, through studies, crafts, and customs."

He then considers what he describes as the "necessary inventions," the loom, yokes, ploughs, windlasses, pressbeams and levers, wagons and ships, balances, weights and measures, millstones, bellows, lathes, - "and so forth." Since such inventions are both common and numerous, he proceeds to discuss "machines which are rarely employed. And first we will explain the machines which must be provided for temples, and for the execution of public works." These involve the basic inventions of antiquity, some more recent than others, namely, the lever, the wheel, also used as roller or drum, the windlass, the lathe, the screw, the pulley, the gear, the catapult, and water and air pressures. Those singled out for description in no way differ from the common home and market machines except that they are bigger and on occasion involve exceptionally clever application.

In general, the attitude of the ancients to science and its application is rather complex and cannot be characterized by one term or sentence. After describing such machines as the block and tackle of derricks, mill wheels, the water screw, a turbine wheel for raising water to higher levels, a water pump, a water organ, and odometer, Vitruvius concludes: "I have thus contrived the execution in proper form of the machines which may be carried out for useful purposes or for amusement in times of peace and tranquility.

"We may now turn to the inventions which serve both to protect against danger and to satisfy the needs of safety." Vitruvius then proceeds to describe scorpions and ballistae (catapults), various movable towers and battering rams used for attack or defense of cities under siege, and many other related contraptions. Among these he cites the borer, climbing machines for demolishing and scaling walls, cranes, rams on wheels, and a tortoise for filling ditches and for storming bridges.

Now, Vitruvius is no biographer like Plutarch, carried away by devotion to his subject. He is an architect, a man of applied science. And yet, he shows the usual deep respect for pure science and for practical applications as well, much as we would in our own day.

There were some who had no use for science, primarily because their major concern was with other aspects of the human mind. Socrates was one such. In his apology (by Plato) rendered to the 500 Athenian representatives before whom he stood trial, he resents the accusation that "Socrates is an evil-doer, --and a curious person, who searches into things under the earth and in heaven." He was indeed pictured as such in the *The Clouds* by Aristophanes, but, says he, it is wholly inaccurate, "not that I mean to speak disparagingly of anyone who is a student of natural philosophy.... The simple truth is, O Athenians, that I have nothing to do with physical speculations." (*The Dialogues of Plato*. Translated by B. Jowett. New York. 1937, Vol. I, p. 403).

In Plato's *Phaedo*, Socrates reiterates the same point. "When I was young, Ceber, I had a prodigious desire to know that department of philosophy which is called the investigation of nature; to know the causes of things, and why a thing is and is created or destroyed appeared to me to be a lofty profession; and I was always agitating myself with the consideration of questions such as these: -- Is the growth of animals the result of some decay which the hot and cold principle contracts, as some have said? Is the blood the element with which we think, or the air, or the fire? Or perhaps nothing of the kind -- but the brain may be the originating power of the perceptions of hearing and sight and smell, and memory and opinion may come from them, and science may be based on memory and opinion when they have attained fixity. And then I went on to examine the corruption of them, and then to the things of heaven and at last I concluded myself to be utterly and absolutely incapable of these inquiries, as I will satisfactorily prove to you. For I was fascinated by them to such a degree that my eyes grew blind to things which I had seemed to myself, and also to others to know quite well; I forgot what I had before thought self-evident truths." For example, Anaxagoras had declared "that mind was the disposer and-cause of all, and I was delighted at this notion which appeared quite admirable, and I said to myself: If mind is the disposer, mind will dispose all for the best, and put each particular in the best place... and I imagined that he would tell me first whether the earth is flat or round; and whichever was true, he would proceed to explain the cause and necessity of this being so, and then he would teach me the nature of the best and show that this was best... and I thought that I would then go on and ask him about the sun and moon and stars, and that he would explain to me their comparative swiftness, and their returning and various states, active and passive, and how all of them were for the best... and I seized the books and read them as fast as I could in my eagerness to know the better and the worse.

"What expectations I had formed, and how grievously was I disappointed!" (*ibid.* p. 480-1) And the reasons for his disappointment lay in the fact that science told him "my body is made up of bones and muscles; and the bones, as he would say, are hard and have joints which divide them, and the muscles are elastic, and they cover the bones, which also have a covering or environment of flesh and skin which contains them," etc. But science could tell him little of purpose, of values, "of the nature of the beast." And Socrates concluded: "So in my own case, I was afraid that my soul might be blinded altogether if I looked at things with my eyes or tried to apprehend them by the help of the senses. And I thought that I had better had recourse to the world of mind and seek there the truth of existence."

It is rather strange that in another dialogue, *Gorgias,* Plato refers to the engineer as well as to the pilot as rather lowly men. Says he: "The pilot, although he is our savior, is not usually conceited, any more than the engineer, who is not at all behind either the general, or the pilot, or anyone else, in his saving power, for he sometimes saves whole cities. And if he were to talk, Callicles, in your grandiose style, he would bury you under a mountain of words, declaring and insisting that we ought all of us to be engine-makers, and that no other profession is worth thinking about; he would have plenty to say. Nevertheless, you despise him and his art, and sneeringly call him an engine-maker, and you will not allow your daughters to marry his son, or marry your son to his daughters. And yet, on your principle, what justice or reason is there in your refusal? What right have you to despise the engine-maker?... I know what you will say, 'I am better, and better born'.... Your censure of the engine-maker, and of the physician, and of the other arts of salvation, is ridiculous." (*ibid.* Vol. I, p. 573)

And so we see that neigher Plato nor Plutarch, both of whom were fully acquainted with the science of their times, pictured the technician or the man of applied science in any other light than as day laborers, menials, necessary servants but not eliciting respect. Awe and admiration were reserved for real science, namely, natural philosophy, ideas concerning nature, numbers and geometry. The fact is that none of the writings of antiquity justifies the notion that science originated from social or economic necessity. Man has always been an inventive being and necessity has always been a stimulating force in one form or another. But when we say necessity, we do not mean the same thing for all people. One person may regard it as necessary to play music, second to dig a sewer, a third to write poetry, a fourth to seek to be liked by neighbors, a fifth to ridicule all the neighbors he can think of, and a sixth to revile only those who are better off than he is. The different notions of what is necessary, held by people, spring largely from individual differences and also from different culture patterns in which they live. Not only can people have different values and goals in life which they regard as necessary for their well-being, but the very means of gratifying basic needs such as food, shelter, faith, group cohesion and the like, may differ from group to group. What we regard as a necessary motive, was not always regarded as such by our ancestors.

2. Science as an Intellectual Pursuit

Man has always devised and invented, improved and modified tools, weapons, dress, operations, shelters, furnishings, ornaments, idols, and what-not. At certain times or under certain conditions his efforts and wits will be guided in a practical direction more than elsewhere, and at other times a given culture will show amazing or even exclusive activity in theoretical, speculative directions. One might say that man is seldom averse to practical considerations and seldom refrains from making some improvement in that field, regardless of other lulls or excitement. Similarly, love of speculation, penetration into the unknown, the emotional-spiritual expression we call religion, philosophy, art and love, are also seldom dormant, and man will also cater to their challenges and demands. While the two lines of activity are always with man, there is variation in his intensity of their pursuit at any time interval in history.

One thing seems certain. Many prominent science writers of modern times, especially in England (a phenomenon associated perhaps with liquidation of empire, hence some decline in cultural, industrial, scientific, and commercial leadership) view society in terms of classes and science as catering only to practical needs. The actual evidence merely supports the view that practical inventiveness and scientific speculations existed in many societies, often side by side. Thus, writes one English science historian: "Astronomy was needed to regulate the calendar, geometry to measure the fields, arithmetic and a system of weights and measures to gather the taxes, medicine had its obvious uses. So, it must be observed, had superstition, and the superstition was such as to preclude the beginning of a scientific cosmology." (Benjamin Farrington, *Greek Science*. 1949, Vol. I, p. 29. Pelican Books) The fact is that fields were measured, allottted, inherited, and divided long before Euclid, and extensively without the aid of geometry, after Euclid. As with Archimedes, it is unlikely that Euclid cared whether or not peasants divided their land one way or another, although he probably was quite naturally pleased to have people use and enjoy his work. Neighter were Rutherford's, Bohr's and Einstein's discoveries "needed" to produce atomic bombs or even electric power from the heat of radioactivity. The search for tools and power is as old as man, and the search for ideas about matter is equally as old. That the two should unite in the course of events is as reasonable as that the act of reading a book should merge with that of smoking a cigarette, or that family feeding be joined with pleasant table talk. Not only is truth perverted by postulating false causation, but the nature of man is being misconstrued in the process.

Seneca, the great moralist, dramatist and Nero's teacher and later essentially his prime minister and also the author of one of a most valuable compilations of the physical sciences of antiquity, *Natural Questions,* saw science quite differently. He begins with: "Some writers have wasted their efforts in narrating the doings of foreign kings, and in telling, as the case may be, the sufferings, or the cruelties of nations.... How much better to make one's theme the works of the gods than the robberies of Philip, or Alexander, or the other conquerors who earned their fame by the destruction of mankind!.. What, I ask, then, is the principal thing in human life? Not to have filled the sea with fleets, nor to have planted the standard of the nation on the shores of the Red Sea... Rather it is to have grasped in mind the whole universe, and to have gained what is the greatest of all victories, the mastery over besetting sins. There are hosts of conquerors who have had cities and nations under their power, but a very few who have subdued self... He is the true freeman who has escaped from bondage to self... its fetters may easily be struck off... if you will say to yourself, 'Why do I rave, and pant, and sweat? Why do I ply the earth? Why do I haunt the forum?' Man needs but little, nor needs that little long.

"To this end it will be profitable for us to examine the nature of the universe. In the first place, we shall rise above what is base; in the second, we shall set the spirit free from the body, imparting to it that courage and elevation of which it stands in need. Besides, subtlety of thought practiced on the hidden mysteries of nature will prove no less efficacious in problems that lie more on the surface. And nothing is more on the surface than these salutary lessons we are taught as safeguards against the prevailing vice and madness -- faults we all condemn, but do not abandon." (London, 1910, pp. 119-114)

Being a stoic and a moralist, Seneca believed that the essence of life is knowledge of fact and nature, submission to the inescapable, improvement of self, and the search for an understanding of man and nature. Science was of importance to him and, as he sees it, to all of mankind only to the extent that it helped expand man's intellecutal horizons. Throughout his great work which encompasses all the knowledge and speculation of the time, the latter half of the first century A.D., concerning meteors, halos, rainbow, light, colors, air, storms, water in all its forms, rivers, winds, earthquakes and comets, his interest in science is never utilitarian, always strictly intellectual. The book is packed with fair and penetrating accounts of the vast diversity of ingenious theories and explanations of the many classes of natural phenomena expounded by the great philosophers, the reasons behind each, and the difficulties which the generalizations overcame or failed to account for.

To Seneca, science is an eternal search. "How many animals we have come to know for the first time in our own days! Many, too, that are unknown to us, the people of a coming day will know. Many discoveries are reserved for the ages still to be, when our memory shall have perished. The world is a poor affair if it do not contain matter for investigation for the whole world in every age.... Nature does not reveal all her secrets at once. We imagine we are initiated in her mysteries: We are, as yet, but hanging around her outer courts.... Of one of them this age will catch a glimpse, of another, the age that will come after....

"Who attends the school of wisdom now? Who thinks it worthwhile to have more than a bowing acquaintance with her? Who has regard for philosophy or any liberal pursuit, except when a rainy day comes round to interrupt the games, and it may be wasted without loss?... Philosophy gets never a thought. And so it comes to pass that, far from advance being made toward the discovery of what the older generation left insufficiently investigated, many of their discoveries are being lost. But yet, on my soul of honour, if we urged on this task with all our powers, if our youth in sobriety braced themselves to it, if the elder taught it and the younger learned it, even then scarce should we reach the bottom of the well in which truth lies. As it is, we search for her on the surface, and with a slack hand." (*ibid.* p. 308)

But while Seneca regarded science as natural philosophy conceived as wisdom and truth about the phenomena of nature, another famous writer of antiquity, Pliny, saw it somewhat differently. Pliny, known as the elder, to distinguish him from his nephew, was the author of a famous work entitled *Natural History,* which constitutes the first popular encyclopedia of nature in western civilization. Pliny loves nature and science, but his approach is that of a gatherer of knowledge and of an enlightened raconteur in the field of adult education rather than of a researcher like Archimedes or Eratosthenes, or of the kind represented by Seneca.

Little wonder, then, that we find him state with admiration: "The people who have achieved distinction in the knowledge of the various sciences are innumerable, but nevertheless they must be touched on when we are calling the flower of mankind; in astronomy, Berosus, to whom on account of his marvellous predictions Athens officially erected in the exercising ground a statue with a gilt ongue; in philology, Apollodorus, whom the Amphictyons of Greece honoured; in medicine, Hippocrates, who foretold a plague... in return for which service Greece voted him the honours that it gave to Hercules... Archimedes also received striking testimony to his knowledge of geometry and mechanics from Marcus Marcellus... Others who won praise were Chersiphron of Gnossus, who constructed the wonderful temple of Diana at Ephesus, Philo, who made a dockyard for 400 ships at Athens, Ctesibius, who discovered the theory of the pneumatic pump and invented hydraulic engines, Dinochares, who acted as surveyor for Alexander when founding Alexandria in Egypt." (Vol. II p. 589) Thus, men of practical achievements were not spurned and are occasionally cited among the greats.

Pliny was the teacher of the common man who was possessed of academic interest and hungry for learning on a level of considerable merit. While he wanders off into some astute philosophical discussion every now and then, and generally exhibits keen knowledge of most of the science of his day, his leanings are toward the empirical and the rather ordinary phases of learning. Thus he ends his great collection of accounts with the following: "However, to return to products pure and simple, the most costly product of the sea is the pearl; of the earth's surface, rock-crystal; of the earth's interior, diamonds, emeralds, gemstones, and vessels of fluor-spar; of the earth's increase, the scarlet kermes-insect and silphium, with spikenard and silks from leaves, citrus wood from trees, cinnamon, cassia and amomum from shrubs, amber, balsam, myrrh and frankincense, which exude from trees or shrubs, and costus from roots. As for those animals which are equipped to breathe, the most costly product found on land is the elephant's tusk, and on sea the turtle's shell. Of the hides and coats of animals, the most costly are the pelts dyed in China and the Arabian she-goat's tufted beard which we call 'ladanum.' Of creatures that belong to both land and sea, the most costly products are scarlet and purple dyes made from shell-fish. Birds are created with no outstanding contribution except warriors' plumes and the grease of the Commagene goose. We must not forget to mention that gold, for which all mankind has so mad a passion, comes scarcely tenth in the list of valuables, while silver, with which we purchase gold, is almost as low as twentieth.

"Hail, Nature, mother of all creation, and mindful that I alone of the men of Rome have praised thee in all thy manifestations, be gracious unto me." (Vol. X, p. 331)

Pliny, the spokesman of the common intelligent man's love of nature, never distinguishes between the abstract and the practical, although quite naturally he leans more to the latter. He is no deep scholar, but shows fairly adequate knowledge of astronomy, geography, zoology, and botany, as well as true admiration for wisdom and learning and the pursuit of science. Clearly, there was no prejedice in antiquity against the practical aspect of science, but there certainly was no concentrated worship of it, either. If anything, the high regard was directed more toward the theoretical and abstract, rather than toward the empirical. Even among the empirical ornaments of science are often cited examples which cater completely to the fanciful, fashion-conditioned and culture-determined notions. In other words, science in ancient civilizations comprised horizons little different from the ones encompassed by it today, with due allowances for the changing stresses introduced by the fashions of the time and the culture.

3. A Unique Feature of Early Science

One unique feature of the science of antiquity and the Middle Ages should be cited, and that is its love of the marvelous, the unusual, the fanciful. True, authors like Pliny or Aristotle, as a rule, append the sincere warning "they say" to their numerous tall stories of marvels, but they recount them none-theless. Pliny, for example, was fully aware of the problems which a science popularizer faced in those days when he was obliged to relate "some things among which I doubt not will appear portentous and incredible to many. For who ever believed in the Ethiopians before actually seeing them? Or what is not deemed miraculous when first it comes into knowledge? How many things are judged impossible before they actually occur? Indeed, the pwer and majesty of the nature of the universe at every turn lacks credence if one's mind embraces parts of it only and not the whole. Not to mention peacocks, or the spotted skins of tigers and panthers and the colourings of so many animals; a small matter to tell of but one of measureless extent if pondered on, is the number of national languages and dialects and varieties of speech, so numerous that a foreigner scarcely counts as a human being for someone of another race!" (*Natural History*. Vol. 2, Book VII, p. 511. Loeb Classical Library) This expresses in concise and simple words the bewilderment of the science writer as well as research scientist in those days. Nature was full of incredible and fascinating novelties, the reports of which an honest and obstinate skeptic might fully reject until experienced by him personally, and thus remain in smug ignorance for the rest of his years. Only a petty provincial mind can blandly reject accounts of natural phenomena with which he is personally unfamiliar or impressive occurrences which seem impossible or implausible to him. Pliny seems aware of the dilemma. Although many historians accuse him of being overly credulous, he is extremely cautious. Says he: "Nevertheless, in most instances of these I shall not myself pledge my own faith, and shall preferably ascribe the facts to the authorities who will be quoted for all doubtful points; only do not let us be too proud to follow the Greeks, because of their far greater industry or older devotion to study." (*ibid.* p. 513) Not only was he cautious but willing to put aside pride of empire and defy popular distrust of the Greeks for the sake of learning.

But nature is full of marvels. We still employ the terms magic, wonders, miracles to even contemporary accounts of science. Both in antiquity and today the human being cannot help being deeply impressed by the sight of the astonishing, the unexpected, the extraordinary. Because they run contrary to what we are accustomed, we quite naturally tend to disbelieve them. If we overdo such skpticism, we fall into the arms of provincialism. To this pitiable state we relegate a person who is so confined by his small world of limited experience that he refuses to broaden his horizons by admitting new facts, concepts, or values into his mental horizons. Aware of this, Pliny, loving marvels himself, cites numerous accounts of fanciful phenomena without authorities, merely adding the phrase "they say", which is good enough since we know what he means.

That skepticism can often go too far is common knowledge. The explorer Marco Polo was derided in his day by people who could not believe his fancy tales of China. About a millenium and a half before him the great explorer from ancient Marseilles, Pytheas, whose fame as scientist and navigator rested on solid achievements, was ridiculed by the historian Polybius and the great geographer Strabo for his claim that Thule, presumably Scandinavia, extended north of Britain. Yet other scholars such as Eratosthenes, Hipparchus, Pliny and Ptolemy, believed him and ultimately proved him to be right. But at the time, there was no way of deciding and one could not be blamed or praised for taking one position or the other.

What folly it is, then, to condemn some scholars of antiquity for being credulous and others for being critical enough to refuse to accept on faith some new idea. One such idea was the revolution of the earth, which admittedly emerged as true, but could not possibly be justly evaluated when first advanced as a possible hypothesis which its author simply preferred to the one commonly honored. There is often a gambling element in the sphere of ideas, or even reports, which involves as much risk as in the support of one of several candidates running for a given post with probabilities of victory wholly unknown and unknowable. Suspension of judgment might be best, but the human mind seems to find this difficult. If it is true that nature abhors a vacuum, it is doubly true that the mind is deeply averse to non-commitment on most issues. Thus judgment is often rendered psychologically unavoidable.

It must not be assumed that particular scientists were even in those days either wholly skeptical or wholly credulous. It is true that some authors tend generally toward caution and others toward credulity; the vast majority of men of science display both features. Herodotus, the so-called father of history, is regarded by most scholars as being overly prone to credulity. Nevertheless, he writes as follows: "For my part I am astonished that men should have ever divided Libya (Africa), Asia, and Europe as they have, for they are exceedingly unequal. Europe extends the entire length of the other two, and for breadth will not even, as I think, bear to be compared to them. As for Libya, we know it to be washed on all sides by the sea, except where it is attached to Asia. This discovery was first made by Necos, the Egyptian king, who on desisting from the canal which he had begun between the Nile and the Arabian Gulf, sent to sea a number of ships manned by Phoenicians, with orders to make for the Pillars of Hercules, and return to Egypt through them, and by the Mediterranean. The Phoenicians took their departure from Egypt by way of the Erythrean (Red) Sea, and so sailed into the Southern Ocean. When autumn came, they went ashore, wherever they might happen to be, and having sown a tract of land with corn, waited until the grain was fit to cut. Having reaped it, they again set sail; and thus it came to pass that two whole years went by, and it was not till the third year that they doubled The Pillars of Hercules, and made good their voyage home. One their return they declared -- I for my part do not believe them, but perhaps others may -- that in sailing round Libya they had the sun upon their right hand. In this way was the extent of Libya first discovered." (*The History of Herodotus*. Translation by G. Rawlinson, New York, 1928, p. 216) As luck would have it, Herodotus chose to be skptical about a report which seems perfectly credible and which has the ring of the truth in every part of it. We know today that the circumnavigation of Africa from the Red Sea southward, then westward around the Cape of Good Hope, then northward to Gibraltar, with the sun rising "upon their right hand," and finally eastward along the Mediterranean to Egypt, need not have been a fantasy. But toward many truly foolish stories, Herodotus demonstrated no skepticism whatever even though on occasion he comments: "If this be true, I know not; I but write what is said." (*Ibid.*, p. 262)

4. A Sample of "Scientific" Instruments

The technological thinking of antiquity followed the culture's general attitude to science, both pure and applied. Continuous progress of varying degree proceeded in the field of practical needs, mostly unnoted and unsung, while in the field of fanciful ingenuity, the efforts were intense, dramatic and gratifying. Let us first survey the field and see the kind of inventiveness displayed and the manner in which the inventions were put to use in society. Hero of Alexandria left two valuable books, *Mechanics* (A. G. Drachmann, *The Mechanical Technology of Greek and Roman Antiquity*. University of Wisconsin Press, Madison, Wis., 1963) and *Pneumatics*, (translated by B. Woodcroft, London, 1851).

The *Mechanics* consists of three books and deals essentially with explanations of the scientific principles and techniques of haulage and lifting, employing gear-wheels, screws, pulleys, levers, wedges, winches, rollers, sleds for dragging loads, as well as pantographs, which are instruments for enlarging or diminishing given shapes, parallelograms of forces, and describing complex presses, cranes, catapults, and various combinations of the simpler instruments. The book is written on a high level in concise and technical language, and the author expects "the student of the science of mechanics" to know considerable mathematics, and also "something about gravity and centers of gravity," geometry, architecture, and to have mastered all engineering skills. It deals in detail with the theory of the five powers, meaning the five simple engines: the windlass, the lever, the tackle-block, the wedge, and the screw, examining their basic uses and principles, and many theoretical examples of their diverse combinations. It instructs the student in the manner of finding the centers of gravity of different shapes, such as triangles, quadrangles, and many polygons.

The following are some of the illustrations pertinent to the text, which give some idea of the material.

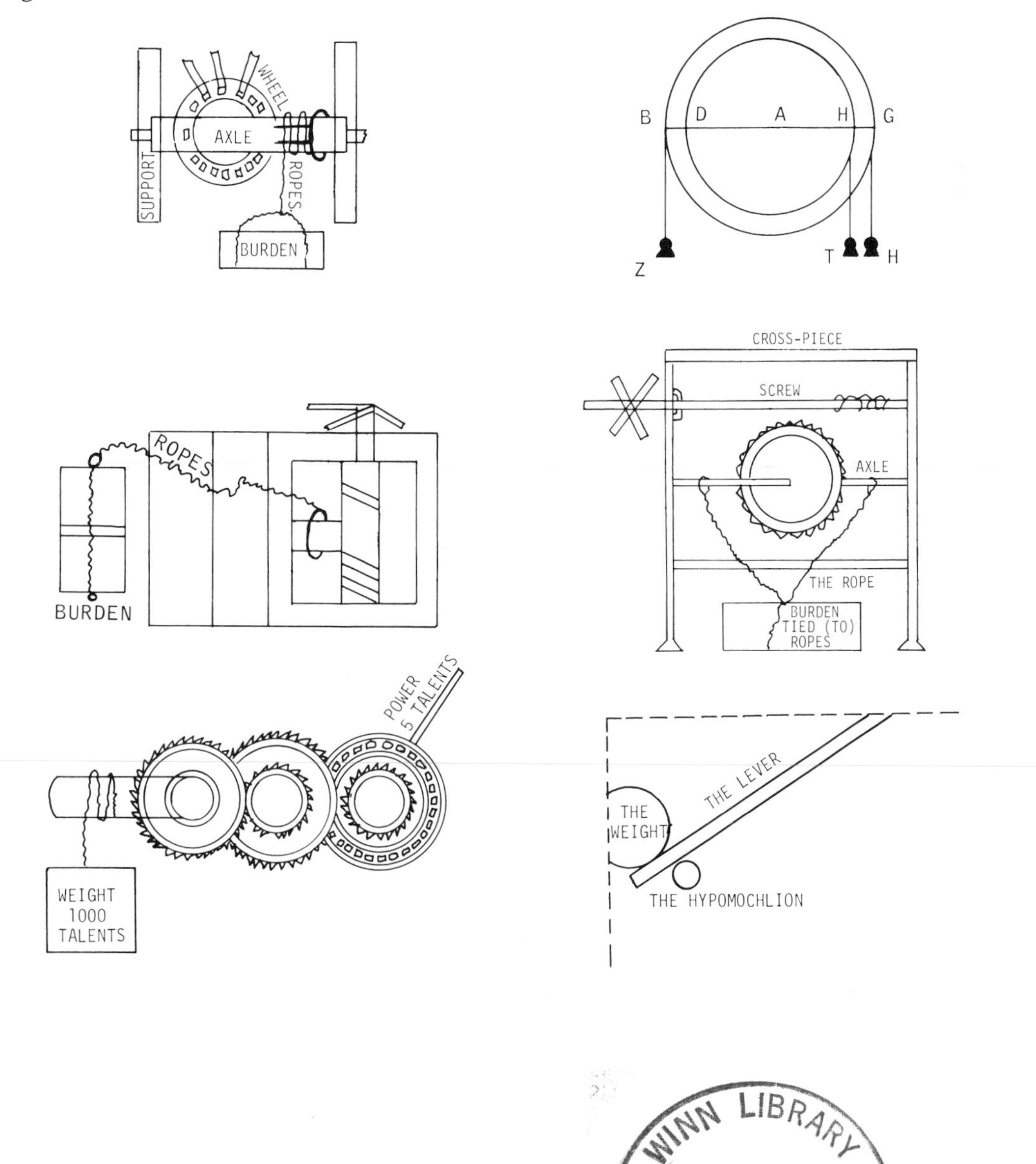

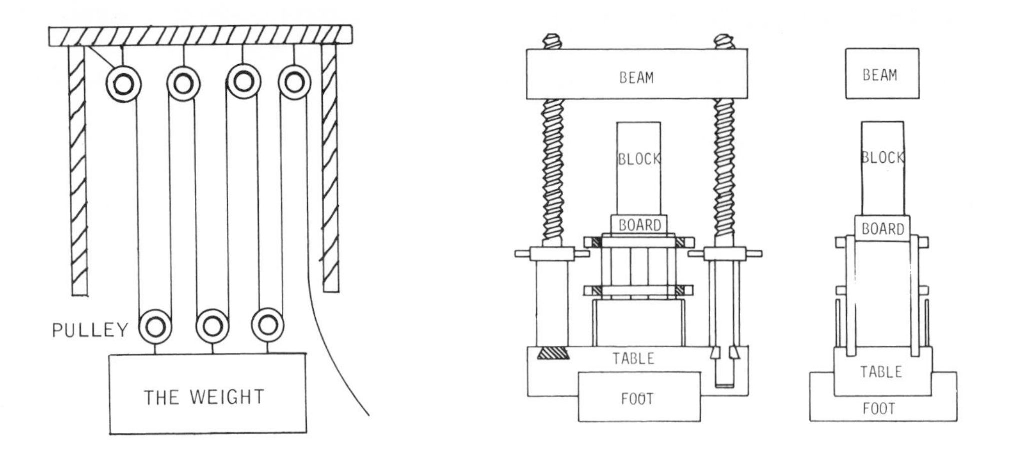

The last of the three books cites a number of complex combinations of the simple machines, which it describes as "engines built for ease and usefulness, by which also great burdens are moved." (*ibid.*, p. 95) Most, if not all, of these machines had no doubt been long in common use. As is shown in the figure (p. 79), Hero demonstrates that the use of either pulleys or gears in a manner shown in the diagram will permit a power of five talents to lift a weight of 1000 talents, thus demonstrating full knowledge of the theory of mechanical efficiency. Yet, his drawings and language indicate that his knowledge of gears was abstract rather than practical, hence that toothed wheels were not used much, and apparently pulleys were more common. Similarly, says Drachmann, "endless chains and ropes are not used; one end is fixed on the axle, the other on the wheel." (p. 199) It would seem from the evidence that up to the time of Hero (circa 60 A. D.) mastery over the gear wheel had not advanced in practice far enough to be effectively exploited. They were used by Ctesibios (circa 280 B. C.) in a fanciful clock and were therefore an inventor's brainchild. The same is true of other applications of the gear such as the endless screw invented by Archimedes (250 B. C.) which was certainly used in war machines. Drachmann, who composed a definitive study of this subject, concludes: "It would seem, then, that the use of the cog-wheel began with the rack-and-pinion arrangement of Ctesibios, and the endless screw of Archimedes, while the direct transmission (i. e. gear to gear) is first known from the Antikythera (instrument showing movements of planets) which is from the second century B. C. The first mention of gear-wheels is from Vitruvius, about 25 B. C., in the water-mills, with the wheels at right angles. Next comes Hero, about 60 A. D., with the barulkos (weight lifting machine) which I refuse to take as a working engine. The gear-wheels were then developed by trial and error, big, wooden ones in the watermills and, later, windmills; small, metal ones in clockwork. But it was not until 1675 that the correct solution was found by Ole Romer." (p. 203)

Thus both Ctesibios and Archimedes were great inventors, one full-time, the other only part-time. Some of their inventions were used, most were not. Inventions for warfare found as a rule quick application when requested by generals or rulers. When advanced as clever devices by their discoverers and offered to the military leaders, more often than not such inventions were not received with enthusiasm, and were frequently entirely spurned. The complex inventions stood a good chance of being disregarded. On the other hand, the basic simple powers--the lever, the wedge, the roller, and the wheel--were very old. "The single pulley has been known from very old times; it is shown in an Assyrian relief from about 870 B.C. It is used for a bucket going down into a well. Also in ships it came into use very early." (p. 203) It was also used for catapults.

The use of the screw, on the other hand, "is the application of a mathematical construction to practical use." The endless screw was used only by surgeons. "For presses the female screw was invented," meaning a cylindrical socket in whose wall a helical groove is carved so that an ordinary or male screw can move along it. The use of the female screw in small holes of either bronze or iron was not within the power of the times and a *tylos* or a peg engaging the screw from the side was employed instead. In general then, it may be concluded that the simple but useful devices arose among the working craftsmen and were widely used. Sophisticated inventions were also forever being designed by clever inventors but not used much because of technical difficulties at the time of their creation. Concludes Drachmann: "Inventors like Ctesibios and Hero strewed their inventions broadcast; but unless the invention found a fertile soil, it could not thrive. I should prefer not to seek for the cause of the failure of an invention in the social conditions till I was quite sure that it was not to be found in the technical possibilities of the time." (p. 206)

Three books entitled *Pneumatics* have come down to us from Greek antiquity and their respective authors are Ctesibios, Philo and Hero, the three great mechanicians. Ctesibios, the pioneer of his times and most original of the trio, was the son of a barber at Alexandria. He worked in his father's shop and lived from about 300 to 230 B.C. The most reliable of the succeeding writers, Vitruvius for example, regard him as the inventor of the fire pump, the water organ, many types of catapults, and "at least one other war engine; also that he improved the water-clock besides providing it with singing birds and other delights. We know further that he wrote a book about his inventions and experiments" which is unfortunately lost. (*Ktesibios, Philon and Heron, A Study in Ancient Pneumatics,* by A.G. Drachmann. Copenhagen 1948, p. 3) Philo of Byzantium whose book has survived even if probably only in part, presents a great variety of curious, ingenious and amusing instruments, and resembles in its entirety the work of Hero of Alexandria. Both books rest upon the genius of Ctesibios, and Hero, who lived around 50 A.D., seems to be the latest of the three. Moreover, since his book is available in its complete text and is provided with lucid illustrations, we shall use it as our source for the kind of instruments the brilliant mechanicians of antiquity created in response to their love of science in their chosen province. Fuller information is available in the detailed work by Drachmann.

Hero's *Pneumatics* deals largely with clever instruments for fancy's sake, designed to serve as parlor entertainment or as impressive temple equipment serving to awe or amuse the visiting or worshipping populace. (Hero of Alexandria *Pneumatics*. Bennet Woodcraft, Ed. London 1851)

Hero begins his work with the statement: "The investigations of the properties of Atmospheric Air, having deemed worthy of close attention by the ancient philosophers and mechanists, the former deducing them theoretically, the latter from the action of sensible bodies, we also have thought proper to arrange in order what has been handed down by former writers, and to add these to our own discoveries.... For by the union of air, earth, fire and water, and the concurrence of three or four elementary principles, various combinations are effected, some of which supply the most pressing wants of human life, while others produce amazement and alarm." This is indeed a concise and complete statement of the manner in which science was developed and exploited in antiquity. It was pursued because man's mind was active and on occasion creative. If human insight saw no practical use for a given invention, then that invention simply was not put to practical use; but, as a scientific invention, it was always interesting, impressive, fascinating and worthwhile. Others were such as to "supply the most pressing wants of human life." With a practical, non-academic artisan like Hero, the latter phenomenon came first.

Hero indicates in that same introduction that quite much was known about air, air resilience, and compression. "While some assert that there is absolutely no vacuum," he himself cannot support such a view, preferring the opinion "that while no continuous vacuum is exhibited in nature, it is found to be distributed in minute portions through air, water, fire, and all other substances... Vessels which seem to most men empty are not empty, as they suppose, but full of air," which "is composed of particles minute and light, and for the most part invisible." Air is, above all, a substance, a body occupying space. Air must leave the space of a vessel if water is to get into it. "This may be seen from the following experiment." An inverted glass inserted into water will not admit water unless a hole in its bottom is opened and air is allowed to escape. Wind is nothing but air in motion.

As usual, side by side with most uncommon insights, we find some logic which makes us smile. Air in cups during the operation of cupping used in the past as treatment for colds, for sucking out poisons or for lancing boils, forms a vacuum because, "the fire placed in them consumes and rarefies the air they contain, just as other substances, water, fire or earth are consumed and pass over into more subtle substances." Cups had a flame inserted into them before being placed on skin. Burned wood cinders, even though they retain their original shape, are lighter because they lost much of their contents to the fire. "Fire dissolves and transforms all bodies grosser than itself.... In the exhalations that rise from the earth, the grosser kinds of matter are changed into subtler substances; for dew is sent up from the evaporation of the water contained in the earth by exhalation," which is "produced by some igneous substance, when the sun is under the earth and warms the ground below." Air can be compressed; hence there are vacua between its particles. Besides, air can be sucked out of a vessel, by which "experiment it is completely proved that an accumulation of vacuum goes on in the globe.... Again, that void spaces exist may be seen from the following considerations: For, if there were not such spaces, neither light, nor heat, nor any other material force could penetrate through water, or air, or any body whatever."

And so we see that Hero possessed great insight into the nature of air, vacua, and pressure in spite of many naive conceptions. Such is the nature of human reasoning at all times. Else, progress could only occur catastrophically, on all fronts at once, which we know not to be so. Man makes progress by seeing a light through one crack while the rest of the wall remains solidly opaque. On another occasion, he will forge another crack in the wall elsewhere. By degrees and against a vast background of ignorance or misconceptions, he slowly erects his universe of order which he calls light.

The practical products of Hero's ingenuity are equally impressive. In his *Pneumatics,* Hero presents 78 inventions of which the following dozen or so may serve as a representative sample, especially since I built them and found them to work as Hero says they do.

1. Libations on an altar produced by fire, or as we might call it today, a self-extinguishing altar. Water is poured into base through a stopcock which is then closed tight. An alcohol flame is caused to burn on the altar. As the air trapped in the altar above the water gets heated, it expands and forces the water to rise in the two tubes and come down upon the flame, thus putting it out.

Figure 5.2

2. The Steam Engine. This is so named in the *Pneumatics,* although the term engine certainly had a different meaning to the ancients from what it has to us. We imply by the term a mechanism which performs as a rule some useful task, thus saving human labor. To the ancients, an engine meant nothing of the kind. It meant instead a mechanism which can perform something impressive, something automatic, something which one does not normally expect from an inanimate object. It is for this reason that most of these automata, namely machines that can perform amazing and entertaining acts, were as a rule placed in temples. A temple was a place of worship, a place for serious emotional experiences of an inspiring nature. Equivalent places are still decorated with great art, such as, the Sistine Chapel or a Buddhist temple, while scientific wonders fill our homes and factories.

Figure 5.3

In this so-called steam engine, water is placed in the basin and brought to a boil. Steam escapes through the two outlets, A and B, thus obliging them by Newton's Third Law to recoil in the opposite direction from that of the escaping steam. The sphere sitting loosely on two pivots, C and D, is thus made to revolve with great speed. Needless to say, we do have the basis of a steam engine here, but the Greeks never dreamed of employing it as a labor-saving device. The whole concept of labor-saving was novel and never real nor urgent. It is likely that if Hero were asked why he did not use the principle of steam pressure as a labor-saving device, he would be surprised and wonder what was wrong with the questioner's wife. Was she sick, or dead? Work was done by wives, by servants, or slaves if you could afford them, but under all conditions by people and beasts. The idea of labor-saving as a formula to be applied wherever possible, was simply unknown and as yet far in the future.

3. As a third and final example of the utilization of air pressure may serve the working model of "Temple Doors opened by Fire on an Altar." The fire on the altar warms the air in the enclosed space beneath it. Note the hole P through which water is poured in. The heated air presses on the water in the sphere below the altar and forces it to escape through a siphon into a bucket suspended from a pulley. The ropes passing over the pulley are attached to shafts that can rotate and open the gates which are attached to the shafts. Opening of the gates is achieved when the bucket fills with sufficient water to force it down and thus rotate the shafts. The counterweight at lower right is raised when the upper gates are opened. However, when the fire is put out, a partial vacuum is created in the space of the altar, and the water from the bucket will be sucked back into the cask beneath the altar. The bucket becomes lighter and returns to its original high perch due to pull of falling counterweight. The gates close and prayer time is over. (Figure 5.4)

It is frequently asserted even by men of learning that, religion functioning as the opiate of the people, many priests will employ various magical tricks or impressive scientific performances to awe the people into terror and obedience. This argument is about as convincing as the postulate that dancing or sex are inventions of the capitalists, designed at keeping the "working class" amused and preoccupied so that the exploited "workers" neglect their true purpose in life, the economic class struggle. This is equivalent to saying that music is performed in churches in order to put the public in a mellow mood so that when the plate is passed around it will extract the maximum donation from the gathered flock. We know that this assertion is false, since men made music in temples long before there was money or plates and long before someone hit upon the idea of combining the two for the support of the temple. Temples were built because people wanted them, and music was played in them because people wanted music to enforce their sense of awe and worship, their emotional gratification in prayer, their tribal experience of collective communion with their gods.

This is the reason that many of the ingenious devices described by Hero found their exclusive application in temples. An interesting scientific gadget yielded an emotional experience much like a religious painting of Giotto, Raphael or Michelangelo did to the pious men of their days. The scientific gadgets impressed and mystified and were expected to find their natural place in temples just as the paintings of the thirteenth or fourteenth centuries were quite naturally placed in churches. Works of art came to be located in palaces and mansions much later, and only in our own times, in common homes. Impressive scientific devices were also subjected to the whims of a variable

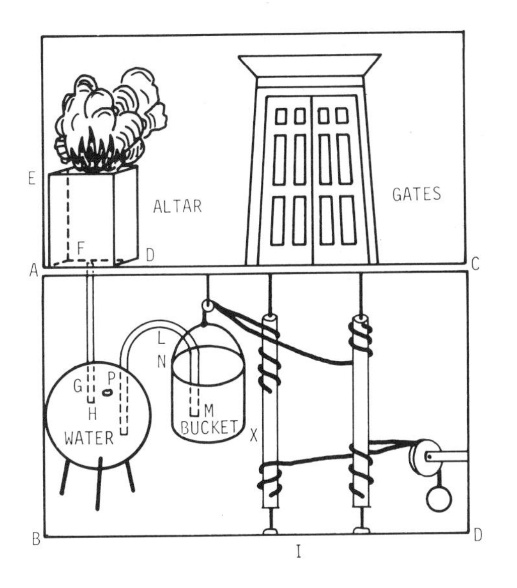

Figure 5.4

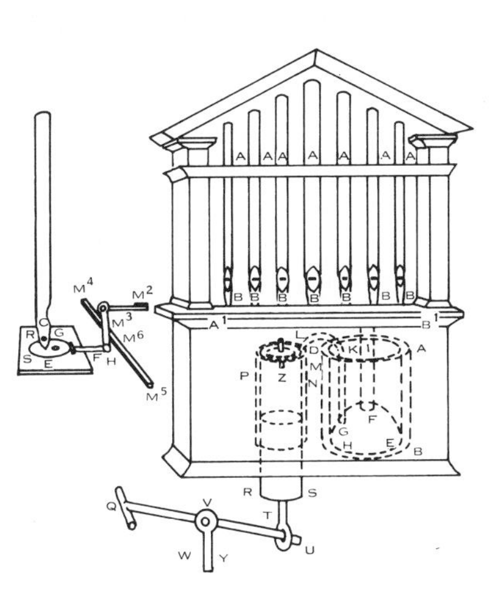

Figure 5.5

fate. From being used primarily for purposes of entertainment and emotional-intellectual stimulation, science came to be employed in every field of man's activities as utilitarian devices.

I made models of all of Hero's devices, not merely to check their validity but also to note their impact on audiences. Invariably the response from all groups was one of curiosity and amusement. There is hardly any reason for doubting that the response of audiences in Hero's time was any different.

4. The bulk of Hero's playthings operated on the principle of work performed by compressed air, since such work stemmed from unseen hence mysterious forces. Most conspicuous of these was "An Altar Organ blown by manual Labor." The diagram presented in Figure 5. 5 explains the operation.

Arm QU operates the piston RS on Pivot V firmly fixed. When RS is lowered, air is taken in through valve Z; when piston is raised, this valve closes and pressed volume of air is forced through siphon LG into hemisphere HE, which rests inverted in water within the large container ABCD. As air enters this hemisphere, water is pushed out of it to the sides and around it so that the water's weight pushes the compressed air in the hemisphere up through the tube FI into the thin, horizontal box marked AB. This long box is then filled with compressed air. The piano keys are made to pull a thin piece of wood, RGSE, back and forth under each organ pipe. This piece has a hole in it. When this hole is directly under the mouth of the vertical pipe, air rushes through it into the pipe, sounding a note. Since Hero also describes valves, it is obvious that he was able to accumulate a modest volume of compressed air in the inverted hemisphere.

The valve at Z of cylinder with piston was "a thin plate under the hole in the lid to close it, upheld by means of four pins passing through holes in the plate and furnished with heads so that the plate cannot fall off." Another valve he describes is illustrated in his book. In this valve, air can be forced through the hole from below to lift a plate. Without pressure from below, the plate is pressed down by air inside the container above it. When the pressure of air forced upward is greater than the plate's weight and the air pressure in the container, then air again rushes inward.

5. Hero's Fountain, pictured in Figure 5.6, is a typical example of a most ingenious device utilizing air pressure obtained through the use of gravity. A glass tube, marked 1 here, with its opening near the bottom of A leads all the way to the bottom of C. As water is poured into A, it flows through tube 1 into C, and forces upward the air of space C through a tube, here marked 2, leading it from top of space C into top os space B. Container B now houses air under pressure due to water from A falling into C and diminishing the over-hanging air volume. This compressed air presses on the water below it in B and forces it upward through tube 3, which begins at bottom of B, going into A and terminating in thin tube with stopcock projecting above A, through which water emerges with fountainlike spray.

To make fountain operate, water is forced through tip of 3 with stopcock open, into B. When this is filled up to a little below open end of tube 2, the stopcock on top is closed and water is poured into A. This water cannot fall into C through tube 1 because the air trapped in C and B, though pressed by weight of water in A, cannot escape. As soon as the stopcock is opened, how-ever, compressed air in overspace of C and B can press on water in B and force it, fountainlike, upward, above original water level of A. The impres-sive aspect is that on opening the stopcock and pouring a little additional water into A for effect, water appears to rise above initial level.

Again, as with the preceding devices, this fountain found no other home but in a temple and played on some predetermined occasion when it partook in some significant ritual. The public was impressed and its inventor felt that he served well the cause of the nation and its gods.

6. "A Vessel containing a Liquid of uniform height, although a Stream flows from it." (Figure 5.7)

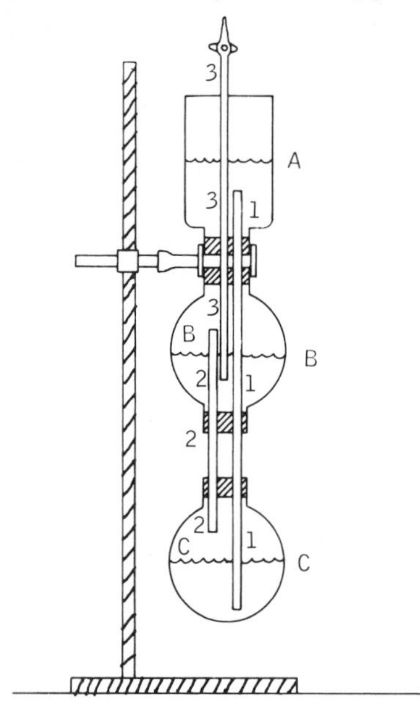

Figure 5.6

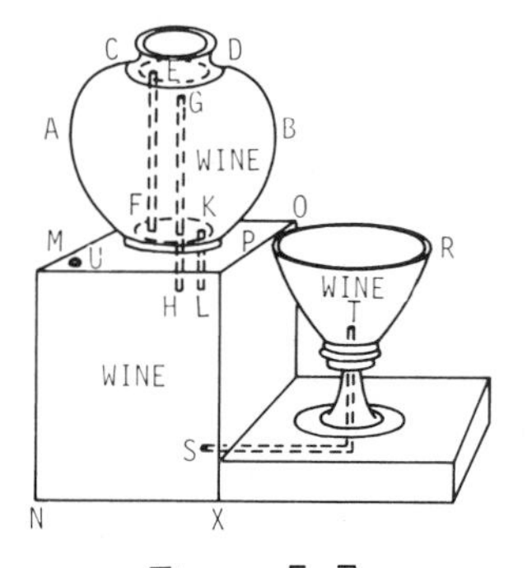

Figure 5.7

The object of this instrument is to keep full the goblet PRT, no matter how much liquid is withdrawn from it. This is rendered possible in the following construction. Vessel ABCD is closed on top except for opening E which leads into a hanging tube attached to the vessel's top and opening above its floor at F. Tube GH is attached to the bottom of ABCD which it pierces; it is open at both ends, G in vessel ABCD and H in vessel MNOX. The third tube, KL, is also inserted in the bottom of vessel ABCD, as shown, and is also open at both ends.

Vessel ABCD is attached to pedestal MNOX which contains wine and which connects by means of tube ST with goblet PR, which also contains wine brought to it through tube ST. The wine gets into MNOX by being poured into ABCD through tube EF. From ABCD its entry into MNXO is made possible by the air flowing out of goblet ABCD through GH, into the upper space of MNXO, from which it escapes outward through hole U. Tube KL being open, some wine will flow into MNXO. However, if KL is closed by fluid in the lower chamber, then ABCD will get filled.

Let wine then flow into MNXO until it reaches heights L and H. "When this is done, close E, and the wine in AB will no longer flow through KL for no more air can enter through E to supply the vacuum created." Thus when wine is withdrawn from goblet PR and orifices U and E are kept open so that air gets into ABCD through EF and HG, more wine will then flow into pedestal MNXO and thereby into PR.

7. "An Automaton which may be made to drink at any time, on a Liquid being presented to it." (Figure 5.8)

In this construction liquid is supplied to funnel YW. Figure PR can turn the horizontal tube QT so that water from the funnel YW will flow into cup MN and fill lower chamber BC. The liquid in this chamber is provided with a siphon, HKL, and the air above it connects with the outside through GFE. When the siphon is made to flow, a partial vacuum is created in space BC above the water within it, and when a beaker with water is brought in contact with mouth E of the swan, the liquid will be sucked in from the beaker. By preventing flow of water from YW into MN by letting its water flow out through arm QT, this process of drinking will be maintained as long as the siphon functions.

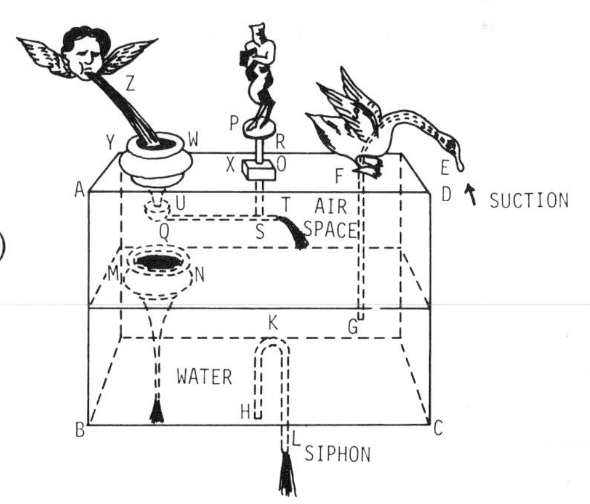

Figure 5.8

8. "A Fountain which Trickles by the Action of the Sun's Rays." (Figure 5.9)

Hero's diagram explains clearly the function of the device. The small volume of air in the globe EF expands when the sun shines upon the air space within it and forces water our through the siphon G. The air chamber ABCD is air-tight so that upon cooling, the air bubble in EF shrinks and causes water from the chamber below to flow

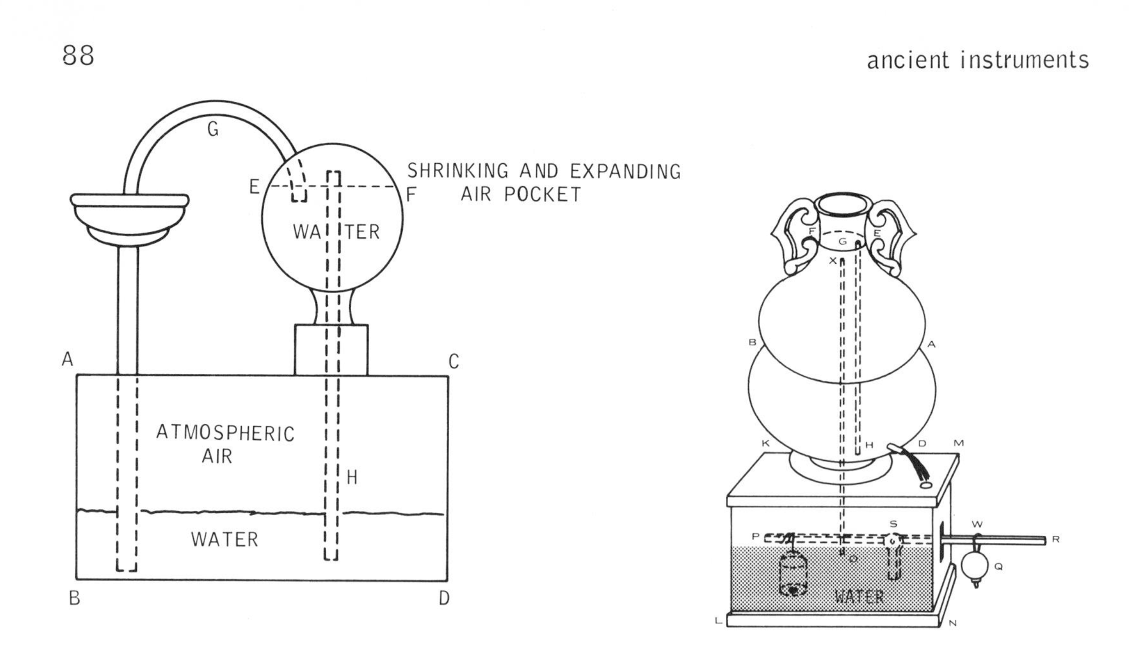

Figure 5.9

Figure 5.10

back through tube H into the globe, thus restoring the original volume from the water available in the lower chamber.

This clearly may well be claimed to be the first combination thermometer of sorts.

9. "A water-clock, made to govern the quantities of Liquid flowing from a Vessel." (Figure 5.10)

In Hero's diagram, tube GH, brings liquid to closed chamber AB. Another tube connects air space of AB with liquid in lower chamber KMNL. Arm P of rod can be raised and lowered on fixed pivot S. This rod is provided on the right side with a movable weight QW, and on the left with a suspended bucket which has a hole in its bottom. The object is to let water flow out of AB through opened stopcock D for a limited time. This is done by filling the bucket and moving the weight QW on arm SR to a desired place. The further to the right we suspend it, the higher the bucket level projects above the water level. Also the larger its volume, the longer it will take for its water to flow out. When the bucket is filled, the water level in lower chamber falls and opens tube end O, thus permitting air to enter AB and water to flow through D. As bucket empties gradually through its small hole, water level in lower chamber rises and in time reaches tube end O, putting a stop to flow at D, since no air can enter upper space in AB.

10. "A Shrine over which a Bird may be made to revolve and sing by Worshippers turning a Wheel." (Figure 5.11)

As can be seen in the Figure this shrine is "provided with a revolving wheel of bronze, termed a purifier, which worshippers are accustomed to turn 'round as they enter." As the outer wheel is turned, gear wheel M rotates shaft with black-cap bird and simultaneously winds rope around pulley L so as to raise attached hemisphere N from the water tank PR. After the outer bronze

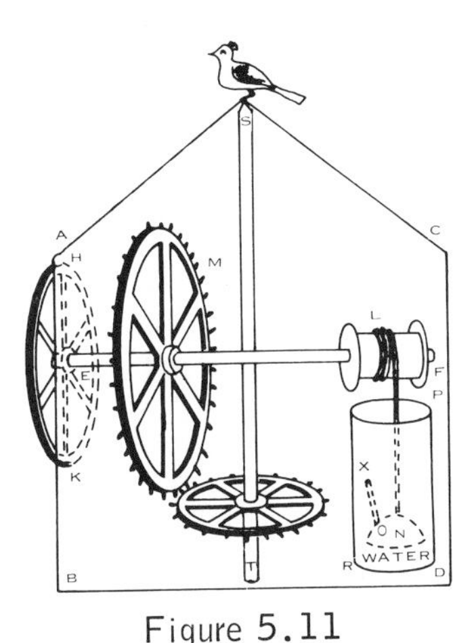

Figure 5.11

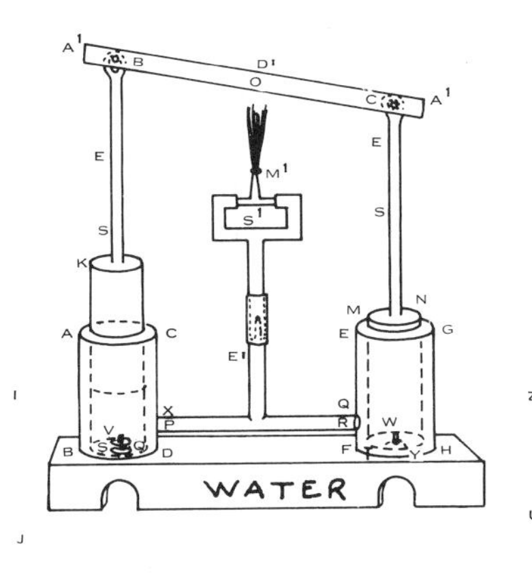

Figure 5.12

wheel is turned and the hemisphere N raised out of the water, then if that wheel is released, the hemisphere N drops, L unwinds, ST rotates with the bird on top of it, and since the hemisphere has a tube X built into it, the trapped air will be forced out of it through that nozzle, which rush of air can be made to emit a sound simulating that of the black-cap or any other bird.

11. The fire-engine represented in the figure demonstrates full knowledge of the application of valves for pumping water to higher levels with the aid of a force pump. The two bronze cylinders, ACBD and EFGH, are provided at their bottoms with valves. A variety of these was available, such as, cups free to rise and fall, a plate moving up and down on four nails, or a hinged flap. Similar valves are seen at P and R. D^1 is a fixed pivot; by working the arm A^1A^1 a stream of water is pumped out through the revolving mouth, M^1. As the piston MN ascends, it opens valve WY and shuts tight valve R, thus raising water into cylinder EFGH. When it descends, it shuts valve WY and opens R, forcing the liquid up the tube E^1S^1. The same applies to the other cylinder, whose action alternates. (Figure 5.12)

It should be noted that there is little evidence that such pumps were employed for extinguishing fires or were ever improved upon in antiquity or in later ages.

12. The flask represented in Figure 5.13 is a clepsydra, a term employed for any flask or container from which water escapes. This flask has a few holes in the bottom and a small hole on top in its neck. The flask is immersed in water or wine which is kept in by closing upper opening with thumb. It is withdrawn and the wine poured into cups by removing the thumb from the neck opening. Closing the hole stops the flow.

Some authors have sought to explain the employment of this method of transference of fluid as a clever means of scooping up all the wine from the bottom of a bowl. This seems dubious when most people in those days would merely turn over the bowl into a flask. Besides, the method proved very ineffective upon being actually tried. It seems more reasonable to assume that this clepsydra was used for the fun of it, in the spirit of the other devices, as playful, magic-like entertainment, now it flows, now it doesn't, by properly or perhaps even clandestinely pressing or easing the thumb over the opening.

Of all of Hero's devices this one seems the least original. A clepsydra of this nature is cited by Aristotle, hence about three centuries before him, to explain the mechanism of inspiration and expiration: water rising in the chest through the pores in the diaphragm forces air out, its ebb draws air in. Anaxagoras, earlier still, (500-430 B. C.), employed it to demonstrate that with one's thumb on the neckhole the pressure or spring of the air was strong enough not to let any water in upon its immersion. Conversely, when water half-filled it, none would flow out as long as the thumb pressing against it forbade air to enter, presumably to help push the water out. He had previously "inflated a wine skin and then twisted the neck of the skin until the compressed air rendered its pliable container firm and hard." (D. E. Gershenson and D. A. Greenberg. *Anaxgoras and the Birth of the Scientific Method.* New York, 1964, p. 40)

13. We finally come to our last illustration of "a Cupping-Glass, to which is attached an Air-exhausted Compartment." (Figure 5. 14)

We have here, in Hero's words, "a cupping-glass, such as is usually applied to the body, but having a partition across it, DE." While the ordinary syringe is also described by Hero, he employs here two modified ones, in reality consisting of a piston within a cylinder. One is fitted tightly into the lower chamber and the other is fitted tightly in a horizontal position in that same chamber but lying against the partition. These syringelike instruments consist of an outer tube or sleeve which holds an inner piston, open at one end but closed and provided with a handle at the other. Both cylinder and piston are provided with holes marked L and M in the vertical syrings, and unmarked in the horizontal one. Place the two holes in the vertical syringe alongside each other, and suck out some air by mouth, turning the inner piston after each suction, so that holes do not match. A partial vacuum can thus be produced through repeated inspirations within the lower chamber. Next, adjust the two holes of the horizontal syrings, the outer cylinder of which is held so that its hole lies against a hole in the partition, DE. By turning the lower vertical piston so that the holes do not face each other, the partial vacuum is locked within the lower chamber. Next, by matching the holes in the upper syringe, the denser air from the upper chamber will rush into the lower one and create a partial vacuum in the upper chamber which is in contact with the patient's skin. "Into the void thus created both the flesh and the matter about it will be drawn up through the interstices of the flesh which we call invisible spaces or pores."

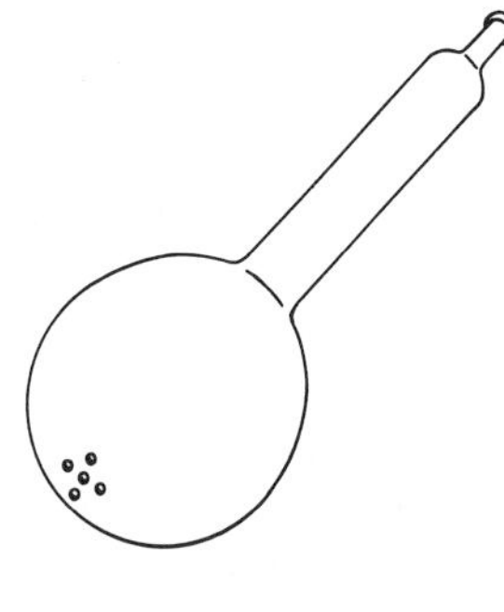

Figure 5.13

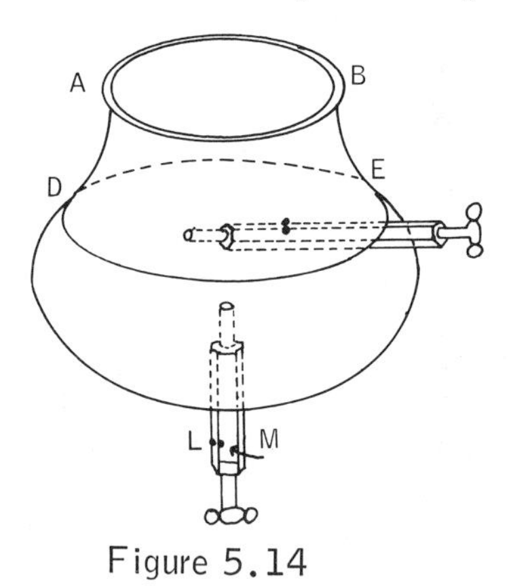

Figure 5.14

Strange that seventeen centuries had to pass before van Guericke and Robert Boyle employed exactly the same principle in developing their vacuum pumps to astound the western world with its lessons concerning the weight of the air and the so-called force of the vacuum. An idea may apparently lie around and go unheeded for a long time before it is seen as if in a new light and comprehended and exploited to its maximum implications. The instruments reported by Hero, whether his own inventions, the products of his brilliant master, Ctesibius, or whether "handed down by former writers," were full of principles that we think of as having introduced the industrial revolution. The great discovery of the eighteenth century fathers of the steam engine, as exemplified by the contributions of Thomas Savery, Thomas Newcomen, and James Watt, was the creation of a vacuum by the condensation of steam. That principle Hero did not make use of, although he might well have possessed it and it might have gone historically unnoticed by calmly resting in the same abysses of oblivion as the other principles which he did uncover and utilize.

5. Their Purpose

Hero of Alexandria composed other treatises in mechanics, such as *On the Construction of Slings; On Automata; On the Method of Lifting Heavy Bodies;* and finally *On the Dioptra or Spying Tube*. Vitruvius in his *On Architecture*, previously referred to, cities the inventions by Ctesibius of the fire pump, the water organ and automatic clock, all of which have been described. He is reported to have constructed the singing cornucopia for the statue of Arsinoe ordered by King Ptolemy Philadelphos about 270 B.C. or thereabouts.

Another mechanician whom Vitruvius mentions is Philo of Byzantium who probably lived only a few decades after Ctesibius. Like his successor Hero, Philo also authored a book called *Pneumatics* and another *Belopoiika* which deals with catapults and other military machines. His *Pneumatics* like Hero's is based upon the same notions of air as a substance and of the vacuum as impossible of attainment on a large scale, which was a fact, and treats mostly of similar inventions.

Some historians of the 19th and 20th centuries demanded that students of ancient science view its concepts in the light of their own parochial values and notions concerning the nature of science and its place in society. It is therefore not surprising that they bemoaned the fact that Philo and Hero neither indulged in philosophic theorizing nor in experimentation for the purpose of testing established scientific theories or laws. Others resented the notion expressed by Vitruvius that besides the water clock, Ctesibius had designed "other things which are not for service, but for the purpose of our delight." Many historians regarded such inventors as amateur playboys and shallow-heads. One should therefore applaud Drachmann's defense of the true scientific spirit when he writes: "When an inventive genius finds a brand new natural force to explore, it seems to me natural that he should explore it to the uttermost, without regard to the practical use of his invention. I fail to see that it was better to invent catapults - which never came into practical use - than singing blackbirds, which led to the invention of the organ, and of which we still find a descendant in the cuckoo-clock. So even by the standards of the critic the blackbirds have proved the better invention. But especially I maintain that the standard is wrong. It is not reasonable to judge of a man's invention by the sole test of time, or of practical use; a most useless invention may be far more clever than an invention that has stood the test of 2,000 years. At any rate, I prefer to judge the inventions as inventions, and not to raise any sort of moral question about them." (A. G. Drachmann, *Klesibios, Philon and Heron*. Copenhagen, 1948, p.3)

There is little doubt that Hero, and probably Philo as well, were not much interested in theory, nor in the manipulation of apparatuses for the sake of testing one theory or another. "He does not use the instruments to illustrate the working of the natural laws, nor does he use the natural laws to explain the working of the instruments, except in rare cases.

"But neither is he interested in the practical employment of the apparatuses. The water-organ and the singing birds, the fire pump and the drinking animals - all is grist that comes to his mill; he never shows any preference. He is not interested in the tricks as such; only once does he even hint that a trick jug is used to trick people, and even there it may just as well be interpreted as an objective remark on the way the jug works.

"What then is the purpose of this seemingly heterogeneous collection? To me it is quite plain! Hero is interested in the technical side of the instruments and nothing else. Himself an inventor, he describes the inventions of others, where he has found them, and adds his own improvements and inventions, simply out of his interest for a nice and clever solution of a technical problem. If he had finished and published his book, we should not have found a treatise on applied physics, still less a vademecum for conjurors; we should have found a technical handbook on the construction of pneumatic instruments, meant for the workshop that had to turn them out." (*ibid.* p. 161)

Few modern students of Hero's book would differ with Dr. Drachmann on his conclusions. We may even go one step further. In the ingenious works of the three great inventors and mechanicians of antiquity, Ctesibius, Philo and Hero, history merely reveals to us a significant facet of science in its course of development. Fascination as my above-cited observations of audiences testify, will always appeal to the human mind. Such fascination is as much a part of science as is the love that men like Ptolemy, Copernicus, Kepler, Galileo, Newton, de Broglie and Einstein, (whom Arthur Koestler so aptly describes as The Sleepwalkers) have for spinning theories on the nature of the universe. Those who apply aspects of theoretical constructs to the practical needs of men, are also workers in the field, and their labors too, constitute a segment of the science spectrum. Moreover, not at all times do the various bands of the spectrum advance at the same rate, or even coexist. In antiquity, as we shall see, the practical or applied phases of science, were only rarely in salient evidence. In modern times, utilitarian applications predominate, and playfulness and ingenuity for their own sake are seldom pursued by men of the calibre of Hero or Philo. Different eras distort differently the spectrum of man's overall pursuit of science.

VI The Usual Advance of Practical Devices

1. Mining and Metallurgy in Antiquity

It seems correct to assert that many primitive cultures remained stationary for varying periods of time. The environmental adaptations of many North American hunting tribes or of sedentary agricultural groups in Africa or Australia, had attained ecological and cultural adjustments of a kind that could remain stable for relatively long historical intervals. Under circumstances in which no challenges arose within the group or outside it, or in which there evolved strong bulwarks against possible impingement on the status quo, a prolonged period of stability could develop. We do know that such conditions prevailed in some regions, though not in the zones which constituted the cradle of our own civilization, and in a few other centers in which cultural development prospered.

Unfortunately, we know little of the forces which conspire to launch some cultures on the road to rapid progress, and contrariwise, of forces that benumb some societies into a state of dormancy. We do know that the Middle East served as the home of several active centers of civilization which seethed with amazing vitality. Some of these were extinguished while others burst forth anew after a temporary decline. Still others struggled along after an initial flareup, radiated ideas and institutions and in turn took over many from neighbors, with the result that both technology and social organization made rapid progress for several millenia in that overall region. These civilizations served as the foundations of our own era of scientific growth and we can therefore speak of them with a certain amount of intimacy.

Once a culture hit upon the use of metals, the making of basketry, pottery, and glassware, the art of weaving, dyeing, agriculture, the domestication of animals, hunting and warfare techniques, irrigation, carving, painting or writing, then these skills tended to remain within the culture by becoming firmly embedded within its warp and woof. Moreover, they also tended to change with time. This does not mean that some pursuits could not freeze in their initial molds and change little if al all for centuries. This did in fact happen at times. Normally, there always exists the possibility that any cultural activity could be fired with explosive vitality and prosper dramatically, as if awakened from slumber. But there also exists within any practice or institution the possibility of stagnation or even of sudden decline.

The cultures of antiquity which we have been considering possessed highly developed technologies in the fields cited above. Let us consider first the field of mining and metallurgy. The great scientific authorities of the time did not leave many detailed accounts of the ordinary activities of the technology of the day, probably because these were too much taken for granted and writing was held in too high esteem for commonplace affairs. There is not much evidence to the oft-repeated charge that all manual work was held in contempt and was generally relegated to slaves. No one ever said anything contemptuous about the occupation of stonecutter as practiced by Socrates. On the other hand, Plutarch, even singles out sculpture and medicine as degrading occupations. It apparently depended on the tastes of the individual author. American culture has never shown any trace of disrespect for manual labor, unlike some contemporary societies which still retain the old world hangover of looking down upon it. Nevertheless, American literature has few descriptions of certain trades and manual skills and few descriptions of zippers, floor shifts in cars, or the types of matches used these days. The same was true of ancient writers, with few exceptions.

The original motive behind the search for metals which subsequently gave rise to a vast metallurgical industry, was not utility but man's love for metals which seemed to him attractive, mystifying, and pleasing. Under such conditions, man invariably tended to ascribe to these substances magical, arcane, and medical powers. Since all metals man ever stumbled upon were rare, they all seemed precious to him. Chemically active metals can only be present in the combined form. Consequently, man could only stumble upon such metals as copper, gold, silver, and an occasional meteorite, invariably in small quantities. Pliny, general, admiral and intimate friend and faithful servant of Roman emperors though he was, continuously berated the use of gold and silver. "It was not enough to have discovered one bane to plague life, without setting value even on the corrupt humours of gold! Avarice was seeking for silver... The enticements of the vices have augmented even art: it has pleased us to engrave scenes of licence upon our goblets, and to drink through the midst of obscenities... And would that it (gold) could be entirely banished from life, reviled and abused as it is by all the worthiest people, and only discovered for the ruin of human life." (*Natural History*. Loeb Classical Library Vol. II, p. 6) When it comes to iron, he is truly a Jeremiah. It is both good and bad, he muses. "With it we plough the ground, plant the trees, trim the trees that prop our vines, force the vines to renew their youth yearly by ridding them of decrepit growth; with it we build houses and quarry rocks, and we employ it for other useful purposes, but we likewise use it for wars and slaughter and brigandage, and not only in hand to hand encounters but as a winged missile, now projected from catapults, now hurled by the arm, and now actually equipped with feathery wings, which I deem the most criminal artifice of man's genius, inasmuch as to enable death to reach human beings more quickly we have taught iron how to fly and have given wings to it. Let us therefore debit the blame not to Nature, but to man." (*ibid*, p. 229)

Both Plato in his *Timaeus* and Aristotle in *Meteorology* have theories of ores and fossils. According to Plato, two elements, earth and water, interact diversely to yield ice, oil, rocks, minerals, and "fusible" earths, or ores capable of melting. Aristotle's theory presupposes the existence of the four basic elements -- earth, water, air, and fire, and the four possible qualities of all matter -- hot, cold, dry and wet. He postulates a vaporous dry and hot exhalation which generates "fossils," by which are implied substances dried out or formed in the ground, meaning by this description homogeneous minerals or compounds such as realgar (As_2S_2, arsenic sulfide), cinnabar, (HgS) and ochre (iron oxides, yellow pigments). Metals, however, were the products of vaporous exhalations that solidified but remained fusible and malleable.

In his work *On Stones,* Theophrastus writes: "Of the substances found in the ground, some are made of water and some of earth. The metals obtained by mining, such as silver, gold, and so on, come from water; from earth come stones, including the more precious kinds, and also the types of earth that are unusual because of the color, smoothness, density, or any other quality. . . . Some things are solifified through heat, others through cold. . . . All types of earth are produced by fire, since things become solid or melt as the result of opposite forces. " Lucretius, in his famous poem *De Natura Rerum* (The Nature of the Universe) describes the mode of formation of earth and heaven thus: At the beginning there was atomic chaos, "a hurricane raging in a newly congregated mass of atoms of every sort. From their disharmony sprang conflict, which maintained a turmoil in their interspaces, courses, unions, thrusts, impacts, collisions, and motions. . . . From this medley they started to sort themselves out, like combining with like. . . . In the first place all the particles of earth, because they were heavy and intertangled, collected in the middle and took up the widermost stations. The more closely they cohered and clung together, the more they squeezed out the atoms that went to the making of the sea and stars, sun and moon and the outer walls of this great world. For all these are composed of smooth round seeds, much smaller than the particles of earth. The first element to break out of the earth through the pores in its spongy crust and to shoot up aloft was either the generator of fire. . . the lakes and perennial water courses exhale a vapour, while at times we see the earth itself steaming. . . On this ensued the birth of sun and moon, whose globes revolved at middle height in the atmosphere. . . When these elements had withdrawn, the earth suddenly caved in, throughout the zone now covered by the blue extent of sea, and flooded the cavity with surging brine. . . So even ampler floods of salty fluid were exuded from its body to swell the billowy plain of ocean. . . As the plains settled down, the mountain steeps grew more prominent; for the crags could not sink in and it was not possible for every part to subside to the same extent. . . All the sediment of the world, because it was heavy, drifted downwards together and settled at the bottom like dregs. " (Penguin Books, p. 185-6)

Proclus, commenting on Plato's *Timaeus,* says: "Natural gold, silver and each metal, like other substances, are engendered in the earth under the influence of the celestial gods and their effluvia. The Sun produces gold, the Moon silver, Saturn lead, and Mars iron. " Many ancient writers believed this process to go on continuously, thus replenishing the diminution caused by man's diggings. Says Strabo, the author of a famous work *Geography* which, like Pliny's *Natural History,* supplies much information on the ancient mind's attitude to nature: "I myself saw these islands when I went up to Poplonium, and also some mines out in the country that had failed. And I also saw the people who work the iron that is brought over from Aethalia; for it cannot be brought into complete coalescence by heating in the furnaces on the island; and it is brought over immediately from the mines to the mainland. . . There is also the fact that the diggings which have been mined are in time filled up again, as is said to be the case with the ledges of rocks in Rhodes, the marble-rock in Paros and, according to Cleitarchus, the salt-rock in India." (*The Geography of Strabo*. Tr. H. L. Jones, Vol. II. Loeb Classical Lib. 1923, p. 356) The seeds of the later alchemical ideas of the evolution of ores and metals in the womb of the earth were widely held in antiquity.

Strange that from earliest times, most scholars regarded mining with as much suspicion and even outright disapproval as they did the rotation and revolution of the earth. Take Pliny, for example: "Our topic now will be metals and the actual resources employed to pay for commodities--resources diligently sought for in the bowels of the earth in a variety of ways. For in some places the earth is dug into for riches when life demands gold, silver, silver-gold, and copper, and in other places for luxury, when gems and colors for tinting walls and beams are demanded, and in other places for rash valor, when the demand is for iron, which amid warfare and slaughter is even more prized than gold. We trace out all the fibers of the earth, and live above the hollows we have made in her, marvelling that occasionally she gapes open or begins to tremble--as if forsooth it were not possible that this may be an expression of the indignation of our holy parent! We penetrate her inner parts and seek for riches in the abode of the spirits of the departed, as though the part where we tread upon her were not sufficiently bounteous and fertile. And amid all this the smallest object of our searching is for the sake of remedies for illness, for with what fraction of mankind is medicine the object of this delving? Although the earth indeed also bestows medicines upon us on her surface, as she bestows corn, bountiful and generous as she is in all her things for our benefit, the things that she has concealed and hidden underground those that do not quickly come to birth, are the things that destroy us and drive us to the depths below; so that suddenly the mind soars aloft into the void and ponders what finally will be the end of draining her dry in all the ages, what will be the point to which avarice will penetrate. How innocent, how blissful, nay even how luxurious life might be, if it coveted nothing from any source but the surface of the earth, and to speak briefly, nothing but what lies ready to her hand!" (*Natural History*, Harvard University Press, 1952. Vol IX, Bk. XXXIII, p. 3-5)

Like all philosophical writers on science in ancient as well as modern times, Pliny never misses an opportunity to bemoan human folly, man's failure to pursue his own good, his greed, cruelty and boundless capacity for injustice. Like others preceding and succeeding him, he proceeds to the business at hand after he is through with his moral sermon. He treats first of gold which he discusses at length, concluding: "And would that it could be entirely banished from life, reviled and abused as it is by all the worthiest people, and only discovered for the ruin of human life." He then proceeds to describe in some detail the methods of ming gold. "By means of galleries driven for long distances, the mountains are mined by the light of lamps--the spells of work are also measured by lamps, and the miners do not see daylight for many months." (*ibid*, p. 55) He will not discuss Indian gold "obtained from ants or the gold dug up by griffins in Scythia," but informs us how Romans obtained gold from river sands by "sinking shafts, or it is sought for in the fallen debris of mountains," each procedure interestingly described. Iron wedges, oxen and "hammer-machines" are employed; "fractured mountains fall asunder in a wide gap... the miners gaze as conquerors upon the collapse of nature." For washing the crushed gold ore so as to float away the lighter expendable rock and permit the heavier gold-containing grains to sink to the bottom, or for carrying away the broken up rock of the fallen mountain wall, canals were dug and streams brought to the mining area, "frequently a distance of 100 miles."

Pliny also relates that "gold is efficacious as a remedy in a variety of ways, and is used as an amulet for wounded people and for infants to render less harmful poisonous charms that may be directed against them. Gold has itself, however, a maleficent effect if carried over the head, in the case of chickens and the young of cattle as well as human beings." (*ibid,* p. 65)

Pliny gives particulars about the mining of silver, mercury, antimony, which "has astringent and cooling properties, but it is chiefly used for the eyes, arrests discharge of blood from the brain, etc.," of amber, litharge or lead monoxide, lead sulfide, cinnabar (mercuric sulfide), copper, lodestone, and many other ores and minerals.

While Aristotle's book, *Meteorology,* describes in the manner of ancient scientists, who invariably regarded themselves more as natural philosophers than technologists, the mode of protean formation of metals and minerals, the classic book of his pupil and successor at the Lyceum, Theophrastus, titled *On Stones,* contains a veritable treasure of practical information of great value. (E. R. Calley and J. F. C. Richards. Theophrastus' *On Stones,* Ohio State University, Columbus, 1956) This author not only presents accurate accounts of the techniques of extraction, grinding, washing and the final separation of various metals and minerals, but offers as well a useful classification, and enumerates their properties free from magical fancy and romance. He reveals to posterity an industry fully mature in its sophistication, in its employment of knowledge of properties, yielding numerous minerals and precious stones, and employing tests for purity of precious metals, besides that of specific gravity used by Archimedes. Magnetism was known, of course, and theoretically explained, as we learn from Pliny, Seneca, and Galen, who argues against the prevailing theory in his *Natural Faculties.* That theory postulated that atoms ejected from the magnet became entangled with the atoms of the iron, and dragged the latter with them on their return trip home. The growth of stones in water, such as corals of different colors, is cited by Theophrastus, and there are references to meteorites as stones which fall from the air. Crystalline shapes were discerned and described, a hardness scale employed, and the "acid test" based upon the liberation of effervescing carbon dioxide by carbonates, chiefly limestone, was known as an Assyrian discovery, although the strongest acid utilized was the acetic acid of vinegar.

It should be borne in mind that mining had been practiced historically since Paleolithic (Old Stone Age) times, five or six millenia B.C., although it did not attain significant proportions until the Neolithic (New Stone Age) era, about 3500 B.C. Plain stones for the making of tools as well as precious stones were sought for earth pigments were made use of and native metals were mined and extracted from workable ores. There is evidence of specializing centers in existence many millenia B.C., which were no doubt worked by individuals with special capacities for polishing stone hammers and knives, or for chipping flint arrowhead flakes or scrapers. Stones were also quarried for megalithic monuments, altars, or temples. Egyptian pyramids began to appear around 3000 B. C., and the famous royal architect Imhotep functioned around 2750 B. C.

Mining presupposes skill in prospecting, surveying, detecting, digging and separating, as well as in evaluating the risk of investing in a given excavation. We know that already in Neolithic times sloping shafts and galleries were undertaken, indicating that open strip-mining had become outmoded and the bold venture of underground mining had been instituted. From that period on, mining grows in complexity. Firesetting develops as a means of splitting rocks within shafts as well as a means of obtaining ventilation. Tunnels are propped up with timbers, shafts and galleries grow more complex, and finally by 500 B. C. we encounter progress in mechanical drainage, in effective transport and ventilation which around the beginning of the Christian Era exploits a few clever, specialized devices. Mines were already worked at several levels in Roman times, and surface refining plants employed large and massive stone hammers for pounding and crushing ore. Stone wedges, chisels, and flint borers were used then on the rock face, deep below. Smelting was carried on early in the history of Egypt, as is evidenced by the large heaps of slag near the refining plants.

The famous copper mines of Sinai were not worked apparently by slaves, but mostly by skilled conscript labor, with some admixture of war prisoners and criminals. Under Romeses IV, the High Priest of Ammon "sent over 9000 men there to quarry stone, for his records mention that he took 8357 men back and left 900 dead behind, mostly soldiers, and only 140 skilled labour." (R. J. Forbes, *Studies in Ancient Technology*. Vol. VII. Leiden, 1963, p. 130) On the other hand, the Ptolemies, who ruled post-Alexandrian Egypt, "worked mainly with condemned and criminals as miners," some of whom were no doubt political prisoners. They mined copper, gold, and iron. The historian Diodorus Siculus (Diodorus the Sicilian, circa 40 B. C.) relates in his *Library of History* how gold was mined "at the extremity of Egypt and in the contiguous territory... where the gold is secured in great quantities with much suffering and at great expense." (Loeb Classical Library. Vol. II, Bk. III, p. 115ff.) The workers, says Diodorus, were men that "have been found guilty of some crime or captives of war, as well as those who have been accused unjustly and thrown into prison because of their anger, and not only such persons but occasionally all their relatives as well... And those who have been condemned in this way--and they are a great multitude and are all bound in chains--work at their task unceasingly both by day and throughout the entire night, enjoying no respite and being carefully cut off from any means of escape; since guards of foreign soldiers who speak a language different from theirs stand watch over them, so that not a man, either by conversation or by some contact of a friendly nature, is able to corrupt one of his keepers. The gold-bearing earth which is hardest they first burn with a hot fire, and when they have crumbled it in this way they continue the working of it by hand; and the soft rock which can yield to moderate effort is crushed with a sledge by myriads of unfortunate wretches. And the entire operations are in charge of a skilled worker who distinguishes the stone and points it out to the labourers; and of those who are assigned to this unfortunate task the physically strongest break the quartz-rock with iron hammers, applying no skill to the task, but only force, and cutting tunnels through the stone, not in a straight line but wherever the seam of gleaming rock may lead. Now these men, working in darkness as they do because of the bending and winding of the passages, carry lamps bound on their foreheads; and since much of the time they change the position of their bodies to follow the particular character of the stone they throw the blocks, as they cut them out, on the ground; and at this task they labour without ceasing beneath the sternness and blows of an overseer.

"The boys there who have not yet come to maturity, entering through the tunnels into the galleries formed by the removal of the rock, laboriously gather up the rock as it is cast down piece by piece and carry it out into the open to the place outside the entrance. Then those who are above thirty years of age take this quarried stone from them and with iron pestles pound a specified amount of it in stone mortars, until they have worked it down to the size of a vetch. Thereupon the women and older men receive from them the rock of this size and cast it into mills of which a number stand there in a row, and taking their places in groups of two or three at the spoke or handle of each mill they grind it until they have worked down the amount given them to the consistency of the finest flour. And since no opportunity is afforded any of them to care for his body and they have no garment to cover their shame, no man can look upon the unfortunate wretches without feeling pity for them because of the exceeding hardships they suffer. For no leniency or respite of any kind is given to any man who is sick, or maimed, or aged, or in the case of a woman for her weakness, but all without exception are compelled by blows to persevere in their labours, until through ill-treatment they die in the midst of their tortures. Consequently the poor unfortunates believe, because their punishment is so excessively severe, that the future will always be more terrible than the present and therefore look forward to death as more to be desired than life.

"In the last steps the skilled workmen receive the stone which has been ground to powder and take it off for its complete and final working; for they rub the marble which has been worked down upon a broad board which is slightly inclined, pouring water over it all the while; whereupon the earthy matter in it, melted away by the action of the water, runs down the inclined board, while that which contains the gold remains on the wood because of its weight. And repeating this a number of times, they first of all rub it gently with their hands, and then lightly pressing it with sponges of loose texture they remove in this way whatever is porous and earthy, until there remains only the pure gold-dust. Then at last other skilled workmen take what has been recovered and put it by fixed measure and weight into earthen jars, mixing with it a lump of lead proportionate to the mass, lumps of salt and a little tin, and adding thereto barley bran; thereupon they put on it a close-fitting lid, and smearing it over carefully with mud they bake it in a kiln for five successive days and as many nights; and at the end of this period, when they have let the jars cool off, of the other matter they find no remains in the jars, but the gold they recover in pure form, there being but little waste. This working of the gold, as it is carried on at the farthermost borders of Egypt, is effected through all the extensive labours here described; for Nature herself, in my opinion, makes it clear that whereas the production of gold is laborious, the guarding of it is difficult, the zest for it very great, and that its use is half-way between pleasure and pain.

"Now the discovery of these mines is very ancient, having been made by early kings."

Coal was also mined in antiquity. Lead was mined in antiquity and because of its softness was widely used to fasten large stones in buildings. Tin was mined for the making of bronze, and zinc for brass.

Tools were made largely of iron. Ancient galleries were low, 2 to 3 feet high and 2 to 2.5 feet wide. The famous silver mine at Laurium, near Athens, had over 2,000 shafts connected with tunnels stretching over a total network close to 90 miles in length. Rocks were heated with vast fires, and cold water was poured on them when hot, so as to cause them to crumble by uneven shrinkage. Canals, or aqueducts, were built to fetch water from remote sources to wash away the broken rock and allow the metal to settle in cisterns, or to wash the ore at the pithead so as to save the labor of carrying the crushed ore to the riverhead. Such streams were often brought from reservoirs or rivers 100 miles away. Says Pliny: "Gorges and crevasses are bridged by aqueducts carried on masonry; at other places impassable rocks are hewn away and compelled to provide a position for hollowed troughs of timber. The workmen hewing the rock hang suspended with ropes, so that spectators viewing the operation from a distance seem to see not so much a swarm of strange animals as a flight of birds."

The transport of the ore from the tunnels was by means of ladders climbed by special porters with the load on their backs. At times, the ore was hoisted in buckets made of leather or of woven strong grasses suspended by thick ropes of hemp and pulled up by means of "capstans, winches, or animal power." Illumination was achieved by resinous torches or oil lamps, which also served for timing the working intervals. Ventilation constituted a serious problem never easily solved. According to Pliny, "if the air at great depth begins to act injuriously, they try to improve it by the constant waving of cloth flaps." Fires were built in side shafts to maintain drafts, and tall chimneys were occasionally erected over others. Although bellows were known in antiquity, the idea of employing them for ventilation was unthought of until the Middle Ages. Current excavations show frequent deaths by suffocation. The fires used in the galleries for breaking rock naturally aggrevated the situation. But there is also evidence of shafts that could serve only for aeration. The system of using a split shaft, U-shaped, with fire at one end so as to cause a draught at the bottom part, was apparently not used until the late Middle Ages.

The most difficult of all operations was that of drainage. Virtually all underground mining necessitates digging below the level of the water table, and therefore entails the need for removal of considerable and steady volumes of gathering water. Occasional sudden floods increase the need. Such superfluous waters were often diverted to cross-adits or made to collect in specially dug wells in a side gallery. Most commonly resorted to was bailing out the water and carrying it to the surface by relays of slaves, in bronze, wooden, or pitch liver basketry buckets. Here and there we see the inceptions of machine drainage. In the ancient mines of Spain, the screw of Archimedes was used. This is essentially a tube of any diameter wound around a cylinder, or a helical pipe, placed obliquely with the lower end of the tube in the water. As the cyliner or helix, suitably installed, are cranked, the water is forced

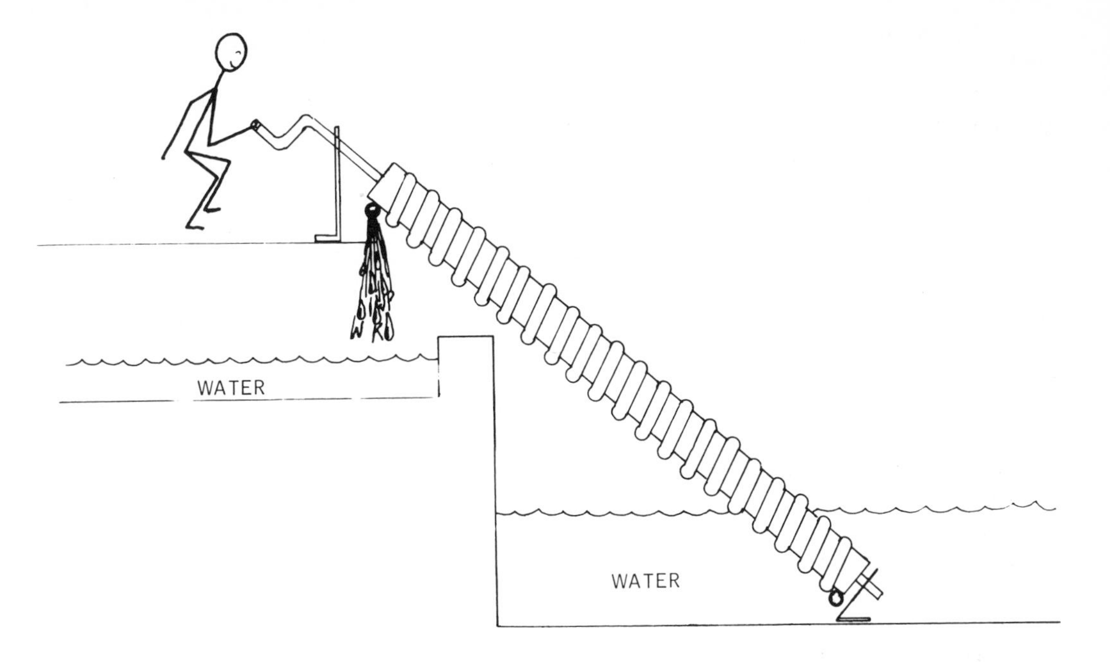

Figure 6.1

to wind its way upward and emerge from the tube's upper end. This screw can therefore raise water to its own height. Diodorus describes its use thus in his *History:* "Not only do they go into the ground a great distance, but they also push their diggings many stades in depth and run galleries off at every angle, turning this way and that, in this manner bringing up from the depths the ore which gives them the profit they are seeking.

"Great also is the contrast these mines show when they are compared with those of Attica. The men, that is, who work the Attic mines, although they have expended large sums on the undertakings, yet 'Now and then, what they hoped to get, they did not get, and what they had, they lost,' so that it would appear that they met with misfortune in a kind of riddle; but the exploiters of the mines of Spain, in their hopes, amass great wealth from their undertakings. For their first labours are remunerative, thanks to the excellent quality of the earth for this sort of thing, and they are ever coming upon more splendid veins, rich in both silver and gold; for all the ground in that region is a tangled network of veins which wind in many ways. And now and then, as they go down deep, they come upon flowing subterranean rivers, but they overcome the might of these rivers by diverting the streams which flow in on them by means of channels leading off at an angle. For being urged on as they are by expectations of gain, which indeed do not deceive them, they push each separate undertaking to its conclusion, and what is the most surprising thing of all, they draw out the waters of the streams they encounter by means of what is called by men the Egyptian screw, which was invented by Archimedes of Syracuse at the time of his visit to Egypt; and by the use of such screws they carry the water in successive lifts as far as the entrance, drying up in this way the spot where they are digging and making it well suited to the furtherance of their operations. Since this machine is an exceptionally ingenious device, an enormous amount of water is thrown out, to one's astonishment, by means of a trifling amount of labour, and all the water from such rivers is brought up easily from the depths and poured out on the surface... The slaves who are engaged in the working of them produce for their masters revenues in sums defying belief, but they themselves wear out their bodies both by day and by night in the diggings under the earth, dying in large numbers because of the exceptional hardships they endure. For no respite or pause is granted them in their labours, but compelled beneath blows of the overseers to endure the severity of their plight, they throw away their lives in this wretched manner, although certain of them who can endure it, by virtue of their bodily strength and their persevering souls, suffer such hardships over a long period; indeed death in their eyes is more to be desired than life, because of the magnitude of the hardships they must bear. And although many are the astounding features connected with the mining just described, a man may wonder not the least at the fact that not one of the mines has a recent beginning, but all of them were opened by the covetousness of the Carthaginians at the time when Iberia was among their possessions. It was from these mines, that is, that they drew their continued growth, hiring the ablest mercenaries to be found and winning with their aid many and great wars. For it is in general true that in their wars the Carthaginians never rested their confidence in soldiers from among their own citizens or gathered from their allies, but that when they subjected the Romans and the Sicilians and the inhabitants of Libya to the greatest perils it was by money, thanks to the abundance of it which they derived from their mines, that they conquered them in every instance. For the Phoenicians, it appears, were from ancient times clever men in making discoveries to their gain, and the Italians are equally clever in leaving no gain to anyone else.

"Tin also occurs in many regions of Iberia, not found, however, on the surface of the earth, as certain writers continually repeat in their histories, but dug out of the ground and smelted in the same manner as silver and gold. For there are many mines of tin in the country above Lusitania and on the islets which lie off Iberia out in the ocean and are called because of that fact the Cassiterides. And tin is brought in large quantities also from the island of Britain to the opposite Gaul, where it is taken by merchants on horses through the interior of Celtica both to the Massalians and to the city of Narbo, as it is called. This city is a colony of the Romans, and because of its convenient situation it possesses the finest market to be found in those regions." (Diodorus of Sicily. Vol. III, p. 197ff.) It is believed that Archimedes saw the screw referred to by Diodorus, in common use in the Nile Valley. No doubt such screws (also called cochleas) were used in storied arrangement, one above the other, much as shadufs, or wellsweeps, were used along the Nile to lift the overflowing waters of the river to the highest plateau. (Figure 6.2)

Another device employed in mines was the wheel described by Vitruvius, in which water is scooped up by buckets on the periphery of a wheel and emptied through a pipe from its center. (Figure 6.3)

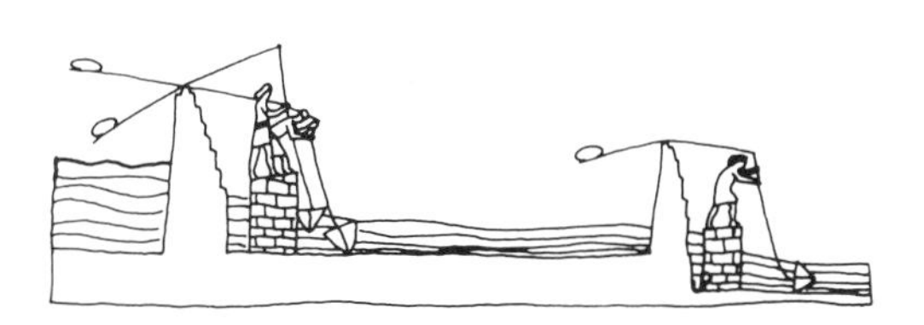

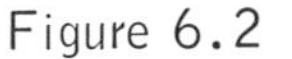

Figure 6.2

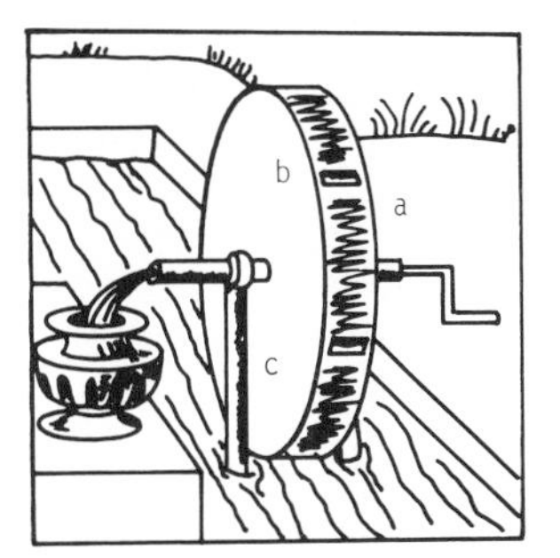

Figure 6.3

Little need be said about the fine work performed by the craftsmen of antiquity in gold and silver, which can be seen in any contemporary museum of note. Like mining, the craft of metalwork advanced from stage to stage, unaided by the natural philosophers. It was advanced by a worker of skill, originality and boldness here and another one there, so that in the course of the productive life of a given culture, which in those days might have been only a few generations, considerable progress was made.

2. Water Supply and the Art of Irrigation

We may next consider the art of irrigation and water supply. All cultures of antiquity evolved in regions where the supply of rainwater could not be taken for granted. Even food-gatherers learned that an adequate supply of water enriched the yield of crops. No wonder that when some cultures took to agriculture or organized crop cultivation, attention was paid to irrigation, or the artificial supply of water to crops where the rainfall is not fully adequate. Conversely, land that became frequently flooded or swampland had to be freed from excess water.

Primitive man obtained his water from springs or man-made wells. He frequently stored it in cisterns hewed out in the rock or in excavations lined with timber, stone slabs, or masonry. When cities grew in size, their inhabitants built huge communal cisterns. From earliest times, water was brought to cities in pipes, open or closed conduits of hollowed out tree trunks as in prehistoric Europe, 3 to 4 feet in diameter, or of terra cotta, earthenware, stone, or metals such as copper, bronze, or lead. Lengths of pipe were tightly fitted into each other and the joints fastened against leakage either with lead or clay.

Cities on rock hills, such as those of Palestine, built vertical stairwells into tunnels which brought water in a conduit from a distant spring. The Assyrians even learned to dig wells deep enough in the local rock to reach a layer on a level with a remote spring, and the records of Assyrian King Sargon II (eighth century B.C.) relate that the king of Armenia, whom Sargon had conquered, "dug a main duct which carried flowing waters... waters of abundance he caused to flow like the Euphrates. Countless ditches he led out from its interior... and he irrigated the fields." Since mining of metal ores had been developed much earlier, it is not surprising that similar techniques were employed in digging for water and tapping it in artifically constructed underground galleries. It was during the first millenium B. C. that closed systems of water pipes for the conveyance of water to fortified cities or for irrigation within their walls became widely used throughout the Near East region. Herodotus states: "The Arabian King, they say, made a pipe of the skin of oxen and other beasts, reaching from this river Corys all the way to the desert, and so he brought water to certain cisterns which he had dug in the desert to receive it. It is a twelve days' journey from the river to the desert track. And the water was brought through three different pipes to three different places." (*The History of Herodotus,* New York, 1944, p. 149) The Assyrian King Sennacherib reports (703 B. C.): "To increase the productiveness of the low lying fields from the border of the city of Kesiri through the high and low ground I dug with iron pickaxes, I ran a canal; those waters I brought across the plain (around) Nineveh and made them flow through the orchards in irrigation ditches." This took place in 691 B. C. The canal, "one of the most impressive works of hydraulic engineering until Roman times," (Singer, C., *et. al.*, editors, *A History of Technology,* Oxford University Press. 1954-58, Vol. I, p. 531) supplied additional water to the city of Nineveh, extended for 50 miles and was paved with well-smoothed and polished stones from a large quarry in the foothills located at the canal's beginning. It is estimated that over two million heavy limestone blocks were conveyed a distance of about ten miles upon wheeled carts along the completed sections up to its point of termination. Water came into the canal from a dam provided with sluice gates. At one point the canal ran across a valley upon an aqueduct 900 feet long placed upon five corbelled arches in its center. Before entering Nineveh, the canal was provided with "a dam that deflected part of the water into subsidiary canals and the irrigation-channels of orchards and gardens outside the city walls." (*ibid,* p. 532)

The prevention of evaporation is most important in regions where water is scarce, such as Mesopotamia. For this and other reasons the local authorities built *qanaats,* a construction still in use today. These are long tunnels built to convey water from a spring in the hills along a gentle incline to a well or a valley stream and supplied with vertical shafts along its length "to provide air to the tunneler and to dispose of the excavated debris." Such structures preserved the least amount of water, demanded constant care, and often extended for many miles. (Figure 6. 4) The city of Sidon also had a pipeline extending for 15 winding miles and crossing gorges and ravines over appropriate aqueducts.

Athens had an underground aqueduct which brought it water from Mount Pentelicus and was provided with vertical air shafts placed about 50 feet apart. There were in Greece also aqueducts which followed a consistent gradient from source to city, were built high on pillars over valleys, and followed tunnels in mountain bases to maintain their straight line. The tunnel of Samos was, according to Herodotus, the most famous. Built in the sixth century B. C. and about two thirds of a mile in length, it was begun from both sides of the mountain, and with the help of a dioptra, or a water level, both teams managed to meet and join up so as to yield a fairly straight line. It was built by the tyrant Polycrates for the water supply of the city of Samos on the Greek

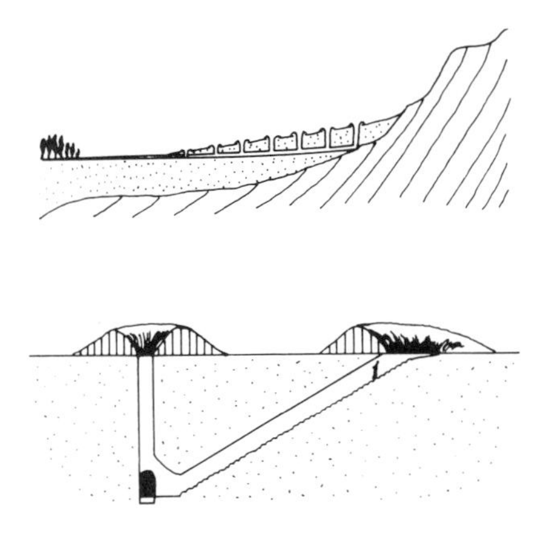

Figure 6.4

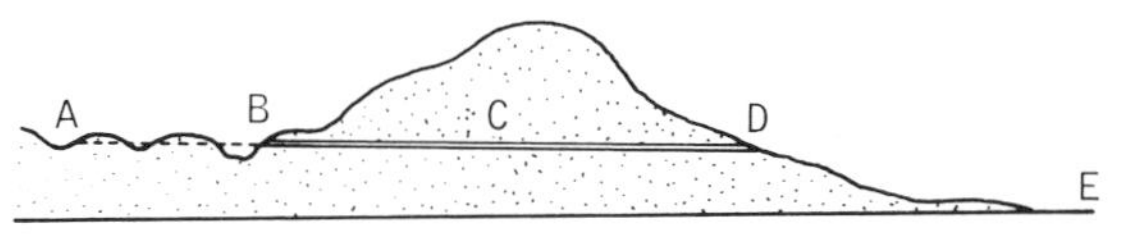

A. Well. B. Entrance to Tunnel. AB. Aqueduct.
C. Point of Contact. D. Tunnel Exit. E. Sea Level.

Figure 6.5

island by the same name in the Aegean Sea, around the year 525 B.C. (Figure 6.5) His engineer, Eupalinus, built that tunnel which was 3,400 feet long, six feet high and six feet wide. Herodotus describes it thus: "I have dwelt the longer on the affairs of the Samians, because three of the greatest works in all Greece were made by them. One is a tunnel, under a hill one hundred and fifty fathoms high, carried entirely through the base of the hill, with a mouth at either end. The length of the cutting is seven furlongs--the height and width are each eight feet. Along the whole course there is a second cutting, twenty cubits deep and three feet broad, whereby water is brought, through pipes, from an abundant source into the city. The architect of this tunnel was Eupalinus, son of Naustrophus, a Megarian. Such is the first of their great works; the second is a mole in the sea, which goes all round the harbour, near twenty fathoms deep, and in length above two furlongs. The third is a temple; the largest of all the temples known to us." (*ibid,* p. 168) The tunnel was dug under Mount Castro which, as Herodotus says, is 900 feet high. Eupalinus made the tunnel to be unseen by enemy eyes and brought water to it so that it passed "under three creek beds enroute." (June Goodfield, "The Tunnel of Eupalinus." *Scientific American,* 1964, Vol. 210, p. 104, June) The fact that the tunnel was dug from its two ends, one on the northern and the other on the southern slopes of Mount Castro, about two thirds of a mile apart, and was successfully joined, speaks for itself.

A dioptra was a U-shaped tube containing sufficient water to rise in both arms to a height that can be sighted on both sides. If the surface upon which it rests is level, the water will rise to equal heights in both vertical arms. Should the surface not be level, then the higher end will show the water lower in its vertical arm, and the lower end higher. The difference indicates the degree of slope. The tube is set upon a circle divided with 360 degrees, so that it can be turned in all directions. (Figure 6.6)

Most sophisticated was the aqueduct of the highly cultured city of Pergamon in Asia Minor (Ionia), constructed in the second century B.C. It entailed the principle of the siphon, known for several centuries prior to that date and used in water clocks and other devices. (Figure 6.7A and 6.7B) The

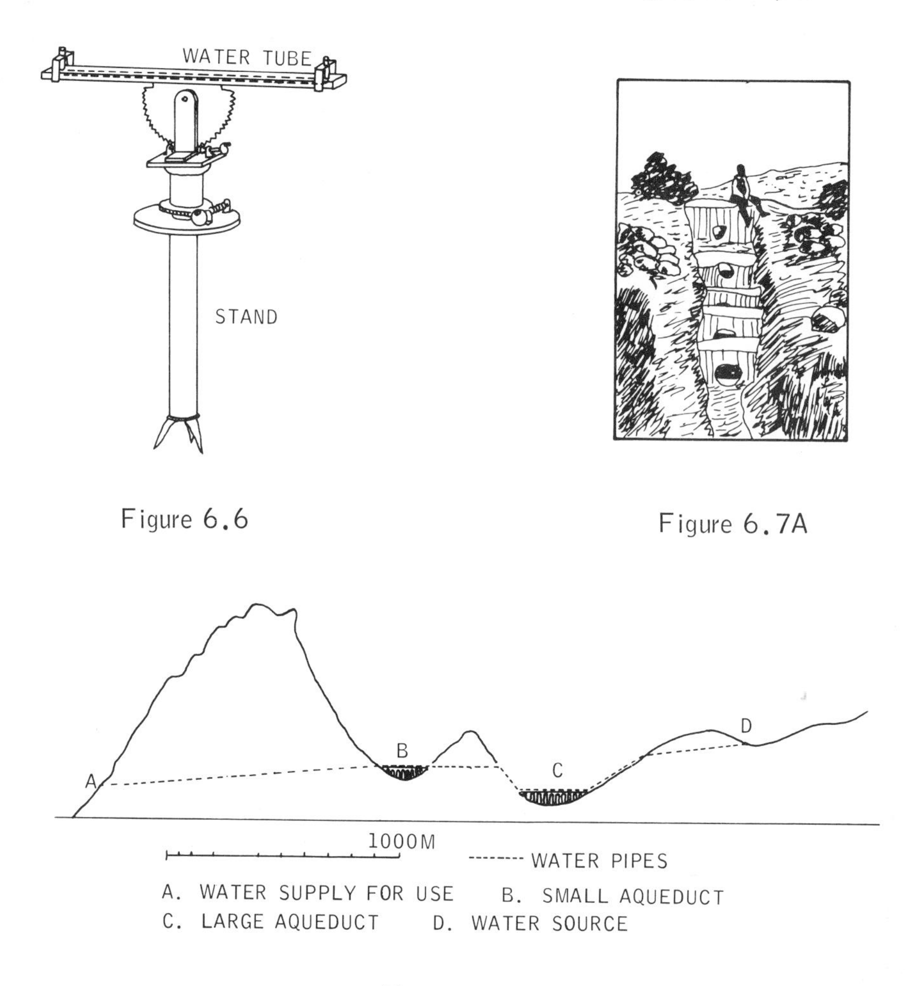

Figure 6.6

Figure 6.7A

Figure 6.7B

siphon did away with the need for the digging of tunnels, a costly and laborious task at best. The water supply system began by conducting mountain spring water at an elevation of 3,800 feet to two settling tanks, or reservoirs, at an elevation of 1,200 feet. From these two tanks, the water was brought in separate pipes to two valleys separated by a ridge and finally up an elevation of 1,100 feet to the fortress, or acropolis. In the lowest points, that is, in the two valleys, the water pressure was very high, about 20 atmospheres, hence about 290 pounds per square inch. Only metal pipes could probably withstand that much pressure. Unfortunately, the original pipes were lost. The pipes composing the siphons consisted of channels one foot in diameter bored in stone slabs positioned vertically. In Roman times, the siphon arrangement was replaced by aqueducts on tiers of arches bridging the two valleys at unequal elevations and running at a gradient in a tunnel at the base of the rock topped by the citadel but not made to climb up it.

In the history of irrigation, the Nile occupies a prime position. Already early in the fourteenth century B.C., the famous King Akhenaten (1375-1358 B.C.), the innovator of sun-worship, sings to his Sun-god: "Thou dost create the Nile in the underworld, and bringest it, according to thy will, to give life to the people of Egypt." The regularity of the Nile's flooding its thirsty plains together with the need for bringing this water to higher plateaus, and the country's total dependence upon this event, singled out the river's annual overflow throughout Egypt's history as the foundation of the country's existence. The Nile waters begin to rise at the beginning of July. "At first, the river is greenish with vegetable scum from equatorial waters. About a fortnight later, muddy silt begins to arrive, and the river takes on a reddish tinge that was associated with the blood of Osiris, from whom new life would presently spring. As the flood swells and reaches the level of the surrounding fields, the dykes are breached and water covers the land to a depth of six feet or more. By September, each village, protected by its dykes, stands like an island, and the shining expanse of water, with archipelagos of trees and houses, stretches from desert edge to desert edge. The waters then begin to subside, and by the end of October the river is again between its banks." (*ibid.* p. 535) Germination begins soon thereafter, and harvesting begins by mid-April.

In Palaeolithic times, rainfall must have been much heavier because most of the present North African desert was then covered with vegetation. No doubt as the rainfall diminished, the erstwhile unperturbed inhabitants were driven toward the riverbanks, which situation obliged them to watch carefully the small islands of wild grasses left behind by each flood. This probably led to the inception of agriculture, and the planting from seed for the enrichment of what nature had provided along the narrow river margins. It also led to the retention of water in small basins or indentations in the land, by erecting a small barrier of stone and mud to prevent its escape. It is from such beginnings in all likelihood that there evolved the idea of irrigation for large basins, so that to this day we still see the Nile valley divided off "into a checkerboard of dyke-enclosed areas of between 1,000 and 40,000 acres each. Canals led the water to areas otherwise difficult to inundate." (*ibid.* p. 536) These basins are so connected by gates and sluices that they can be inundated at will for desired lengths of time, since the water can be allowed to run off to a lower level when necessary. The silt brought by the waters is very rich in decomposed vegetable matter and in minerals, so that no fertilizers are needed. Obviously, this kind of work could not be done by individuals, but was an organized social effort suited to the disciplined tribal atmosphere of the times. The king, or ruler, had to have an eye for organization and skill in coordinating this kind of agricultural preparedness and overall activity. No wonder King Amenemhet I, circa 2,000 B.C., could justly boast: "I grew corn, I loved Neper the grain god; in every valley the Nile greeted me; none hungered, none thirsted during my reign." District governors had the title "Digger of Canals," and ineffectiveness in leadership could be disastrous. Excessive inundation meant flood and destruction, and "nilometers," or scales on walls usually of temples on the quay, were scattered along the river and watched over for the daily rise of the waters, lest the dykes become inadequate. Maximum heights were recorded annually with pious devotion, and messengers ran downstream with news of the river's doings in its upper regions.

The Theban Dynasty that ruled Lower Egypt between the years 2000 to 1788 B.C., after the empire of the pyramid builders had fallen apart due to internal strife, instituted the first reclamation project in known history. They decided to convert the Faiyum desert into a fertile valley by diverting the waters of the Nile westward into its territory. "They threw dams across the ravines leading into the basin to impound the rains of the wet season against drought. One of these dams in a 250-foot wide gorge had a base 143 feet thick, four times its height. It was built in three layers, the bottom of rough stones embedded in clay. The next of irregular limestone blocks and the top of cut stone laid in steps so that the water pouring over the brim was checked in its fall and would not erode the stucture. The Egyptians had also a canal from the Nile, known today as the Bahr Unsuf, a Canal of Joseph, to carry flood waters into the artificial Lake Moeris. There was developed a complex system of dikes, flood-control gates, canals, and bridges. Many buildings appeared, some of them regal palaces.... According to William Willcocks, principal designer of the modern Aswan Dam, it was the management of these dikes and gates of Moeris by the rulers of Upper Egypt that reduced the flow of the Nile in Lower Egypt and caused Joseph's famines there. Recapture of the dikes by the king of Lower Egypt put an end to the hardship. Similar manipulation of local dikes and levees aided the escape of Moses and the Israelites from Pharoah's host." (*Engineering in History* by R.S. Kirby, S. Withington, A. B. Darling and F.G. Kilgsur. New York, 1956, p. 34)

Irrigation canals require much care and skill. They must flow down a slight gradient and lie above the land to be irrigated. Too steep a slope erodes the bed, and too slow a flow causes weeds and silt to choke the channels. Both sluices and embankments must be kept in endless repair and the canal bed must be kept free from silt. All this is equally true of all water conduits, and their neglect for one season is sufficient to ruin the well-being of a region for years to come. Without a strong and intelligent centralized government, both water supply and irrigation systems can hardly come into being or function properly.

Toward the end of the fourth century B.C., Rome got its first underground aqueduct, the Aqua Appia, to which in subsequent years more were added as the city prospered and expanded. We are fortunate in having on this subject a work entitled *The Aqueducts of Rome,* by Sextus Julius Frontinus, who after a great military career became water commissioner of Rome from 97 to 104 A.D. This post was founded by Augustus and its first occupant was Marcus Agrippa, the emperor's great friend and brilliant architect and organizer. It was indeed a most responsible post, and Frontinus knew it, since he proudly exclaims: "With such an array of indispensible structures carrying so many waters, compare, if you will, the idle Pyramids or the useless, though famous, works of the Greeks." (Loeb Classical Library. London, 1925, p. 357) Five of the aqueducts rose "to every point in the City, but of these, some are forced up with greater, others with lesser pressure." They were eight in number in his day, but later reached a total of fourteen. In our modern water supply system, the water is gathered in a reservoir and conducted to the city by main pipelines from which branch pipes run into various districts, and from these, street lines issue with offshoots to individual houses. The ancient system was different, in that the water was gathered in a collecting tank and from there dispatched to town by pipe, where it was made to gather in a water-tower, representing our reservoir. From this spot it was directed to three subsidiary tanks, one of which supplied the baths, the

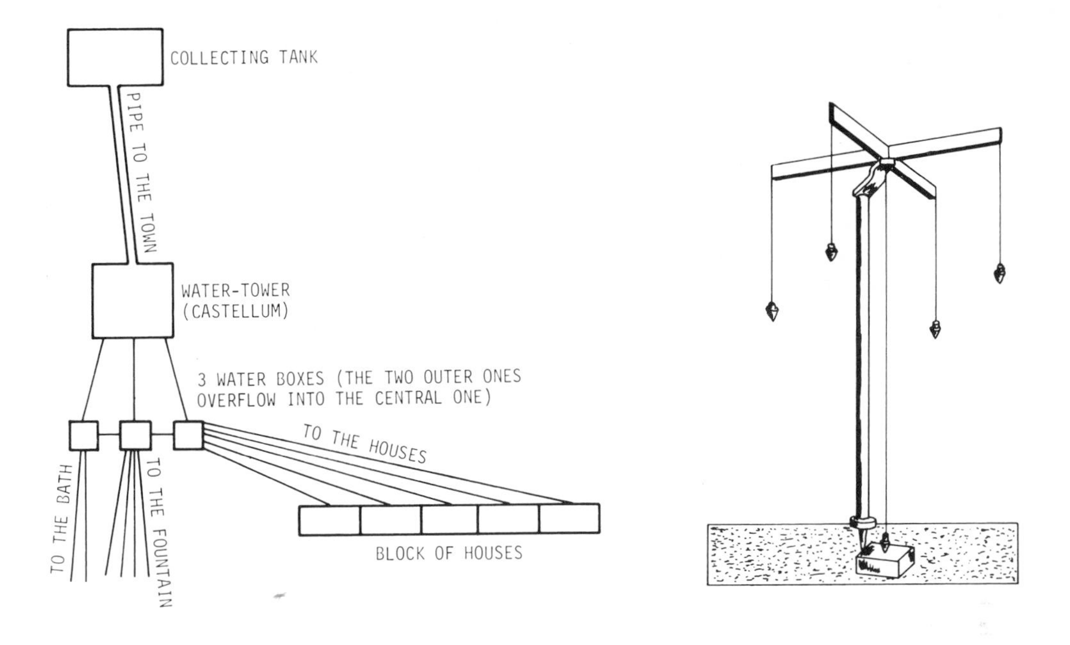

Figure 6.8

Figure 6.9

second private homes, and the third which received the overflow from the other two, led its contents to the city's numerous fountains. Rome had a veritable passion for water, and as late as 1936, still consumed more per capita than any other capital in the world. In antiquity the rate of water consumption was still greater. (Figure 6.8)

Before considering the still impressive stone causeways and arched aqueducts of the Roman builders and engineers as well as their magnificent temples and domed structures, one should bear in mind that the only instrument employed in building that we know of is the groma. It consists of a vertical rod that carries a cross from which four plumblines are suspended. In the absence of any adequate description of its uses, we can safely surmise it yielded lineups of right angles. It was in use in Greece originally and was known there as the Grecian Star. (Figure 6.9)

The first aqueducts of Rome were located underground, while the later ones were constructed along a straight gradient and ran through tunnels under mountains and on arched columnar viaducts across valleys. This far more laborious and costly method had to be resorted to because the water was brought from remoter sources after the more proximate ones had been exhausted. Also, keeping the conduits consistently underground resulted in great pressures which the pipemaking of the time could not accommodate. When the aqueduct ran overground, it consisted of a channel lying on a causeway built upon arches supported by columns in close succession. All was made of masonry and many of these aqueducts carried two or three channels, one on top of another, with the topmost also covered to prevent evaporation or dirt. (Figure 6.10, Pont du Gard at Nîmes, France).

Figure 6.10

Providing for an adequate water supply to growing cities was not man's only contact with water. Man's very interaction with it stirred him to the discernment and study of related problems, such as, the use of lead in pipes and cisterns, the role water can play in health and disease, effective irrigation and storage, methods of filtration and purification, drainage of swamps, and finally the conveyance of water into the home and its use in the disposal of sewage and refuse. To some extent all of these aspects cropped up in antiquity and met with varying degrees of success.

Hippocrates, the great medical authority of antiquity and the first pioneer in medical wisdom and observation, called attention to the role of water in health and disease in his book, *On Airs, Waters, Places*. Vitruvius discussed its purification "by percolation" through layers of sand or by allowing it to stand in a settling tank. Aristotle recommended filtration through porous pottery and prescribed methods of distilling off sweet water from salt water, while the addition of salts to water in order to remove its impurities and render it sweet and wholesome, is even mentioned in the Bible (II Kings 2:21-22). Elsewhere, herbs are believed to accomplish the same objective (Exodus 15:25). Hippocrates, Galen, Vitruvius, and other authors warned against the harmful effects of lead in waterpipes. Vitruvius comments that "if water is boiled in a copper vessel and is allowed to stand and then poured off, it will also pass the test, if no sand or mud is found in the bottom of the copper vessel."

In drainage, too, ancient Rome was quite successful. Large water tunnels were built for sewage removal, with air-shafts at regular intervals, as in the conduits of a water-supply system. Lake Albano, which was situated in a crater of an extinct volcano and became frequently flooded for lack of an outlet, was duly emptied by constructing such a tunnel to allow the waters to flow out along a 15 mile open channel to the Tiber. Thirty thousand men worked eleven years to complete, in the first century A. D., a system of canals that drained Lake Fucinus which lay in a closed mountain basin. The tunnel that emptied the lake was over three miles long. Equally successful was the drainage of the Po Valley in the second century B. C., the district around Bologna and Piacenza. On the other hand, the famous Pomptine Marshes south of Rome were never really drained, though the need for it was frequently mentioned. The very boldness of some schemes bears testimony to the level of competence achieved. Nero, for example, had begun to dig a 160-mile ship canal from Ostia, near Rome, to Lake Avernus, near Naples, in which two five-bank ships could pass each other.

Strangely enough, although Ctesibius and Hero employed water pumps operated by suction or by hot or compressed air, such devices were rarely put to practical use. Machines for raising water to higher levels were used, however, as we have seen, but they were man-operated. To this group belonged the screw of Archimedes, the shaduf or swipe, the tympanum of Vitruvius, and the wheel of buckets. Occasionally such machines were operated by an animal turning a treadmill. These same machines were also used as we saw in draining water from mines or in the drainage of swamps.

But just as it is true that many good technological principles were never put to practical use in antiquity, it is also true that occasionally a clever device was fully exploited. The use of the water turbine for the grinding of corn, by which is meant not maize, but the grain of wheat, rye, barley, or millet, into flour, is a case in point. Many authors have stated that the existence of slavery discouraged the invention or use of machinery. As R. J. Forbes points out, (*Studies in Ancient Technology,* Volume II, Leiden, 1955, p. 80), it can with certainty be stated that this assertion has no evidence to support it, even if we take into consideration the fact that the 3, 500 years covered by the term Antiquity saw many changes in the structure and vigor of the institution of slavery. It is a fact that in Egypt slavery played a minor role and few, if any, slaves were employed in the building of the pyramids. Besides employing much skilled labor, Egyptians were conscripted by the king to serve as laborers, much as our young men are called up for military service. In spite of many statements to the contrary, Forbes seems fully justified in asserting that: "Apart from the temple slaves and those belonging to the state, the proportion of the unfree population in every country and at almost every time was insignificant in relation to the free population. Estates or mining industry employing masses of slaves were non-existent. The large land-owners preferred tenants to slaves, as the latter proved expensive on the farm as well as in the shop. The basis of the Near-Eastern economy was the free tenant farmer and share cropper in agriculture and the free artisan and day laborer in the workshops. The slave had his place in the household, and always remained half free and half property. The Near East also knew the bondman who worked as a kind of contract-coolie to pay off a debt or to earn a lump sum of money. He was always a paid servant and never a slave." (*Ibid*)

Slaves were too expensive to maintain and if unmotivated, failed, even when hired out, to produce anything beyond their keep. This meant that they had to be given more and more privileges and inducements, which fact no doubt accounts in largest part for the rapid rise of freedmen in Rome and for the gradual decline of the institution. The rise of the Stoic philosophy and of humanitarianism also contributed greatly to the weakening of slavery as an institution. By the time of the establishment of Christianity, the total abolition of slavery was readily attained as if of inner disintegration.

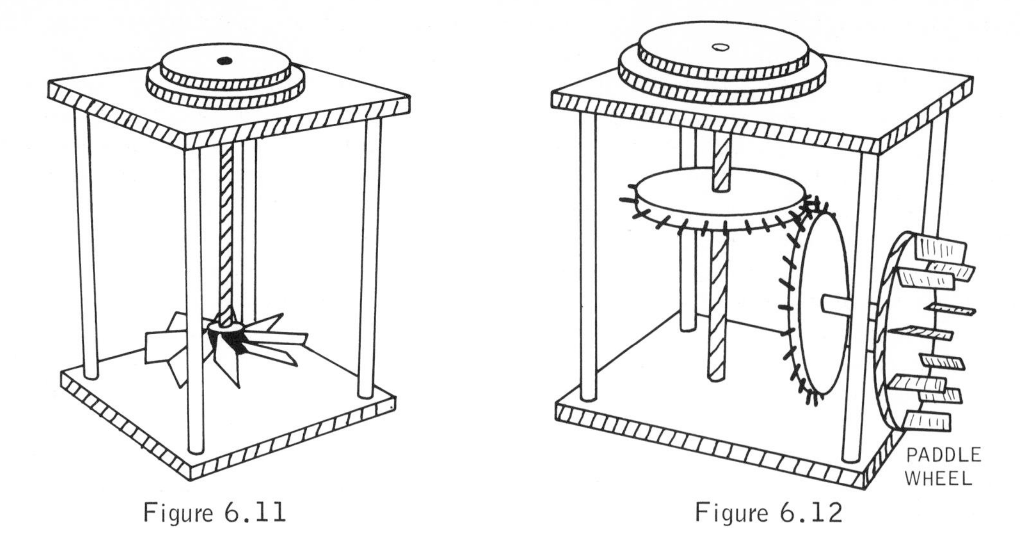

Figure 6.11

Figure 6.12

During the first century B. C., two kinds of water mills for the grinding of corn made their appearance.

The simplest kind was called the Greek or Norse mill. It has a horizontal grinding wheel, to which was fastened a vertical shaft that passed through a lower stationary millstone that was fixed to the upper stone by a crossbar. As the stream propelled the wheel, the upper millstone rotated above the lower one and ground the corn into flour. This type of mill is not very efficient, since it gives one revolution of the millstone per revolution of the turbine. (Figure 6.11)

Far more efficient was the Vitruvian or horizontal mill, in which the paddle wheel is placed vertically and the shaft lies horizontally; motion is transmitted to the millstone through intervening gears, with the result that one revolution of the water-wheel results in five revolutions of the stone. Such mills could be of either the overshot-wheel type, or the less efficient undershot. They require steady and regulated water-power of considerable strength, which can only be obtained from draining a river to raise the water level to a desirable falling height and allow the water to act on the turbine vanes through a sluice to the millrace and thus exert the maximum force. (Figure 6.12)

Flour mills gained quickly in popularity so that by the second century A. D. corn-grinding constituted a significant industry in Rome, which possessed 300 mills. These were probably not water mills, since they were operated by horses and "when the Emperor Caligula confiscated the horses in the bakeries of Rome, a bread famine resulted." (*Ibid.* p. 94) Others were worked by slaves, free laborers, or criminals. However, a century later when Rome suffered from acute labor shortage, water mills became the chief means of preparing Rome's flour. As a source of energy for other purposes, the principle of the water-wheel largely was neglected until the Middle Ages.

From Herodotus we learn that on occasion the ancients undertook some very courageous measures in diverting river beds. Thus the Babylonian Queen Semiramis "raised certain embankments well worthy of inspection, in the plain near Babylon, to control the river, which, till then, used to overflow and flood the whole country 'round about." A later queen and "a wiser princess than her predecessor," named Nitocris, dug out a large reservoir near the Euphrates River above Babylon, used the dug up soil to build embankments, paved the "entire margin of the reservoir" with stones and made a new winding channel for the river across the road which the threatening Medes would have to take to approach her city. Moreover, the river flowed originally through Babylon, separating the city in half, so that "if a man wanted to pass from one of these divisions to the other, he had to cross in a boat; which must, it seems to me, have been very troublesome." She therefore diverted the flow of the river into the above large reservoir and "while the basin was filling, the natural channel of the river was left dry. Forthwith, she set to work, and in the first place lined the banks of the stream with quays of burnt brick, and also bricked the landing places opposite the river-gates," and then, "built, as near the middle of the town as possible, a stone bridge, the blocks whereof were bound together with iron and lead. In the daytime, square wooden platforms were laid along from pier to pier, on which the inhabitants crossed the stream; but at night they were withdrawn, to prevent people passing from side to side in the dark to commit robberies. When the river had filled the cutting, and the bridge was finished, the Euphrates was turned back again into its ancient bed, and thus the basin, transformed suddenly into a lake, was seen to answer the purpose for which it was made, and the inhabitants, by help of the basin, obtained the advantage of a bridge." (Herodotus, pp. 69-70)

A word should be said about the use of ducts for the removal of sewage. Ancient Rome adopted from the Etruscans the system of sewers. The famous Cloaca Maxima, or large subterranean sewer, fourteen feet high and eleven wide, was built around 500 B. C. and served to drain the area of the Forum. Rome originally had three small brooks used for sewage removal, but in time these became part of one sewage system. The main pipe connected with outlets from private homes, all of which were provided with latrines and baths. The Cloaca also gathered the wastes from public baths and public lavatories which were to be found in most cities of Italy. In the year 315 A. D., Rome was reported to have had 144 public latrines flushed by running water, and 116 "Necessariae," or emergency places.

Figure 6.13
Upper photo: Cloaca Maxima Rome
Lower photo: Its exit into Tiber

3. The Technology of Warfare

It would take us far afield if we considered the long history of progress in agriculture, domestication of plants and animals, the multiple arts of ceramics, the preparation of leather, metal work, glass, ship or road building, fire-making and fireplaces, beer and wine culture, the extraction of dyes, edible oils and perfumes, spinning and weaving of cloth, architecture and sculpture, the alphabet and writing, and a number of other skills and pursuits, each of which constitutes a vast study by itself. Each serves to demonstrate that whatever human activity we may choose at random for careful analysis, we invariably find that it hardly ever stands still in the light of history, but that small and detectable changes constantly occur in it to make growth practically inevitable.

Since we cannot consider all the practical activities subject to this law of evolution, let us take as our last example the arts related to warfare. This distinctly human activity is of particular interest, because it is apparently the one area in which there is the least gap between inventiveness and application.

This does not mean to imply that no sooner is an idea presented than the rulers of the land immediately adopt it. We know that this was not so from two specific instances. First, there is available to us a plea by a Roman engineer to his Emperor, offering to build for his armies some fantastic military weaponry. The anonymous author of *De Rebus Bellicis,* written about 350 A.D. when as he says, "above all it must be recognized that wild nations are pressing upon the Roman Empire and howling 'round about it everywhere, and treacherous barbarians, covered by natural positions, are assailing every frontier." He therefore suggests twelve military inventions, and hopes the Emperor will forgive his boldness in submitting them or in criticizing the existing state of preparedness. "I think I should be protected by your indulgence, for if I am to carry out my promise, I must be assisted for the sake of the freedom of science." (E.A. Thompson, *A Roman Reformer and Inventor*. Oxford, 1952, p. 108) After listing his plans for defense, he pleads: "Invincible Emperor, you will double the strength of your invincible army when you have equipped it with these mechanical inventions, countering the raids of your enemies not by sheer strength alone but also by mechanical ingenuity, particularly when with keen perception you find machines that will be effective on all the elements." (p. 120) In spite of all this, there is no evidence that either the Emperor or any of his advisors did anything but disregard this fascinating document.

We also know from the letters of Leonardo da Vinci that all his clever inventiveness and florid military promises did not suffice to induce Count Sforza to employ him as military construction engineer to carry out his grandiose designs of fantastic weapons. In his plea to Lodovico Sforza of Milan, Leonardo wrote, "I can construct light and strong bridges... easy to take to pieces and set up again. I also know how to fire and destroy the bridges of the enemy... In laying siege to a fortress I know how to empty the water out of moats and construct siege bridges, mantlets, scaling-ladders, etc.... I shall manufacture bombards, mortars, and catapults of the most beautiful and serviceable forms. For combats at sea, I have methods of making many instruments excellently adapted for attack and defence--and ships that can resist fire..." Finally toward the end of his appeal he states: "In time of peace, I think I can give the best of satisfaction, well bearing comparison with anyone else, in architecture, in the designing of buildings, whether public or private, and in the conducting of water from one place to another. I shall carry out sculptures in marble, bronze, and clay, and similarly paintings of every possible kind, to stand comparison with anyone else, be he who may." (Antonina Vallentin, *Leonardo da Vinci*. New York, 1952. p. 75ff.)

In spite of all this, Leonardo was not hired and his biographer says: "In reality, these all too marvelous proposals fell at first on deaf ears." Not one of his fascinating military inventions was ever put into practice. Moreover, when Sforza's trusted expert, the architect Bramante, once submitted a report on the improvement of some fortification, Sforza commented: "Bramante cannot understand the subject as well as a soldier," thus rationalizing his opposition to perhaps valuable military innovations. This seeems to be true of all military leaders, small or great. Our own atomic physicists in 1939 found it far from easy to induce the Army or Navy to welcome their idea of the atom bomb, and required the intervention of no lesser a personality than Albert Einstein to influence favorably the President of the United States. Hence men of defense, like all other people, show, as a rule, considerable resistance to new ideas. True, such resistance is only temporary and is rooted in some psychological pattern. In time, resistance is overcome and new adjustments are attained. There seems little doubt that new weapons often meant certain supremacy to its possessors. Tribes or nations, imbued with determination or vision, welcomed new weapons, skills or auxiliary innovations, and were led into the business of empire-building, for good or for evil. Often, however, leaders resisted useful novelties to their own destruction.

The art of warfare involves a large variety of skills, such as the art of building roads and bridges, the domestication of the horse, the construction of chariots, the forging of diverse weapons, the art of shipbuilding, the designing of siegecraft, general defense technology, the building of walls, fortification, tunnels and earthwork ramparts, and finally the sending of messages, the making of maps, and the keeping of records. Those nations of Antiquity which attained positions as empires did so by virtue of excelling at least in many, if not in all, of these areas. This is true of Egypt, Babylonia, Assyria, Persia, the Greece of Athens, Alexander the Great and his successors, Carthage, and Rome.

Consider the matter of roads. No empire can exist without a network of roads to be used not only by armies on the march but also for communication later on. No roads to speak of existed before the appearance of ancient empires because trade alone was never sufficient to generate them. Water traffic was easier to come by and was therefore the first to reach significant exploitation. The first land tracks were pathways, log-roads across marshes, or artificial ruts cut into the soil to guide the cartwheels. The oldest paved streets consisted of slabs of stone set in bitumen mortar and appeared first as processional highways linking temples within the city walls with shrines or with temples beyond the walls. The sacred statues of gods were carried on carts along these special streets. Such construction dating to 1,200 B.C. is found in Asia Minor in the cities of the Hittites. In 1,100 B.C., the Assyrian

King Tiglath Pileser I already had a corps of engineers who laid pontoon bridges and levelled roads for carts and large siege apparatus. He writes: "I took my chariots and my warriors and through their wearisome paths I hewed a way with pickaxes of bronze, and I made possible a road for the passage of my chariots and my troops." (K. K. Luckenbill, *Ancient Records of Assyria,* Chicago, 1926, Vol. I, p. 75)

Neither Babylonia nor Assyria, however, built the complex network of highways so characteristic of the vast Persian Empire (ca 550 B. C.) which introduced as well the first messenger service and an empire-wide, stable currency. The Persians had pushed to a high level the advancing art of horse-riding and chariot construction. Primitive vehicles were sleds pulled on land by human efforts, while two-wheeled carts are known from before 2,000 B. C. Generally speaking, the third millenium B. C. abounds in two-wheeled carts and in war chariots, as well as in four-wheel wagons, both open and covered. Mycenaean Greece and the Hittite cities of the second millenium B. C. employed chariots and horses in warfare, each carrying one driver and one warrior. The first draught animals were oxen harnessed in pairs and pulling the wagon by the pole that was attached to the chassis resting on the axle in the rear but having a wooden yoke in the front end, to which the oxen were tied. "Tractive power was transmitted to the wheels by the pole and to the pole by the wooden yoke." (*History of Technology,* Vol. I, p. 720) Beginning with about 2,000 B. C., horses are harnessed instead to onagers or rolling battle catapults. It is at about that time that records from Persia reveal chariots with spoked wheels. These records also supply us with references to horse-breeding. In the subsequent centuries, the use of horses in warfare becomes quite widespread. This entails the development of saddles, bridles, cheekpieces and bits, organized campaigns and novel methods of offense and defense. It is believed that the horse and chariot brought the first successful invasion of Egypt at the beginning of the second millenium B. C. and probably enabled the Hellenic Achaeans to invade Greece, the Aryans to conquer the Indus Valley, and effected changes within China as well. But it is with the later Persians that both chariotry and cavalry reach their peak effectiveness. Alone, the spoked wheel entailed great skill in woodwork and in the making of its required tools, as well as the need for bending pieces into felloes (rim of wheel with spokes) and for other related tasks. The use of the horse as a riding animal derived from the nomadic tribes of Asia early in the first millenium B. C. Horse-riding brought with it the need for a padded saddle (Rome, fourth century A. D.), the spur, and later the stirrup, a most significant innovation without which the rider could hardly be secure in combat. The shoeing of horses was subsequently added by the Romans and seems to have completed the efficiency of the horse as a most serviceable animal for draught and cavalry.

At the very inception of the Persian Empire, we find Cyrus the Younger telling his army: "You gentlemen who are in command of the roadmakers, you have the lists of soldiers I have disqualified from serving as javelin-men, bowmen or slingers, and you will make the old javelin-men march with the axes for falling timber, the bowmen with mattocks and the slingers with shovels. They will advance by squads in front of the wagons so that if there is any road-making to be done, you may get to work at once, and in case of need, I may know where to get the men I want."

At that, Persian roads were makeshift constructions compared to Roman roads which in time came to cover all the occupied territories of the Roman Empire. Neither did Greece achieve sophistication in road building, although Greek roads contained well-laid ruts of uniform gauge in which the chariot wheels ran as forcedly as trains do on tracks. But Persia did have an excellent and dependable postal service the like of which had never previously existed and which Alexander's successors sought to preserve. Aside from roads, traffic by ship did prosper uninterruptedly throughout the Greek era, and covered not only the entire Mediterranean and the Black Seas, but also the Nile, the Red Sea, and the Indian Ocean to China. Ships of considerable dimensions plied the seas, equipped with sails, rudders, several rows of oars, powerful ramming devices, and they were run by men of exceptional skill and courage.

Figure 6.14

The Roman art of building roads was intricate and the products proved sturdy. As a rule, they were composed of four layers, but were modified in harmony with local needs and conditions. The excavated bed was first made level and covered with a twelve-inch layer of fist-sized rocks. If the bottom was soft, piles were driven into it, a cover laid upon them and the above layer of stones put on. Next came a layer of broken brick or rubble mixed with lime, which was packed down with heavy wooden stamps or with rollers of wood or stone, until nine inches thick when packed. Next came a six-inch layer of powdered pottery mixed with lime and packed down, then overlaid with a pavement of either flat stones, concrete, or fine crushed stone or gravel, giving a total thickness of about four feet. The flat pavements slabs were embedded in lime mortar. Concrete was obtained from gravel or chipped stones or bricks mixed with mortar. The latter consisted of lime mixed with powdered volcanic rock and sand. Drainage of the foundation was provided for, but not shrinkage and expansion by changes in temperature. The main road or "agger publicus" was only about 40 feet wide, containing a path for carriages as well as sidewalks for pedestrians, the latter marked off by a low stone wall or strip of grass.

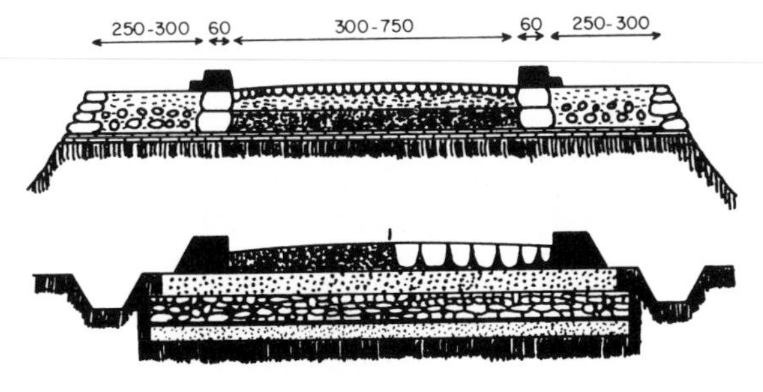

Figure 6.15

Let us consider now the technology of war machines. Again we must return to Greece, because it was there that mechanical was devices originated and were put to use. As already stated, such mechanized weapons were virtually the only product of the mechanical inventiveness of Greece that was generally put to what we would call practical use. The Persian Empire had demonstrated that organized cavalry could be an almost invincible power, and Alexander the Great continued the policy begun by his father, Philip II of Macedonia (359-336 B. C.), and built a cavalry to match that of Persia, equipped as well with sword, thrusting spear, and heavy body armor. But the major advances made by Greek military science went even further. They increased the power of the bow by adding a stock to it and also a lock so that the string could be held taut, the arrow loaded and the aim sighted with the bow ready to discharge at the proper instant. This was the crossbow.

The same principle was applied most effectively on a larger scale in the siege catapults which appeared as early as 400 B. C., when Dionysius of Syracuse employed them in his war with Carthage. These machines were adopted by Sparta and Athens only a few decades thereafter. There were four types of such heavy stone-throwing catapults. First came the tension catapult, which was merely a giant crossbow. The ordinary bow used by the infantry was either simple, that is, made of one piece of yew-tree wood bent by a string of twisted animal gut, or a composite of two pieces of horn joined by a piece of wood and held in place by sinews. It possessed far more elasticity than the simple bow, but required greater skill in bending to put the string in position for us, since proper care of the bow demanded that it be relaxed when not in use. The tension catapult, being a large crossbow, had the two horns fixed to a heavy wooden beam, or stock, that ended in a curved piece (b). The stock had a groove in it (c), and a rack on its side (k). A sliding piece (d) rode dovetailed in the groove and pulled along with it the bow's string. The sliding piece was provided with a pawl (h), which engaged the rack and prevented the tautly bent horns from pulling back the string to its initial position. The front end of this crossbow was held against the ground or a wall, and the upper part of the body pressed against the curved end of the stock to pull back or charge up the string. An arrow was placed in an appropriate slot (f) to load the bow, which could then be raised, aimed, and then fired by releasing the trigger. This crossbow is described by Hero of Alexandria. (Figure 6. 16)

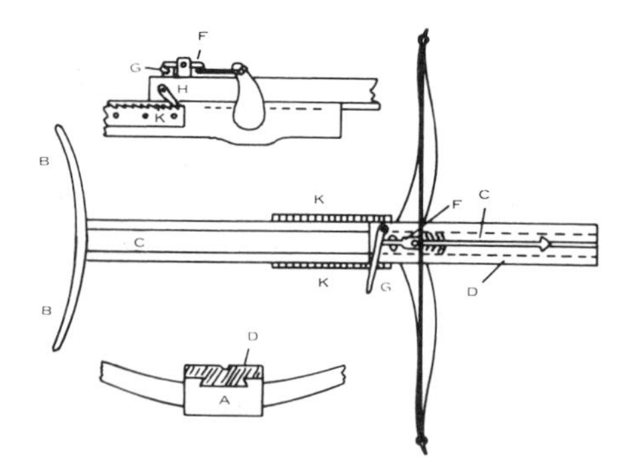

Figure 6.16

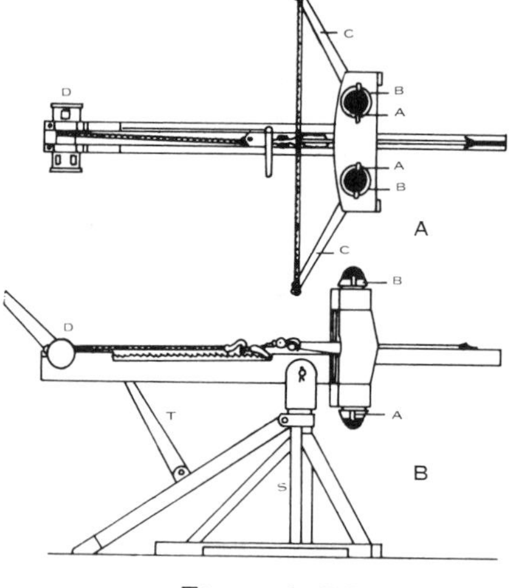

Figure 6.17

The second projectile-ejecting machine was artillery-type in nature, (Philo's euthynon) and was intended for heavier missiles. Here the power was obtained by the principle of torsion. A pair of twisted cords, sinews, or ropes of hair (A) was wound taut into skeins on two iron pins projecting from two stout collars of bronze or stout wood (B). The rods (C) were inserted into the skeins and their ends joined by a tough string or rope to produce a bow, mounted on a solid stand and loaded either with an arrow or a stone by stretching the string with power delivered from a winch situated at the end of the stock. (Figure 6.17)

The third type of artillery-piece, described by Philo of Byzantium, was similar in structure but employed bronze springs, as shown in the drawing. As the bow was bent, the two arms attached to the bow string pressed against the two springs which in the violent return to their free shape straightened the string and propelled the missile. This kind of catapult is reported by Philo to have been modified into an engine with a machine-gunlike mechanism in that it could be charged with several arrows, which were then fired, as if automatically, in rapid succession. (Figure 6.18)

Finally, there was the onager, or a torsion machine still employed as a toy. An arm provided with a sling and stuck within a single skein of taut rope could be bent backward by means of a winch held in place by a catch and released by a blow with a hammer. The arm would then spring forward and hit against a straw-filled sac placed at an angle of about 15 degrees from the vertical so as to give the arm ample room for the rebound forward and be arrested in the right position for hurling a large stone from the sling attached to its apex. (Figure 6.19) None of these catapults had a very long range, but were capable of throwing fairly heavy loads for distances a little over a quarter of a mile.

Mention should be made of the battering rams and movable towers that were already in use through the greater part of the first millenium B. C. The cleverness of ancient fortifications are common knowledge with their battlements, towers, ramparts, glacis, ditches, moats, and the use of burning tar or pots of naphtha with missiles from the various catapults or from the walls of a fortified city. The multiple skills involved in the building of chariots and the use of harnesses, should not be overlooked.

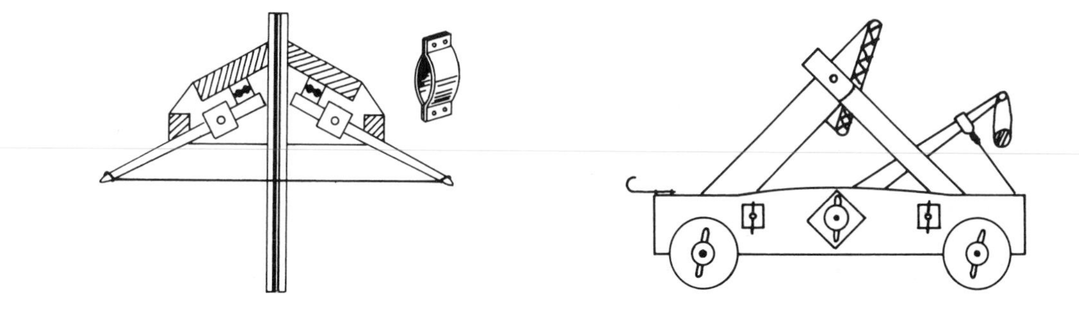

Figure 6.18

Figure 6.19

Figure 6.20

Figure 6.21

A cursory look at some of the suggested military machines designed by the above cited anonymous author of *De Rebus Bellicis* should complete our argument that whatever the practical task man becomes aware of, progress in it is virtually inevitable. The above author suggested twelve machines.

The first is a ballista, by which is meant the general missile-throwing machine "that is able to discharge arrows against the foe on every side with the free movement of an archer's hand." It is a large bow worked by a windlass but situated upon a screw so that it can turn in all directions as it moves forward. Next comes a rolling machine for the protection of a ballista by having unseen soldiers in it; walls equipped with lances and tridents, horizontally placed, protect its outside, and fascines, or bundles of twigs, cover the top. The next invention consists of a shield with projecting nails. It has room for a javelin that can be thrown by hand and is provided with feathers to smooth its flight much like an arrow but having projecting nails and sharp points so that "it pierces the foot of anyone who treads on it," should it miss its victim. This javelin can also be used as a spear. Next comes a shield-piercing spear, then a combat vehicle provided with projecting knives in the rear and with scythes attached to the axles. (Figure 6.21) These scythes can be raised and lowered by the soldiers on the vehicle. Next, a smaller model of the above. Next comes "an astonishing machine (which) possesses a certain novelty." It is equipped "with automatic lashes to urge the horses on, and is defended with shields surrounded by iron spikes." Only one driver guides two horses in it; otherwise it is like the piece already described. Next, "for relieving physical discomfort" caused by heavy armor, he recommends one of soft wool. Any soldier bedecked with this garment plus boots, iron greaves (leg-shields), a helmet, a shield, sword and lance, "will be fully armed to enter an infantry battle." Next comes a bridge made of rafts produced by air-filled leather bladders fastened by thongs. "If iron stakes are fixed on both banks and strong ropes are stretched beneath the skins themselves in mid-stream so as to bear the weight of those walking upon them, but above the skins on the banks so as to steady them, this contrivance will provide a ready means of crossing a river in a short time by a novel and unfamiliar piece of marching equipment." (Figure 6.22)

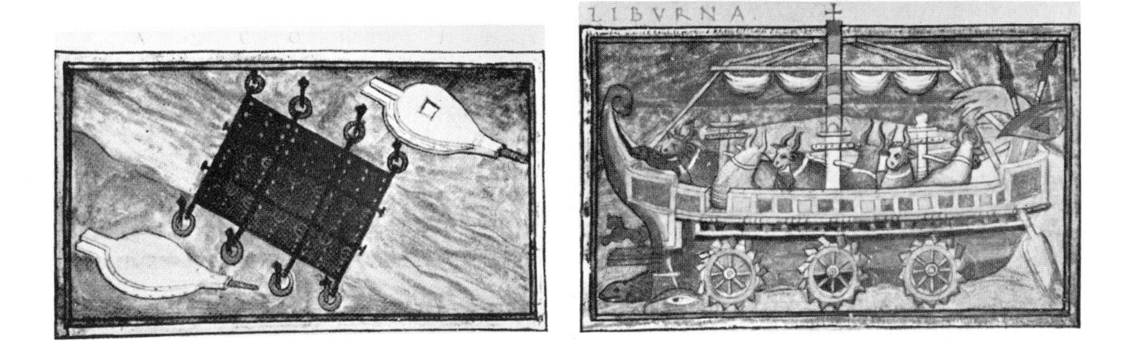

Figure 6.22 Figure 6.23

Next comes "A Liburian ship suitable for naval warfare, so large that human weakness more or less precluded its being operated by men's hands, is propelled in any required direction by animal power harnessed by the aid of human ingenuity to provide easy locomotion." As can be seen, "oxen are yoked to machines, two to each, and turn wheels attached to the ship's sides." With such power, a sturdily built ship can "easily crush and destroy all opposing warships that come to close quarters with it."

Last comes a ballista equipped with an iron bow, worked by two powerful winches, and capable of being raised and lowered for better control of the trajectory. Above all, "it is controlled, for the purpose of simply applying the motive force to the arrow, by the agency of a single man at his ease, as it were," says our anonymous author. (Figure 6.20)

We may well close the present chapter by concluding that we consider our point well proved with these few examples. We may profitably repeat the lesson learned: Take any practical activity of a culture and you will find that time will willy-nilly and, in historical perspective, almost continuously supply novelty to it, even if at various rates. A practical activity once set in motion implies awareness of a need. Contrary to the theory of economic determinism, the existence of a need is not an independent objective phenomenon like rain or cold. A human need is subject to the decree of the intervening mind, except in extreme cases. Beliefs, values, judgments affected by the culture and modified by the individual personality, more often than not determine a need. Antiquity possessed all the basic principles for the use of a vast variety of machines for mass production of goods and services; it also had everything needed for greater efficiency, hence greater productivity, which would spell a higher standard of living; it had everything necessary for trade and greater profits, which would mean greater investments and autocatalytic growth, for collective bargaining, for greater democracy than the relatively high level actually attained in both Greece and Rome, for universal education, and many other social institutions. All these measures were feasible, since the tools and social means were at hand. What was lacking was the fact that people did not experience the need, or did not think of taking steps necessary for the realization of measures to fulfill even a partial need, and consequently the measures were not undertaken. Putting the matter in such succinct form is merely another way of saying that conditions were such that people had other values, other motives, other drives, other goals, other notions of what was important, other ideals to get angry or pleased about. They lived in a different culture, hence dreamed, quarreled, acted, lived, emoted, and despaired differently, in spite of being as human as we are today.

Once a need was recognized or an activity conceived and begun, such as that of growing edible plants from seeds, domesticating some animals, irrigating the ground, bringing water to a city, heating houses in winter, having ice-cold drinks in summer, using metals, ceramics or glass, writing and painting, using weapons in war, metallurgy, etc., then growth, progress, modification, diversification and general improvement were almost inevitable. Apparently, man has an adequate supply of technical competence, both in carrying out tasks and in ingenuity for their betterment, to carry out this process of accretion. We shall see that this process is not so direct in the field of scientific generalization, in the realm of hypotheses or theories. There we shall encounter a situation in which progress can be stymied for many centuries for want of a constructive and fertile hypothesis, and no progress worth the name will transpire until a mind arises that supplies a new hypothesis, a new opening, which once supplied delivers a vitalizing impulse to the erstwhile stunted and debilitated corpse, bringing it as if by magic to life and efflorescence. But in the theoretically stymied interim, practical activities entailing the elements of that very science, may be seen to forge nicely ahead at their usual pace. In modern times, with science as an organized activity that unceasingly gives birth to new ideas for possible needs and enjoyments, such as radio, TV, lasers, plastics, hi-fis, interplanetary rockets, a variety of toys, games and gadgets, underwater travel, and the like, the relationship between the two is entirely different. We are fully conscious of the value of application of scientific principles, and skill in such application has become a full-grown activity, an industry in its own right.

VII Geometry in the Service of Science

1. Distances to Sun and Moon

It is a fact of no little significance that among the very first scientific works to be composed and circulated should be Euclid's *Elements of Geometry* in thirteen books. The term book implied in those days a somewhat enlarged chapter covering a coherent topic. The *Elements* contains 148 demonstrations dealing with plane figures entailing mathematical properties, all of which are worked in algebra by us today. In addition, the work contains 25 demonstrations of proportionality and about 70 demonstrations involving three-dimensional or solid geometry. Three books (7, 8, and 9) deal with arithmetic. If we take into account that this volume still dominates or influences much mathematics today and is an indispensable text for student and scholar alike, it is easy to realize its phenomenal intrinsic merit.

Euclid was not the sole creator of the vast beauty and wisdom encompassed by his work. Proclus, the great ancient mathematician and commentator on Euclid says: "Not much younger than these is Euclid, who put together the *Elements*, collecting many of Eudoxus' theorems, perfecting many of Theaetetus', and bringing to irrefragable demonstration the things which were only somewhat loosely proved by his predecessors." Like Aristotle a few years before him and Ptolemy four and a half centuries after him, Euclid was not only an enlightened and competent gatherer and organizer of knowledge, but a thoroughly ingenious and creative scholar in his own right. We must especially marvel at the vast store of mathematical wisdom he brought together at about 300 B.C. when we bear in mind that consistent mathematical reasoning based on logic and proof seems to have begun in ancient Greece with Thales, who lived during the first half of the sixth century B.C. He is credited with being the first who placed certain clever though simple statements about geometrical relationships upon an unshaken logical foundation called proof. By this method the number of fundamental notions accepted as reasonable, self-evident, or on faith, meaning that they gained common agreement due to their universal appeal to man's common sense, was reduced to the five so-called postulates and the five additional "common notions" which are cited by Euclid. All else is built up as a solid logical edifice resting upon these ten foundations.

What do we mean by proof, by a firm logical construction? Let us take the five geometrical truths commonly known and accepted, but first proven by Thales. They are: 1. A circle is bisected by any diameter; 2. The base angles of an isosceles triangle are equal; 3. The vertical angles formed by two intersecting lines are equal; 4. Two triangles are congruent if they have two angles and one side in each, respectively, equal; and finally, 5. An angle inscribed in a semicircle is a right angle, a conclusion known to the Babylonians fourteen centuries earlier.

We do not know what proof Thales actually used to establish the first theorem, but we may reason as follows. It can be demonstrated that within any circle if two chords are equal, the arcs determined by them are equal. [The proof of this theorem requires joining the two ends of each chord with the center of the circle. Such lines are radii and are equal; hence triangles built on equal chords are equal and so are their corresponding central angles. Hence the arcs are equal.] Given a circle with AB as its diameter, this circle has two arcs, x and y. Since AB = AB, then arc x on AB to the right must be equal to arc y on AB to the left. Hence the right half of a circle equals the left half. Now, common sense alone would tell us that a diameter divides a circle into two equal halves. It is obvious that you can cut the circle in half along a line through its center and superpose the two halves, etc. But logical proof is a unique type of evidence and it is upon such evidence that a foolproof system can be built. At that, one must inevitably start with some definitions and postulates and then proceed from there. Given the tool of logical proof, the edifice one constructs is, however, far more securely sound, consistent and reliable. It remains so forever, as long as the definitions are adhered to and the postulates honored. With the fall of a postulate or misuse of a definition, the entire structure falls. What Thales presumably did, was to lay down the method, so fully and beautifully carried out by Euclid a few centuries later. The upshot of this method was that beginning with clearly laid down definitions and with the minimum number of plainly stated postulates, one proceeded with unimpeachable logic to build up a system of steadily increasing complexity, held together by the powerful cement of proof. Thales presumably pointed the way, while many others contributed to the general effort, and Euclid finally organized, perfected, and synthesized the fruits of close to three centuries of growth.

Euclid's assemblage of geometrical logic found immediate application in the sphere of astronomy. This was fully to be expected, because in spite of the origin of its name--earth measurement--there is really no satisfactory evidence that the science was ever put to practical use.

It is true that Proclus (410-485 A.D.), in his *Commentary on Euclid's Elements,* quotes "the remarkable Aristotle" as having stated that geometry began with the Egyptians. Says Proclus: "It owed its discovery to the practice of land measurement. For the Egyptians had to perform such measurements because the overflow of the Nile would cause the boundary of each person's land to disappear." (M.R. Cohen and I.E. Drabkin, *A Source Book in Greek Science,* New York, 1948, p. 34) Herodotus also reports that King Sesastris (circa 1300 B.C.) divided the land equally among the people and "would send men to... measure the space" for purposes of taxation. Yet, Aristotle himself viewed the social role of mathematics in a different light. Says he in his *Metaphysics:* "At first he who invented any art whatever that went beyond the common perceptions of man was naturally admired by men, not only because there was something useful in the inventions, but because he was thought wise and superior to the rest. But as more arts were invented and some were directed at the necessities of life, others to recreation, the inventors of the latter were naturally always regarded as wiser than the inventors of the former, because their branches of knowledge did not aim at utility. Hence, when all such inventors were already established, the sciences which do not aim at giving pleasure or at the necessities of life were discovered, and first in the places where men first began to have leisure. This is why the mathematical arts were founded in Egypt; for there the priestly caste was allowed to be at leisure." (*The Basic Works of Aristotle*. ed. Richard McKeon, New York, 1941, p. 690) Aristotle here develops his ladder of values. On the lowest rung are those individuals who merely use their senses; next come "men of experience," or empirical doers; next, skilled mechanics, then master-workers, and finally the men of knowledge, or theoreticians. To him, the last group is wiser than mere inventors for utility or pleasure.

It is, nevertheless, a fact that peasants seldom divide their lands by hiring a surveyor; they make use, as a rule, of some natural markers, and where nature fails to provide such, put some conspicuous stone marker in the desired spot, or drive in a stake. Besides, at best the percentage of theorems that could be practically employed was miniscule. Geometry was born, evolved, functioned, and has remained to this day an intellectual quest, an innate, human pursuit, a mental challenge which may even prove to be less prone to dismissal, replacement, or evasion than wine or meat or a comfortable bed, which man often consents to do without when some belief dictates that he do so. Geometry, like learning, can become as necessary and as dear to him as life itself, once he becomes aware of it and tastes its delights.

Little wonder, then, that no sooner had Chaldean astronomy reached Greece, where it began its upward climb with its own inspired momentum, than it promptly joined hands with geometry and exploited its theorems to the fullest with greatest speed. With the aid of the simplest possible geometry, a number of significant relationships were determined. We shall consider some of them.

It is generally known how Eratosthenes determined the radius of the earth, hence its circumference, $2\pi r$. Eratosthenes, the learned librarian of Alexandria who mastered virtually all the knowledge of the times, accomplished the first determination of the dimensions of the spherical earth with the aid of geometry, in the third century B.C. He knew that at Syene (modern Aswan) the sun can, on the day of the summer solstice (June 21), be seen reflected at noon in the very center of a deep well. This meant that the sun was at the zenith there, and that the locality was at the edge of the Tropic of Cancer. He knew that Alexandria was about 500 miles north of that place, and believed it to lie on the same meridian. The rays of the sun falling upon the earth were generally assumed to be parallel because of the sun's vast distance from the earth. The sun's altitude in the sky at Alexandria on June 21 at noon, was seven and a fraction degrees south of zenith. Eratosthenes therefore assumed that this angle would be the same at the center of the earth, since the earth's radius is insignificantly small in relation to the earth's distance from the sun. On this basis, seven and a fraction degrees on the earth's surface; hence one degree equals about 70 miles. The circumference of the earth's sphere consists of 360 degrees, and its measure in miles will amount to 360x70, or 25,400 miles. The circumference of a circle being 2 r, the radius of the earth's sphere is 25,400/2x3.14 or approximately 4040 miles. The fact that the unit in which his measurements have come down to us is in stades which is still an uncertain measure in our terms, and the fact that both the longitudes of the two localities were not quite identical, and the assumed distance between them slightly in error, are of relatively minor importance. The method was ingenious and the results somehow turned out to be almost perfect.

A slightly different experimental procedure in obtaining the dimensions of the earth was made use of by another great scholar, Posidonius (135-51 B. C.). A pre-Ptolemaic Greek astronomer and author of a text in the field, Cleomedes, regarded Posidonius' method as simpler than that of Eratosthenes (T. L. Heath, *Greek Astronomy,* cited by Cohen and Drabkin). Both methods rest upon the same working principle, except that while Eratosthenes employs the concept of simultaneous measurement of the height of the sun from two different localities on the same meridian, Posidonius measures the height of a star, Canopus, in the constellation Argus, lying about 53 degrees south of the celestial equator. Says Cleomedes: "Now Rhodes and Alexandria lie under the same meridian circle, and the distance between the cities is reputed to be 5,000 stades. Suppose this to be the case."

Posidonius then divides the zodiacal circle into 48 parts, hence each of the twelve signs of the zodiac into 4, thus assigning $7\frac{1}{2}$ degrees to each division. He similarly divides the circle of the meridian. "Now meridian circles are circles which are drawn through the poles of the universe and through the point which is above the head of any individual standing on the earth." Hence one such segment on the meridian is also equal to $7\frac{1}{2}$.

Now Canopus is so far south in the sky that it is not seen in Greece proper, just as the Southern Cross is not. But as one travels southward, one reaches a point at which it begins to be seen barely above the horizon. The island of Rhodes is such a place. As one travels further south, Canopus will be higher and higher in the sky. As the traveler reaches Alexandria, he has covered, says Posidonius, 5,000 stades, and Canopus is exactly one quarter of a zodiacal sign, or $7\frac{1}{2}$ degrees, above the horizon. Hence one degree of the sky is equivalent to 666 stades. Both measurements, the distance between Rhodes and Alexandria and the difference in latitude of Canopus, happen not to be correct. The latter is 5°13', and the former is considerably less than 5,000 stades, being only 380 miles. Moreover, Rhodes and Alexandria differ by about $1\frac{1}{2}$ degree in longitude. Posidonius' logic and general procedure is, however, as sound and as brilliant as the logic of Eratosthenes. Says Cleomedes: "Since, then, the part of the earth under this segment is reputed to be 5,000 stades, the parts (of the earth) under the other (equal) segments (of the meridian circle) also measure 5,000 stades; and thus the great circle of the earth is found to measure 240,000 stades [48 x 5,000], assuming that from Rhodes to Alexandria is 5,000 stades; but, if not, it is in (the same) ratio to the distance. Such then is Posidonius' way of dealing with the size of the earth."

Since the angle of difference in latitude was far too big, Posidonius obtained a smaller circumference for the globe of the earth than it is in actuality. He made it smaller by 44%. For reasons of his own, Ptolemy adopted the figure obtained by Posidonius rather than the more correct one found by Eratosthenes. The medieval world, having based itself largely on the great work of Ptolemy, thus obliged Columbus to ascribe to the earth in general and the Atlantic ocean, lying between Europe and Japan, (Cipangu) in particular, smaller dimensions than they possess in reality. This error served, however, to strengthen his conviction that the region he was after could readily be reached by sailing westward only about 2,400 instead of 3,450 miles. His sailors threatened rebellion probably because toward the end of September or early October, 1492, they realized that their captain's calculations were inaccurate. It may also be that Columbus' original failure to win the support of Portugal was due to the fact that he had put his faith in Posidonius' value for the circumference of the earth, while the Portuguese navigators perhaps put more trust in the figure obtained by Eratosthenes.

The method of reasoning employed by Posidonius exemplifies rather simple geometrical logic. Let us examine relatively more refined methods, though remaining within the confines of elementary geometry. Consider next the determination of the distance to the moon, which the ancients had little difficulty with and ascribed it to Hipparchus.

Select two cities, A and B, on the same meridian of longitude, and measure either altitude, or zenith-distance of moon at exactly the same time at both places, with the kind of astrolobe already described. Altitude is the angle which designates the elevation of moon above the horizon, hence the angle which line AM makes with the horizon at A, and line BM with the horizon at B. The zenith distance is the complement of these angles, namely, the angle between the moon and the zenith. To perform the measurements at exactly the same time is relatively easy, since they can be done at midnight,

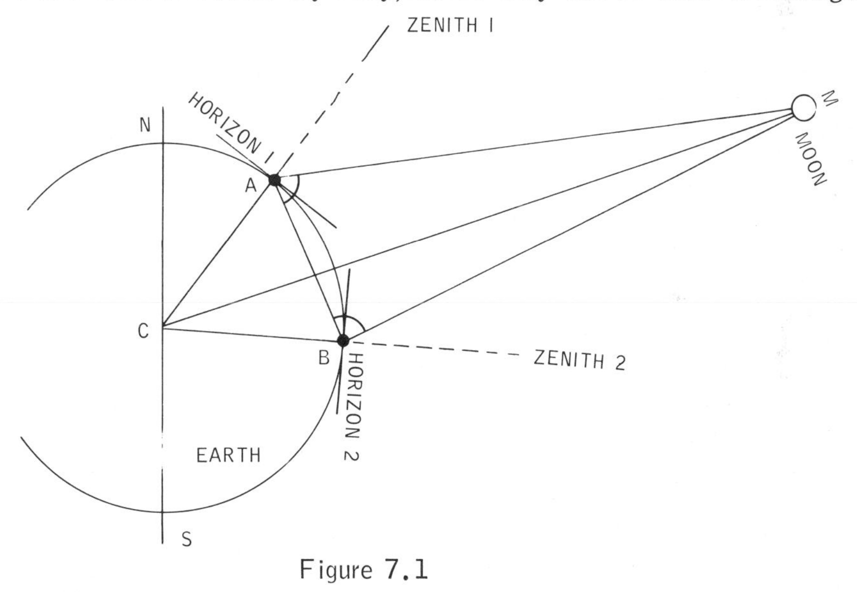

Figure 7.1

hence when the center of the moon is crossing the meridian. In this manner all the angles of △ABM can be known. △ACB is isosceles, since AC = CB = radius of earth, already determined. Side AB can be known if latitudes of localities A and B are known or the distance between them. AB is a chord and knowing the arc AB, hence angle ACB, one knows the length of the chord. One then knows the angles CAB and CBA, and the zenith distance angles ZAM and ZBM, one readily obtains the angles BAM and ABM. Knowing this, one can calculate the length of lines AM, BM, and CM, the latter being the distance between the centers of the two bodies.

Hipparchus measured the distance to the moon in the following manner. A solar eclipse occurred apparently in the year 129 B. C. It appeared as a total eclipse at the Hellespont but only as a partial, with four-fifths of the sun obscured, as seen from Alexandria. "Since the distance between these places, expressed in the earth's radius, could be computed, Hipparchus was able to derive the parallax of the moon, hence the distance from the earth; he found it variable between 62 and 74 radii of the earth." (A. Pannekoek, *A History of Astronomy,* New York, p. 129) In other words, Hipparchus constructed a triangle with the distance from Hellespont to Alexandria as base and an angle of parallax of 6' (1/5 of 30' which is the diameter of the moon) as apex. The altitude of this triangle is the distance from the earth to the moon.

To Hipparchus is attributed another clever method of determining the moon's parallax. Consider the following figure representing the situation at the end of a lunar eclipse. It can be seen from Figure 7.2 that angle a + angle b = angle c + angle d, because 180 - (angle a + angle b) in the triangle in which these two angles are to be seen, is equal to 180 - (angle d + angle c) as seen along the straight line Sun-Earth-Apex. This being so, it follows that,

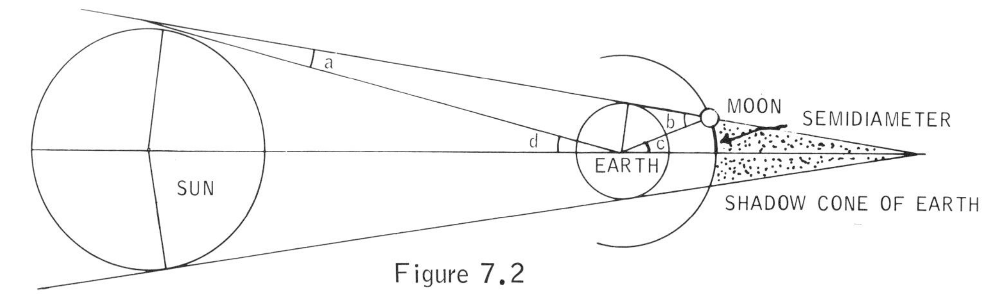

Figure 7.2

calling these angles by their names, parallax of sun (∠a) + parallax of moon (∠b) are equal to the sun's radius (∠d) plus the semidiameter of the shadow as seen from the earth (∠c). Since the parallax of the sun is very small, it can be neglected without much error in the calculation. We are left then with the result that the moon's parallax is equal to the sum of apparent semidiameters of the sun and of the shadow.

Aristarchus of Samos, who lived circa 310-230 B. C., next succeeded in obtaining a rough approximation of the relative distance of earth to sun. The angle at the moon when that body is observed from the two localities A and B, the parallax, is relatively small. When the same measurement was applied to the sun, the ancients realized at once that the sun was much farther away from us than the moon, because its angle of parallax was extremely minute. They also measured the sun's and moon's diameters in degrees and found each to subtend an angle of $\frac{1}{2}°$ or 30 minutes of angle. Clearly the sun was both much bigger, brighter, and much farther away.

Aristarchus bypassed this seemingly insuperable obstacle in an ingenious manner. He observed that when the moon appears to us exactly halved, that is when it is in first or last quarter, it is not exactly on the meridian at sunset but a bit to the west of it. Now, when the moon has the dark line (the terminator) exactly at the center of the surface it presents to us, then the sun must be so situated as to be perpendicularly placed to that line, as is shown in the diagram. At such times, exactly at sunset, he believed that the moon was found by actual measurement to be three degrees to the right of the meridian. It could not be on the meridian because under these conditions, the setting sun, being on the plane of our horizon, would be simultaneously perpendicular to a north-south line on our horizon and to one on the moon's, which would mean that the earth and moon would have to be at the same place, and the distance between them zero or at infinite distance from the sun. Actually, the angle subtended at the sun, △MSE, happens to be ten minutes (10'). Aristarchus' crude measurement yielded 3 degrees instead. But proceeding from this fact, he ingeniously showed by means of simple Euclidean rules that in any right angle triangle the side opposite an angle of 3° must be in about the ratio of 1:19 to the hypotenuse. That is, EM/ES = 1/19, or the distance of earth to sun is about nineteen times greater than the distance of earth to moon. And since the diameters of both sun and moon subtend the same angle at the human eye, 30', and further, since the size, or linear dimension of an object varies inversely with distance

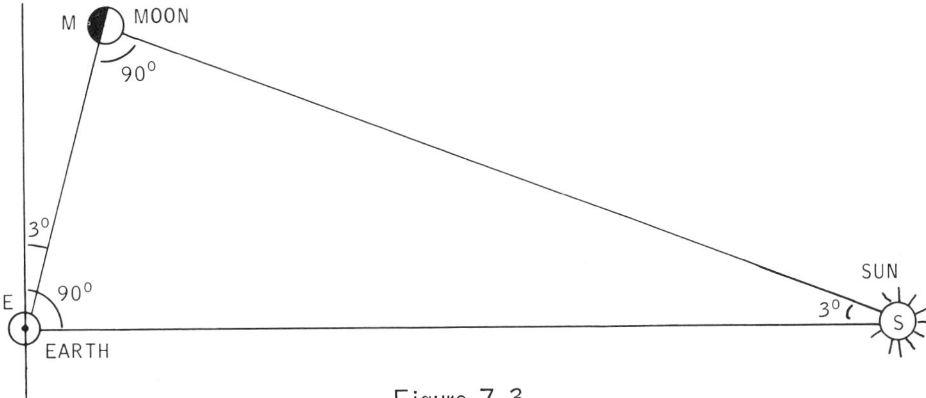

Figure 7.3

from eye, it follows that the diameter of the sun must be nineteen times larger than the diameter of the moon. Since the distance to the moon was known to be about 240,000 miles, the distance to the sun had to be approximately four and a half million miles.

From these data one could go further and deduce the actual orbit of the moon, since the circumference of a circle is $2\pi r$, which yields an orbit of 1,507,000 miles ($\pi = 3.14$). Also, the diameter of the moon, being a measurable one-half a degree, is equal to this figure divided by 360 and then by one-half, which yields about 2,070 miles. And the same calculation can be made for the sun, yielding an orbit of about 28,728,000 miles and a diameter of circa 40,000 miles, about 19 times larger than the moon's diameter.

Aristarchus pushed the process of geometrical reasoning still further with the following brilliant idea. Consider the case of an eclipse of the moon, a lunar eclipse, which occurs less frequently than the solar eclipse, but is seen more often at any place. The brilliant hunch of Aristarchus was to time the passage of the moon as it sails through the shadow cast by the earth. The nature of eclipses had been known for some time. Aristotle (4th century B.C.), a century before Aristarchus, had used the lunar eclipse as demonstrative evidence of the sphericity of the earth. Says he in his book *On the Heavens:* "Further proof is obtained from the evidence of the senses. (i) if the earth were not spherical, eclipses of the moon would not exhibit segments of the shape which they do. As it is, in its monthly phases the moon takes on all varieties of shape--straight-edged gibbous and concave--but in eclipses the boundary is always convex. Thus if eclipses are due to the interposition of the earth, the shape must be caused by its circumference, and the earth must be spherical. (ii) Observation of the stars also shows not only that the earth is spherical but that it is of no great size, since a small change of position on our part northward or southward visibly alters the circle of the horizon.... For this reason those who imagine that the region around the Pillars of Heracles joins on to the regions of India, and that in this way the ocean is one, are not, it would seem, suggesting anything utterly incredible." (Loeb Classical Library, 1953, p. 253)

Eclipses were well known in antiquity and meticulously observed and recorded. The first Greek attempt at predicting an eclipse is attributed to Thales of Miletus, who lived probably from 624 to 547 B.C. and was declared one of the Seven Wise Men in 581 B.C. The eclipse he predicted occurred in 585 B.C. Plato tells an interesting episode about him; while absorbed in observing the sky, he fell into a well. "A clever and pretty maid-servant from Thrace" who happened nearby, upbraided him for being so "eager to know what goes on in the heavens when he could not see what was in front of him, nay, at his very feet." This story may well be true, since we have little reason to doubt it, any more than the one told by a contemporary, Xenophanes, and a little later by Herodotus. The latter relates: "Among their battles (the Medes and Lydians) there was one night engagement. As, however, the balance had not inclined in favor of either mation, another combat took place in the sixth year, in the course of which, just as the battle was growing warm, day was on a sudden changed into night. This event [eclipse] had been foretold by Thales, the Milesian, who forwarned the Janians of it, fixing for it the very year in which it actually took place. The Medes and Lydians, when they observed the change, ceased fighting, and were alike anxious to have terms of peace agreed on." (Herodotus 1, p. 27) The prediction was thus for the year in which it occurred rather than the day, which seems to have been the usual meaning of prediction in those days, even among the Chaldean experts in astronomy. "It is probable that the Chaldeans arrived at this method of approximately predicting the times at which lunar eclipses would occur by means of the period of 223 lunations, which was doubtless discovered as the result of long-continued observations. This period is mentioned by Ptolemy as having been discovered by astronomers 'still more ancient' than those whom he calls 'the ancients,'" explains Sir Thomas Heath, the great student of ancient astronomy, in his book, *Aristarchus of Samos* (Oxford, p. 16).

By the time of Aristarchus of Samos (ca 310-230 B.C.) who was known as "the mathematician" and had succeeded Theophrastus as the head of Aristotle's Lyceum, eclipses could be more accurately predicted than in the days of Thales. Consider first the movements of the moon in the sky as the ancients observed them, hence purely factually. Anyone can see that the moon rises about 51 minutes later every day. In other words, if we see a full moon rise at 6 p.m. tonight, at the moment the sun sets, then tomorrow night it will rise at 6:51 p.m., and so forth. This means that relative to the stars, the moon shifts backwards, or eastward against the sky. This is to be related to our describing the diurnal revolution of the sky as forward. The moon's motion eastward is about 13 degrees each day, completing the circle as it does in $29\frac{1}{2}$ days. The moon's position against the stars can be readily noted on successive nights and its apparent path determined. It will then be seen that for half a month the moon moves along its orbit above the ecliptic, about 5 degrees, and the other half, below it. This is what is meant by the inclination of the moon's orbit by 5 degrees and nine minutes to the ecliptic. The points where this circle of the moon's path cuts the ecliptic are the nodes, or the points of intersection; the descending node when the moon moves south of the ecliptic, and two weeks later the ascending node, when it crosses it on its way up.

Any consistent recorder of these events will detect that the moon's orbit keeps the same angle of inclination to the ecliptic, but shifts its nodes to the right, or westward, as seen in our southern sky. The nodes return to any initial position, in about 18.6 years. Thus, if one node is in the constellation Taurus now, then in about nine years from now, the node will be seven constellations to the right, or in Libra. This is called regression, or precession, because the node shifts so as to oblige the moon to be in line with the sun in fewer days than expected for the normal length of the solar year. The moon is in line with the sun and the earth, or in conjunction when the moon's orbit is at a node, because a node occurs only when the moon is on the ecliptic, meaning in that part of the sky where the sun is. Eclipses can therefore occur only then, with the sun, moon and earth in a straight line. For this very reason that path is called ecliptic.

We can also picture these same events in terms of the moon's orbit around the revolving earth, hence not in terms of the actual observations, but in terms of our own explanatory conception. We say that eclipses, either solar or lunar, occur as rarely as they do, roughly every six months, because the orbit of the moon lies at an angle of inclination of 5°9' to the earth's orbital plane. As the earth revolves around the sun in its plane, the moon revolves around the earth in its own plane, which retains its position in space exactly as the earth's axis retains its position and points in the same direction all through its annual revolution. Similarly, as we have already learned, the axes of the moon's eliptical orbit always point in the same directions, and the angle of inclination remains unchanged as well. (Figure 4.3) In Figure 7.4, assume the plane of the earth's revolution to be the plane of the table, with sun at the center. Assume further that the moon's orbit is inclined to this plane at an angle of 5°9', as shown. Only when the earth is in positions A and B can there be solar eclipses (moon at M_2 and M_3, resprectively) and lunar eclipses (moon at M_1 and M_4, respectively).

It is easy to see why this is so; you place a card (3" x 5") between yourself and a small object, say a glass or salt shaker on the table in front of you. Hold the card vertically on its small side with its plane perpendicular to your chest. Next, incline it at an angle to the table. Draw a small earth at the center of the card with the moon revolving around it in an elliptical orbit. The card then represents the earth with the moon revolving around it. One revolution of the card around the glass completes one year since the card carries the earth. Hold the card at a constant angle (to the table), preferably larger than the necessary 5°9', and without changing the angle of the card, place it in the four positions indicated in the diagram. Since your card represents the moon's plane of rotation around the earth, you can readily see that only at A and B will the moon, earth, and sun be in line. You will also note that in any

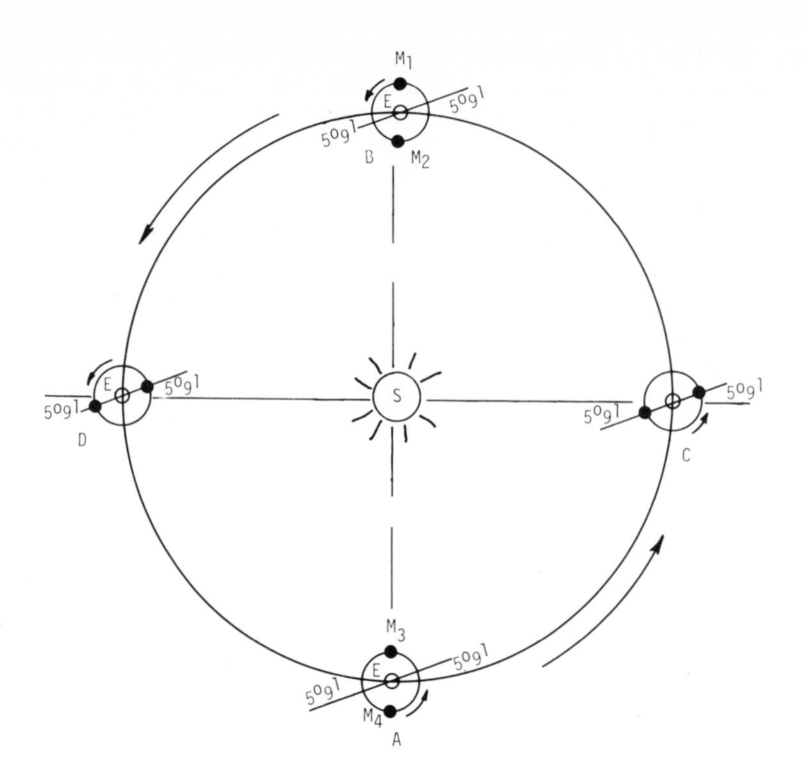

Figure 7.4

other position besides A and B the moon will not be in a straight line with the earth and sun. Allow the moon to complete a month while you hold the card at position C. Follow the moon along its mild elliptical orbit. Observe that the moon will never be in a position for an eclipse except at A and B; only at these points will the three celestial spheres be lined up for both solar and lunar eclipses. Clearly, these can occur only about six months apart.

The line joining M_1 with M_2, and M_3 with M_4, is called the line of nodes. Draw this line on your card. Note that this line does not change its direction during the year, which means that it remains parallel to itself. However, during the year, hence in one revolution around the sun, the nodal arrangement, M_1EM_2, shifts a little in a clockwise direction. Position B, with its possibilities for eclipses, will at the end of one revolution actually be located to the right of its previous position, and arrangement A will shift to the left. What this means is that the line of nodes will be in line with the sun before a full year has been completed since the angle of the orbit remains the same. We thus have an *eclipse year* which is half a month shorter than a solar year and consists of 346.62 days. This is the shift in the line of the nodes. This shift is essentially due to the sun's attraction which acts so as to rotate the plane of the moon's orbit once in 18.6 years. The angle of inclination of that plane to the earth's orbit remains the same but the lunar nodes, or points of intersection of the two orbital planes, slide along the lunar orbit.

Since the eclipse year shifts against the solar year by about half a month, expected eclipses occur each year that much earlier. In time, positions A and B will return to their initial places. These annual shifts add up to a full round for positions A and B in a little over eighteen years, or 223 lunations, specifically 18.6 years. This cyclical occurrence of eclipses was observed by the ancients and was called a saros. It is easy to see that when eclipses are feared or honored, they will be carefully recorded. A clever man can then notice the periodicity in their occurrence. Rough predictions of their approximate appearance could be made even without careful measurements of the nodal movements, hence with such observations as had been made since old Babylonian times.

Aristarchus of Samos made use of observations of eclipses to determine the distance of the earth to the sun in the following manner.

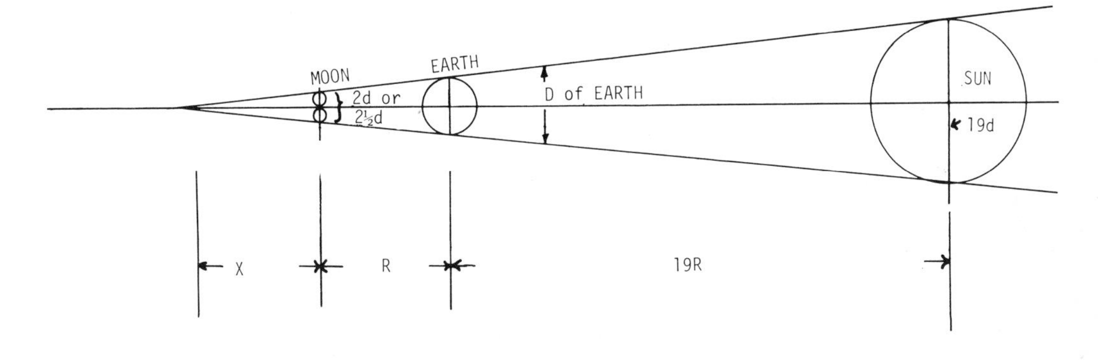

Figure 7.5

It is not too difficult to measure the time interval from the beginning of a lunar eclipse to its termination. The moon travels faster in her orbit than a point on the surface of the earth rotates around the earth's axis. The moon travels at the rate of one km/sec and the earth rotates in the same direction at about $\frac{1}{2}$ km/sec; the moon will enter the earth's shadow at her eastern rim and leave it at her western. The time the moon stays within the full shadow (see Figure 7.5) can thus be measured. Aristarchus found that interval to be equal to the time it takes the moon to travel eastward a distance equivalent to two of its diameters. The estimates of the exact angle subtended by the moon's diameter differed according to the observer. Proclus, Hipparchus, Ptolemy, Sosigenes and others had figures that varied from 20'26" to 35'20". Let us regard it as 30', or $\frac{1}{2}°$. If the distance to the moon is around 240,000 miles, which as we saw the ancients knew, then the moon's orbit, the circumference of a circle with a radius of 240,000 miles, = 240,000 x 2 x 3.14 = 1,5000,000 miles. This route is covered in 27.3 days or 656 hours, hence the moon travels about 2,093 miles per hour, or 50,000 miles per day. The earth's radius is 4,000 miles, which times 2 x 3.14 yields about 25,000 miles for its circumference at the equator. Since the earth rotates once in 24 hours, the linear velocity of a spot on the the equator is about 1,046 miles, or exactly half the moon's velocity. This means that with regard to a given point on a line joining the sun, earth, and moon, the moon will run ahead of a spot on the earth.

The moon moves eastward in the sky, retrogrades 13.2° per day, which is its orbital velocity. This figure is obtained by dividing the moon's revolution about the earth, hence 360° over 27.3 days, the duration of a sidereal lunar revolution. The moon thus travels the distance of two lunar diameters, or 1° of its orbit (4180 miles), in 1.8 hours. As Aristarchus saw it, it took the moon less than two hours from the moment she entered the earth's full shadow to the moment she cleared it. Ptolemy changed the time of passage to 2 1/2 lunar diameters, which made the crossing distance of the shadow's cone equal to 5,225 miles, which means that it lasted in reality 2 1/4 hours. Hipparchus clocked one of his eclipses at 5 1/8 hours.

Incidentally, Aristarchus also used the transit of the moon across the earth's shadow as a means of checking on the moon's orbital velocity. He measured the time that elapsed betwen the instant when the moon first entered the cone of the shadow, until it was totally obscured. This would be the time the moon traveled 30', or 1/2°, or 1/720 of its total orbit of 27.3 days, its sidereal period. He next found that the moon remained fully hidden for an equal interval of time, and then began emerging. As already stated, other observers got different results. The method was, however, brilliant.

Now, let us see what he did with his findings. The breadth of the earth shadow where the moon crossed it is 2d, if d is the moon's diameter, known from measurements previously described. The value for D, the earth's diameter, is known from the measurement of Eratosthenes. The distance X is unknown but the distances from the earth to the sun are known, as are the respective diameters of moon, earth and sun, as previously described.

In the diagram, we have three similar triangles with altitudes X, X + R, and X + 20R, which yield the following relationships.

$$\frac{X}{2d} = \frac{X + 20R}{19d}; \text{ Solving for X we obtain:}$$

$$19X = 2X + 40R, \text{ since d cancels out.}$$

$$\therefore X = \frac{40R}{17};$$

We also have the following relationship:

$$\frac{X}{2d} = \frac{X + R}{D}; \qquad DX = 2d(X + R)$$

Substituting the value for X obtained above in terms of R, we have:

$$\frac{D \times 40R}{17} = 2d \times \frac{40R}{17} + 2dR$$

$$\text{or,} \quad \frac{40DR}{17} - \frac{80dR}{17} = 2\ dR;$$

Multiplying both sides by 17 and dividing by 2R, we obtain:

$$20D - 40d = 17d,$$

$$\therefore 20D = 57d; \quad d = \frac{20D}{57} = 0.35D.$$

Other scholars found the value for d to range from 0.16 to 0.36, times the diameter of the earth, D.

The moon's diameter being 0.35 the diameter of earth, the earth's diameter is about three times that of the moon. (The modern value is four times.) Next, the sun's diameter is 6 2/3 times the diameter of earth. The modern value being about 109, clearly, any measurements regarding the sun were far off because of basic difficulties in any measurement involving large distances. Further, the orbit of the moon around the earth was 720 x d, and the orbit of sun was 720 x 19d.

Subsequent mathematicians employed the above scheme of Aristarchus in different ways. This was done by Hipparchus of Nicea in Asia Minor, who is regarded as the greatest astronomer of antiquity and was the authority most admired by Ptolemy. Hipparchus (2nd century B.C.) made great contributions in the geometry of spherical triangles and in what we now regard as trigonometric functions, and made also remarkable contributions in mathematical geography, particularly in astronomy.

In books now lost, he apparently laid the foundations for Ptolemy's great work, *The Almagest*. He is also the author of the first catalogue of stars. Pliny writes of him as follows: "Now Hipparchus, who cannot be praised too highly and who, more than anyone else, exemplified man's kinship with the stars and proved that our souls are part of the heavens, detected a new star that had appeared in his own time. Because of its motion on the day on which it shone, he was led to wonder whether this happened at all frequently and whether those stars moved which we consider fixed. He went so far as to attempt--what would seem rash even for a god--to number the stars for his successors, and assign names for the various groups. For this he contrived instruments by which he might mark the location and magnitude of each star. Thus it could readily be discovered not merely whether stars perished and were born, but whether any of them moved and whether they grew or diminished. He left the heavens as a bequest, as it were, to all who were found capable of receiving the inheritance." (Pliny, *Natural History* 11, p. 95). How pointless it is to talk of the "authority of Aristotle" when even in antiquity, popularizers like Pliny whom one would least expect to be independent, diverges considerably from the Aristotelian scheme of the immutability of the heavens whenever he deems it necessary. Hipparchus pursued his own path of research or theorizing, and so did everybody else, for that matter. Strabo, for example, the famous author of the *Geography,* who lived in the first century B.C., criticized the astronomer, Geminus, for "being too interested in causes in the manner of Aristotle." Galen, the great physician (second century A.D.) criticizes Aristotle repeatedly, as did indeed most ancient and medieval scholars.

Lunar eclipses were exploited by Hipparchus in the following manner.

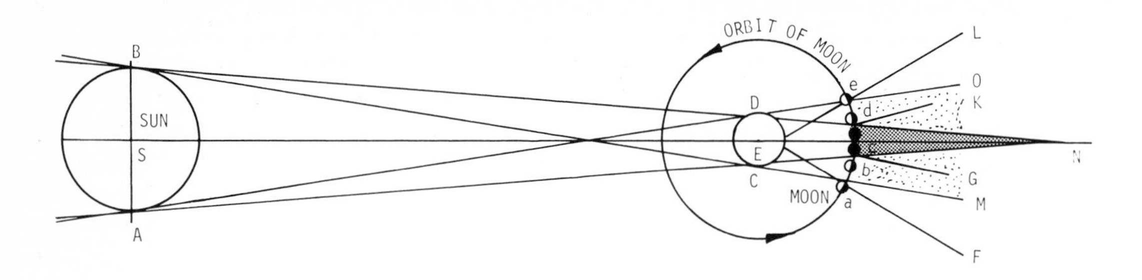

Figure 7.6

Cone CND = umbra, or total shadow. In this region an observer on earth sees full eclipse of moon and an observer on moon sees total eclipse of sun by earth. Cones MCN and NDO are penumbras, or regions of partial visibility of moon. According to Hipparchus, ten hours elapse while moon journeys from a to e. The moon's rate is 13.2° per day; hence entire eclipse occurs while moon traverses this arc of 5.5°; (= FEL). Angle of complete obscuration, GEK, or bEd, lasted about 5 1/8 hours, equivalent to an arc of 2.6°, rather long by comparison with other eclipses of moon, which vary normally in duration. Diameter of moon as seen from earth is 30'. Also, moon travels eastward in her monthly orbit 30' per hour, or the length of one lunar diameter. Angles BCA and CDA are each also 30' since sun subtends the same angle as moon. All angles made by moon at E are known. Distances to moon and sun can therefore be determined by geometry.

Hipparchus' method resembles that employed by Ptolemy, although both made use of different values for the initial distances. Pappus gives the following account: "In his first book about sizes and distances, Hipparchus starts from this observation: There was an eclipse of the sun which was exactly total in the region about the Hellespont, no portion of the sun being seen, whereas at Alexandria in Egypt about four-fifths only of its diameter was obscured. From the facts thus observed, he proves in his first book that, if the radius of the earth be the unit, the least distance of the moon contains 71, and the greatest 83 of these units; the mean therefore contains 77. After proving these propositions, he says at the end of the first book: 'In this treatise I have carried the argument to this point. Do not, however, suppose that the theory of the distance of the moon has ever yet been worked out accurately in every respect; for even in this question there is an investigation remaining to be carried out, in the course of which the distance of the moon will be proved to be less than the figure just calculated,' so that he himself admits that he is not quite in a position to state the truth about the parallaxes. Then, again, he himself, in the second book about sizes and distances, proves from many considerations that, if we take the radius of the earth as the unit, the least distance of the moon contains 62 of these units, and its mean distance 67 1/3, while the distance of the sun contains 2,490." (T. L. Heath, *Aristarchus of Samos*, p. 342)

Concerning the measurements of the diameters of the sun and moon, Ptolemy, who left us descriptions of most if not all the more sophisticated astronomical instruments used in antiquity, has the following to say in a section of his great work, the *Almagest,* (Book V, Chapter 14) entitled, *"On the Magnitude of the Apparent Diameters of the Sun, Moon and Shadow During the Syzygies."* The term syzygy means the period during which the sun, moon and earth are in line, hence conjuction and opposition, or period of new moon and full moon. Says Ptolemy: "Of the methods for such an inquiry, we rejected all those which measure these luminaries by means of waterclocks or the times of equatorial ascensions, (i. e., rising and settings while sun and moon are on equator) because of the impossibility of getting what is proposed by such means. But constructing ourself the four-cubit (six feet) rod dioptra described by Hipparchus and making observations with it, we find the sun's diameter everywhere contained by very nearly the same angle with no variation worthy of mention resulting from its distances. But we find the moon's diameter contained by the same angle as the sun's then only when during the full moon it is at its greatest distance from the earth." The sun being very far, his diameter showed little variation, while the moon being closer to the earth, differed slightly in her elliptical orbit.

The instrument used above is called a dioptra. Pappus described it as follows: On the base AB have a groove PO, in which "a little block is easily moved as we wish along the whole length of the rod without falling from it. At one end of the rod, where the eye will be applied, have a fixed plate FG with a very small hole in it, K. At the other end, have a ring or plate CD with a diameter SR across it, placed on the movable block. Place your eye at K and move CD until SR just covers diameter of moon, or of sun viewed through dark filter."

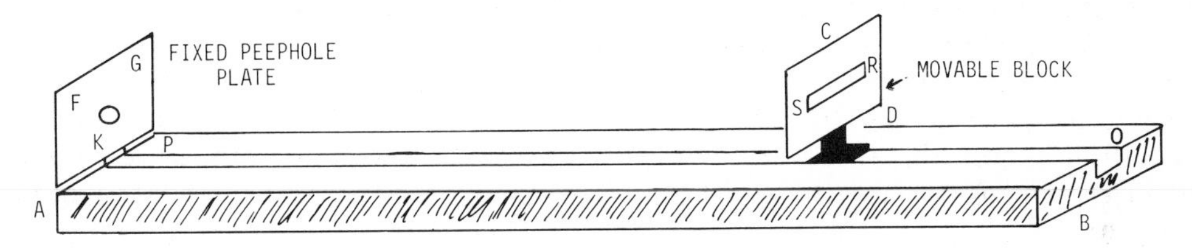

Figure 7.7

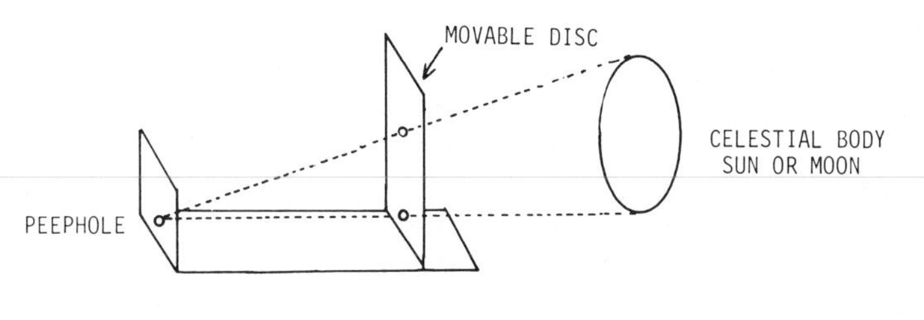

Figure 7.8

Figure 7.8 shows a variation of dioptra in Figure 7.7.

2. The Phenomena of Optics

Although the ancients built their knowledge of optics upon what we know with certainty today to have been a basically false conception of vision, they gathered considerable data and described many aspects of that science with enduring skill. Had they not organized their observations in accordance with geometrical logic, they would have made no contribution. With the aid of geometry, however, they left to posterity a worthy modicum of optical knowledge encompassing reflection, refraction, some notions of focal lengths, the relation between angle of vision, distance, and size, some properties of mirrors and of light beams, and related matters.

As usual, the practical phase of the science went forward on its own power, as in the other fields already discussed. Mirrors were invented independently of the geometrical study of optics, and their capacities in distorting, minimizing, magnifying, and igniting objects were similarly noticed. The subsequent major discoveries of corrective eye-glasses, of the telescope and the microscope, were again largely independent of any scientific or mathematical progress made in the field of geometrical optics.

The ancient Greek theory of vision resolved the puzzling problem of the relation between the observer's eye and the illuminated object by assuming that vision emanated from the eye. Characteristic of the hopeless confusion on the subject of light is the writing of Theophrastus in his *On the Senses.* He rejects the idea that light is indispensable; he rejects the idea that "vision is a function of the body as a whole"; he dismisses the notion of Democritus and Lucretius that objects peel off images and send them flying through the air thereby accounting for vision, an action that suits transmission by water better than air; contrary to Aristotle he believes images to be a fire within the eye, witness our inability to look into the sun because a more powerful light extinguishes the weaker one; besides one sees the fire in the eyes of nocturnal animals; both colors, white and black, lack light; sight arises when objects are reflected in the pupil, but the act requires external and internal air. There seems no end to the subject's bedevilment. (On the Senses, in G. M. Stratton. *Theophrastus and the Greek Physiological Psychology before Aristotle.* London, 1917) There were other theories, but none of them stood up well. Democritus, for example, assumed that objects produced an imprint on the air, or an actual image, which then traveled to the eye, where it reflected in its moisture. The intervening air and the distance which the image had to traverse, functioned so as to distort that image. In the absence of intervening air, that is, in a vacuum, the image would reach the eye in its full clarity. Says Lucretius, his spokesman: "I maintain therefore that replicas or insubstantial shapes of things are thrown off from the surface of objects. These we must denote as an outer skin or film, because each particular floating image wears the aspect and form of the object from whose body it has emanated.... Cicadas, for instance, in summer periodically shed their tubular jackets; calves at birth cast off cauls from the surface of their bodies; the slippery snake sloughs off on thorns the garment we often see fluttering on a briar. Since these things happen, objects must also give off a much flimsier film from the surface of their bodies." (*The Nature of the Universe.* 1951. Penguin Books, p. 131)

Aristotle argued against this view. A medium is necessary for vision, he reasoned, and that medium may be air, or then again it may be light. But "light itself is not a 'body,' or a corpuscular emanation." The general hypothesis that vision somehow consisted of a cone of rays that emerged from the eye and conveyed to the brain knowledge of shapes and colors of all objects they encountered in the presence of light, was accepted as unquestioned by almost everybody. This hypothesis is, of course, the contrary of our present view of the nature of light and vision. We regard light as a form of energy generated by an oscillating electron, or electrical charge, hence a form of energy invariably associated with an electromagnetic field and traveling in space through a vacuum or through various media, at different velocities. Its velocity in a vacuum is constant and maximal. Light enters the eye where its beams are focused by the cornea and lens upon the retina, which contains a photosensitive pigment. When light falls upon this pigment, it causes it to undergo chemical changes which are of such a nature as to stimulate the optic nerve. By stimulation is meant that a chemico-physical change is produced in the nerve, of the kind that travels along its trunk, ultimately arriving at a brain center where its sudden presence results in the unique sensation which we call vision.

The ancients knew nothing of this entire range of knowledge, but went boldly and logically about their efforts at gaining a mental foothold upon the problem. With light they could get nowhere at all. Light is visible, says Theophrastus in his *On the Senses,* but he agrees with Aristotle that somehow it is not an indispensable condition for sight, nor is it universal since we do see in real darkness. While light was utterly baffling, the problem of vision proved more amenable, and all they could come up with was the theory that the power of vision lay in the eye; that a ray could emerge from it at all times, and that in the presence of light that ray could see. In the dark the eye still functioned as usual, just as a stomach functions as usual but leads to no effective digestion in the absence of food. A sick eye sees poorly because being sick, its beams are inadequate, or disturbed. Smoke, fog, and opaqueness, generally hinder the path of the beam. One ancient author, Damianus of Larissa, actually had among his "hypotheses" one that stated: "What emanates from us is light," and gave as evidence the fact that in some animals one can discern the luminous nature of their eyes and also the fact that eyes can see in the dark. Euclid, Ptolemy, and others never stated the matter thus, but merely assumed that light was needed.

Actually, we shall see that the science of optics which the ancients founded was in no way affected by the acceptance of one theory of light or another. This is the beauty of scientific observation and mathematical abstraction. If the facts are carefully observed and the mathematical reasoning sound, which it usually is since the rules are clearly laid down and readily checked, the results are necessarily sound in the light of the fundamental assumptions. These can often be changed without affecting entire segments of the superstructure, although the change may radically revise the models of the mechanisms involved, and initiate new outlooks, approaches and stresses.

The study of optics as a science is generally held to begin with Euclid (ca 300 B.C.), whose *Optics,* deals with the principle of geometric laws of reflection and refraction. His book *Catoptrics,* probably only attributed to him, deals with the application of optical principles to mirrors--plane, convex, and concave. These two works are like Euclid's *Elements,* the first organized summaries of all the geometrical knowledge concerning visual rays. In his *Optics,* Euclid lays down twelve definitions, or assumptions, from which he develops some sixty geometrical demonstrations or theorems. Among his suppositions, or definitions, are the following:

"1. That visual rays issue from the eye and proceed in straight lines and diverge indefinitely; 2. That the figure contained by a set of visual rays is a cone of which the vertex is at the eye and whose base is at the surface of the subjects seen; 3. That only those objects are seen upon which visual rays fall; 4. Those things are not seen upon which visual rays do not fall; 5. That things seen under a larger angle appear larger; 6. Those under a smaller angle appear smaller; 7. And those under equal angles appear equal; 8. That things seen by high visual rays appear higher; 9. And things seen by lower visual rays appear lower; 10. That, similarly, things seen by rays further to the right; 11. And things seen by rays further to the left appear further to the left; 12. That things seen under more angles are seen more clearly." The angle in the last definition refers to the angle of the visual cone as in Definition 2.

The propositions which follow these assumptions are stated geometrically in the exact manner in which such concepts are developed in his *Elements.* For example, Proposition I states: No visible object is seen completely at one time. In the diagram, B is the eye and AC the visible object, and "BA, BD, BE, BF, and BC are the visual rays from B to the object. Then, since the incident rays move at an interval from one to another, they cannot fall continuously over AD." This conclusion is based on Definition 1, which declares that visual rays emanate from the eye and "diverge indefinitely." This means that the further the object is from the eye, the further apart the rays have to be, since they go off into space maintaining an ever-increasing distance between them. Thus, since only that object is seen which has visual rays fall upon it, objects near the eye have many rays per given area, while equal objects further away have fewer. Hence far objects are seen less clearly. Moreover, when an object is so far away as to be situated in the diverging space between rays, or if it is small enough not to intercept any, it will not be seen. All these points are established by propositions of which we may consider a sample.

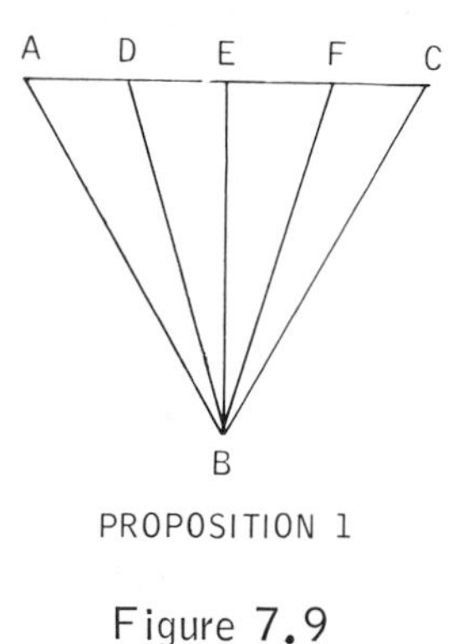

Figure 7.9

Proposition II states: "Of equal magnitudes situated at a distance, those that are nearer are seen more clearly." Again: "Let B be the eye and GD and KL the visible objects, which we are to consider equal and parallel, GD being nearer the eye." The lines from B to points G, D, K and L are visual rays. "The visual rays to KL will not pass through points G and D. For if they did, in the resulting triangle DLKGB, KL would be larger than GD. But they were assumed to be equal." GD must have more rays going through it than KL and will therefore be seen more clearly, from which follows that all objects nearer the eye are seen more clearly.

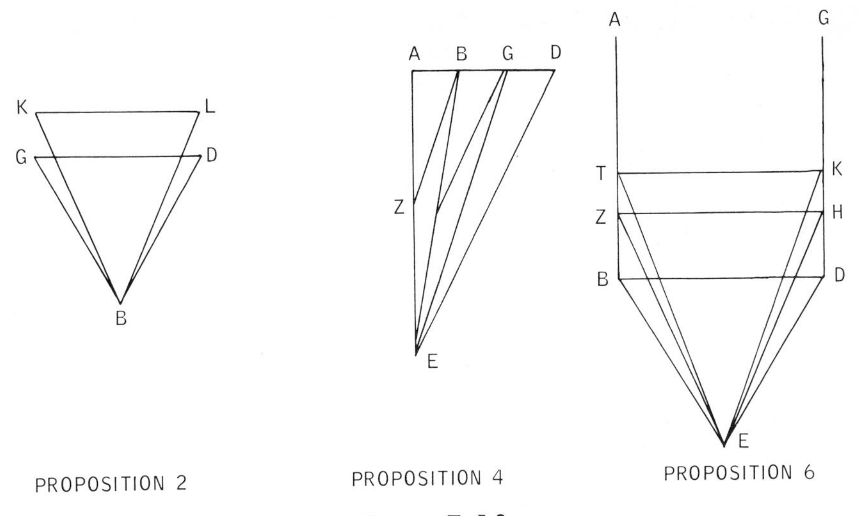

Figure 7.10

Let us take another example of the power of the geometrical method. Proposition IV states: "Of equal intervals on the same straight line, those seen from a greater distance appear smaller." "Let AB, BG, and GD be equal intervals on the same straight line. Draw AE perpendicular to this line; let the eye be at E. I say that AB will appear larger than BG, and BG larger than GD.

"Let EB, EG, and ED be incident visual rays. Draw BZ through B, parallel to GE. AZ = ZE, for since BZ was drawn parallel to one side, GE, of triangle AEG, it follows that EZ:ZA = GB:BA.

"Hence, as we have said, AZ = ZE.

"But BZ > ZA (since BZ is the hypotenuse), therefore BZ > ZE, which means that $\angle$ZEB > $\angle$ZBE, because the former angle lies opposite a bigger side of triangle EZB than does $\angle$ZBE. Further, $\angle$ZBE = $\angle$BEG (since ZB and EG are parallel and these two angles are alternate interior angles). Therefore $\angle$ZEB > $\angle$BEG. Consequently, AB will appear larger than BG. Similarly, if a parallel to DE be drawn through G, it may be shown that GB will appear larger than GD."

The text also deals with rules of perspective. Proposition VI states: "Parallel lines when seen from a distance appears to be an unequal distance apart," and proof of it is given along similar lines. AB and GD are two parallel lines and E is the eye. All lines emanating from E are visual rays. On the basis of proof already given, it follows that the further the distance between AB and GD (e.g. BD, ZH, TK, etc.), the smaller are the angles at E (BED, ZEH, TEK), which they subtend, hence the smaller respectively appear to be the intervals between the two parallels.

Lastly, we may take Proposition XLV, which also deals with perspective. "There is a common point from which unequal magnitudes appear equal."

"Let line BG be greater than GD. About BG describe a segment of a circle greater than a semicircle, and about GD describe a segment of a circle similar to that about BG, i.e., a segment containing an angle equal to that contained in segment BZG. The segments, then, will intersect, let us say, at Z. Draw ZB, ZG, and ZD.

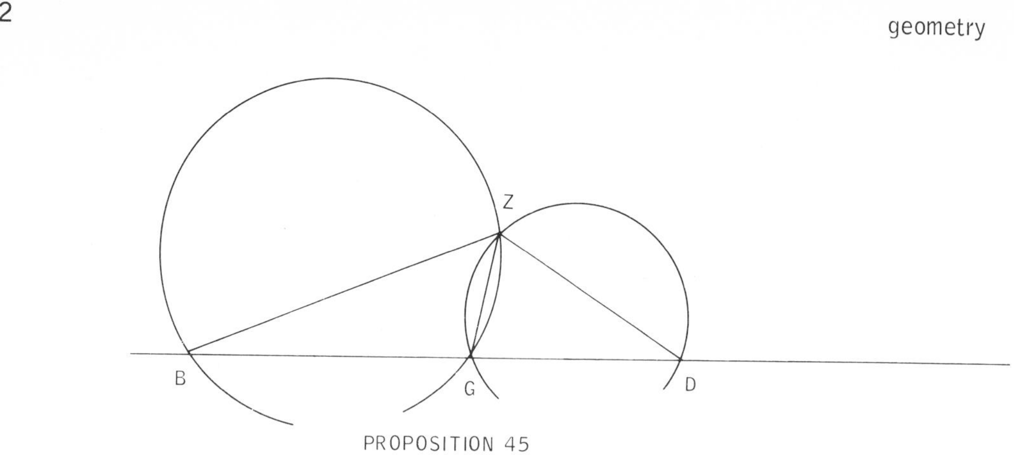

PROPOSITION 45

Figure 7.11

"Since angles inscribed in similar segments are equal, the angles in segments BZG and GZD are equal. But things seen under equal angles appear equal. Therefore, if the eye is placed at point Z, BG will appear equal to GD. But BG > GD. There is, then, a common point from which unequal magnitudes appear equal."

The problem of reflection and refraction is considered by Euclid, Hero of Alexandria, Archimedes, and Ptolemy, in books usually entitled *Catoptrics*, or mirrors. The Catoptrics of Euclid is according to best judgment a compilation prepared many centuries later and falsely attributed to him. It reports, nevertheless, an interesting experiment. "If an object is thrown into a vessel and the latter is removed to such a distance that the object can no longer be seen, it will become visible at the same distance if water is poured into the vessel." (E. Mach. *The Principles of Physical Optics.* Dover, p. 29) The work of Archimedes is lost, but the *Catoptrics* of Hero and the *Optics* of Ptolemy are available and show how complex the science of mirrors had become by the time of Christ. Says Hero: "Catoptrics, too, is clearly a science worthy of study and at the same time produces spectacles which execute wonder in the observer. For with the aid of this science, mirrors are constructed which show the right side as the right side, and, similarly, the left side as the left side, whereas ordinary mirrors by their nature have the contrary property and show the opposite sides. It is also possible with the aid of mirrors to see our own backs, and to see ourselves inverted, standing on our heads, with three eyes, and two noses, and features distorted, as if in intense grief. The study of catoptrics, however, is useful not merely in affording diverting spectacles, but also for necessary purposes. For who will not deem it very useful that we should be able to observe, on occasion, while remaining inside our own house, how many people there are on the street and what they are doing? And will anyone not consider it remarkable to be able to tell the hour, night or day, with the aid of figures appearing in a mirror?... Again, who will not be astonished when he sees, in a mirror, neither himself nor another, but whatever we desire that he see? Such, then, being the scope of the science, I think it necessary and proper to describe the views held by my predecessors, that my account may not be incomplete." (Cohen and Drabkin. *Source Book in Greek Science,* p. 262)

Hero reiterates that the "rays proceeding from our eyes are reflected by mirrors and the reflections are at equal angles." These rays travel extremely rapidly, "with infinite velocity, "for which reason their paths are straight lines. A visual ray "strives to move over the shortest possible distance, since it has not the time for slower motion, that is, for motion over a longer trajectory." The angle of incidence is equal to the angle of reflection "in the case of plane and spherical mirrors."

"Consider AB a plane mirror, G the eye, and D the object of vision. Let a ray GA be incident upon this mirror. Draw AD, and let △EAG = △BAD. Let another ray BG also be incident upon the mirror. Draw BD. I say that GA + AD < GB + BD.

"Draw GE from G perpendicular to AB, and prolong GE and AD until they meet, say at Z. Draw ZB.

"Now △BAD = △EAG and △ZAE = BAD, since they are vertical angles formed by the crossing of two straight lines. Therefore, △ZAE = △EAG. And since the angles at E are right angles, ZA = AG because the two triangles are congruent, and ZB = BG for the same reason. But ZD < ZB + BD, since it is one side of the triangle ZBD and ZA = AG; ZB = BG. Therefore, GA + AD < GB + BD. Now △EAG = △BAD and △EBG < △EAG, and △HBD > △BAD [△HBD is an external angle of △ BAD]. Therefore, △HBD is a fortiori, greater than △EBG, which is even smaller than △BAD." (Cohen and Drabkin, p. 264)

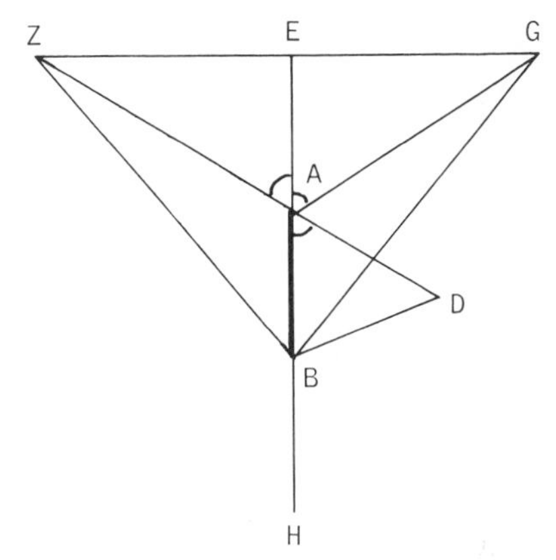

Figure 7.12

We see from this proof that when the angle of incidence (△EAG) is equal to the angle of reflection (△BAD), the path of the ray is shortest [GA + AD < BG + BD]; also, that there is only one incident ray which can be reflected if the two angles are to be equal. The same relationship is next shown to be true for spherical mirrors, both convex and concave.

Hero does much with mirrors. He proves, for example, how, when "one mirror is kept unmoved, while another is moved up and down, the ray will reach a point where the image of the foot of the observer will appear in the mirror and he will think that he is flying." (Figure 7.13)

As in the case of the playful and ingenious automata, Hero offers several combinations of mirrors that lead to intriguing and fanciful deceptions. Thus in Figure 7.14 he shows how an observer can look into a mirror and see not himself but a statue.

Ptolemy's *Optics* is a large work which summarizes virtually all the knowledge of antiquity bearing on the subjects of both optics and catoptrics. Several simple but ingenious instruments are described with which a considerable number of experiments were performed and many sound and lasting properties of mirrors and images were arrived at. In summarizing his section on reflection, Ptolemy concludes: "The truth of the principles which we have assumed is, then, evident from our illustrations, and it may readily

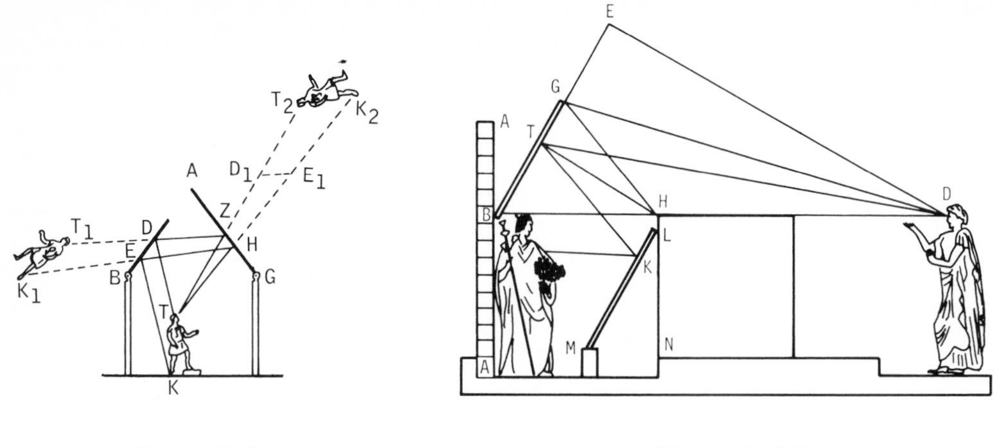

Figure 7.13

Figure 7.14

be seen that in these cases our reasoning accords with the evidence of our senses. Now it is the nature of a visual ray to proceed in a straight line from its source to all objects which are seen directly. A reflected ray, however, which proceeds from a mirror is not, in general, collinear with the visual ray. Our senses, therefore, must have recourse to an action which is natural and customary, and so we join the reflected ray to the first part of the visual ray, the part before reflection." [What Ptolemy means to say is that given an object at B, the observer's eye at A, and a plane mirror at MR, then the incident ray is AO and the reflected ray is OB. The observer at A, who expects light to travel in straight lines, joins the reflected ray OB to the first part of the visual ray AO and obtains AB^1, where B^1 lies beyond the mirror, on a perpendicular from object to mirror, forming line B^1B.] Ptolemy continues: "Thus we have the impression that both parts constitute one straight ray, as if that were actually the case and nothing had happened to the ray. Hence the image of the object will be seen as if it were an object in the direct line of sight." (*Ibid.*, p. 271) Moreover, it is always seen the same distance back of the mirror that B is in front of it, since B-mirror = mirror B^1.

Ptolemy's greatest achievement was his study of refraction, or the bending of visual rays as they pass from one medium into another. He demonstrates that "a visual ray may be naturally bent only at a surface which forms a boundary between two media at different densities; that the bending takes place not only in the passage from rarer and finer media to dense but also in the passage from a denser medium to a rarer; that this type of bending does not take place at equal angles but that the angles, as measured from the perpendicular, have a definite quantitative relationship."

Ptolemy explains the demonstration with the coin in the cup, previously cited from the pseudo-Euclid, in terms of the bending of the visual ray in the presence of water. He next describes an instrument known as a *planca,* which consists of "a round copper disk of moderate size," and having "edges of the circumference well rounded and smoothed." It has engraved two diameters at right angles and each of the four quadrants is graduated into 90 degrees. The disk has one movable arm the length of a diameter and another one the length

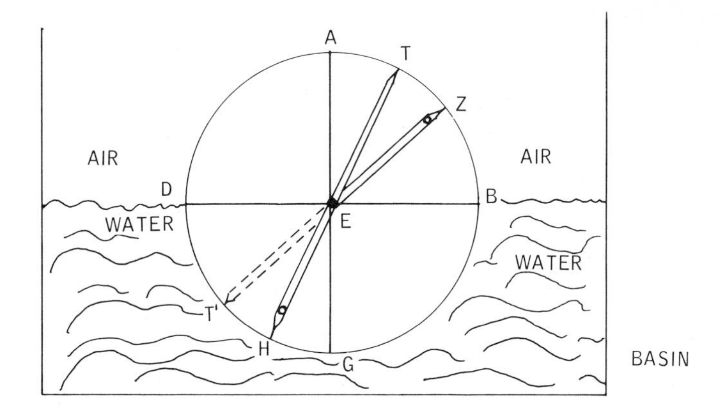

Figure 7.15

of a radius, both revolving about the disk's center. "Set the disk upright in a small basin and pour into the basin clear water.... Let the surface of the disk, standing perpendicular to the surface of the water, be bisected by the latter, half the circle, and only half, being entirely below the water."

Note the ringlike marker at the lower end of the movable diameter, hence in the water. Note a similar marker at the upper end of the movable radius. "With one eye, take sightings until the markers at Z and at E appear on a straight line proceeding from the eye." That is, place eye at Z and move TH until H seems in line with eye at Z.

"Now arc GH will always be smaller than arc AZ. Angle AEZ will always be greater than angle GEH. But this is possible only if there is a bending, that is if ray ZE is bent toward H, according to the amount by which one of the opposite angles exceeds the other," hence by $\triangle$TEZ or T^1EH. "If, now, we place the eye along the perpendicular AE, the visual ray will not be bent but will fall upon G, opposite A and in the same straight line as AE." In all other positions there is a bending. Ptolemy then gives a table of degrees of HG for angles from 10 to 80° for angle or arc AZ. "This is the method by which we have discovered the amount of refraction in the case of water. We have not found any perceptible difference between waters of different densities." He thus obtains measures of refraction in air and water.

He next takes a semicircle made of glass and places it over the DGB half of the disk out of the water. He now sights Z and lines it up with H through half air (ZE) and half glass (EH) and notes the amount of bending. He finds the bending (TZ) to be greater than between air and water.

He next places the glass semicircle on top and immerses the disk again in water as in the first experiment. This means that semicircle DGB is in water up to diameter DEB, and semicircle DAB is covered by glass. Repeating the same experiment, he finds that when the visual ray goes from glass into water, the corresponding bendings or refractions are less than in the opposite arrangement tried before. His data are extremely good when compared to modern findings.

Ptolemy then applies his findings of refraction to "the boundary between air and ether", where he expects "a bending of the visual ray because of a difference between these two bodies. We find that stars which rise and set seem to incline more toward the north when they are near the horizon and are measured by the instrument used for such measurement. For the circles, parallel to the equator, described upon these stars when they are rising and setting are nearer the north than the circles described upon them when they are in the middle of the heaven." This means that the small circles parallel to the equator that represent the daily (diurnal) apparent path of a star appear to be at a greater distance from the celestial equator when the stars are low on the horizon, hence at their rising and setting, than when they are high in the sky. As Ptolemy correctly concluded, when the star is high in the sky, the bending of its rays is less than when it is lower in the sky, hence nearer the line of the horizon. A visual ray from the eye of an observer on earth goes through a layer of air and is deflected away or down on reaching the surface of separation of air and ether; therefore any object which it reaches, even while still below the horizon, will become visible.

A is an observer on the surface of the earth. A star at point K will appear at Z. The bending occurs away from the zenith, at E, and the star appears higher above the horizon than it actually is. But, Ptolemy points out, since we do not know the relative extents of the atmosphere and ether, astronomical refraction cannot be measured.

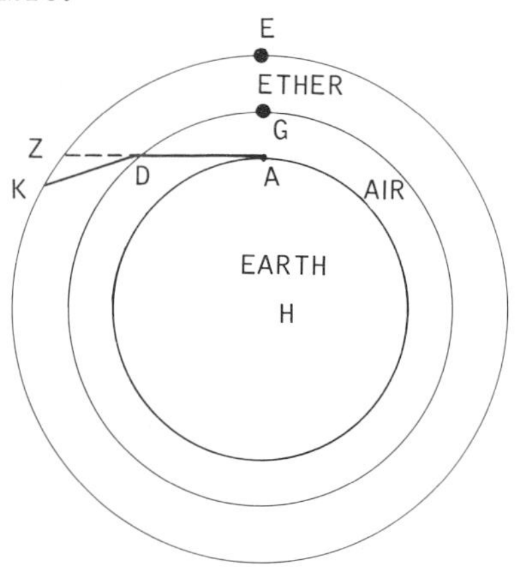

Figure 7.16

We see that geometry laid the foundations of a vast science and that although its basic postulate concerning the nature of the visual ray was the opposite of what it is for us, the language and logic of geometry were so precise that their scientific merit is mostly still valid today. Again, as in previous incidents, the only application of the science of catoptrics was in temples and for the call of fancy. How can it possibly be maintained that natural philosophy, or science, developed as a result of the pressure of economic circumstances? Precisely what made the wise men of Greece devote their time to these matters? What made the sages of Israel, who lived in the same period, devote their energies to such problems as vessels rendered impure because they contained meat and cheese, or whether eggs laid on the sabbath could be eaten or not? Certain it is that periods, like cultures, have a vitality and direction all their own; neither is an absolute indicator of the attainment potential of their participants. At a particular time in history, one group possessing as much active brainpower as another, may deliver productions that prove of fundamental and lasting merit, while the other yields labors that are trivial and transitory. At other times the roles of two such groups may be reversed.

3. The Foundations of Cartography

Another area in which the abstract-logical mode of reasoning that is geometry, produced remarkable results is the field of geography. Two great works of antiquity on this subject have come down to us and stand as monuments to high attainment in scientific and scholarly pioneering. One is the vast *Geography* of Strabo of Pontus (63 B.C. to after 21 A.D.), and the other is the smaller but more solidly mathematical *Geography* of Claudius Ptolemy. These works represent the two currents that composed Greek geography: the descriptive and the mathematical. Both branches had many contributors during the thousand years that elapsed from Homer to Ptolemy, and their labors culminated in the above two works.

It is commonly agreed that Eratosthenes (third century B.C.), who was librarian at the famous school of learning at Alexandria, measured the dimensions of the globe, estimated its inhabitable section, and represented it with parallels of latitude and meridians of longitude. His book *Geography* is lost, but we have some idea of its contenets from Strabo's work by the same name.

As can be seen from the map, the first meridian, or zero longitude, begins west of the Pillar of Hercules, our Rock of Gibraltar, and was presumably located on the Canary Islands. The last line of longitude is located east of India with oceans encircling the oikoumene, or inhabited world. The world was further divided by Posidonius into zones of climate. First came the torrid zone, or "the region that is uninhabitable on account of heat", and extends through the tropics north and south of the equator. Next came the central equatorial zone, with no rain or rivers but suitably strange creatures. Next to the tropics were the temperatre zones and then the cold polar regions, the arctic circles. "For the regions on the equator and in the torrid zone are uninhabitable because of the heat, and those near the pole are uninhabitable because of the cold; but it is the intermediate regions that are well-tempered and inhabitable." (Strabo, *Geography,* Vol. 11, 3, p. 1) The actual number of zones varied with each philosopher.

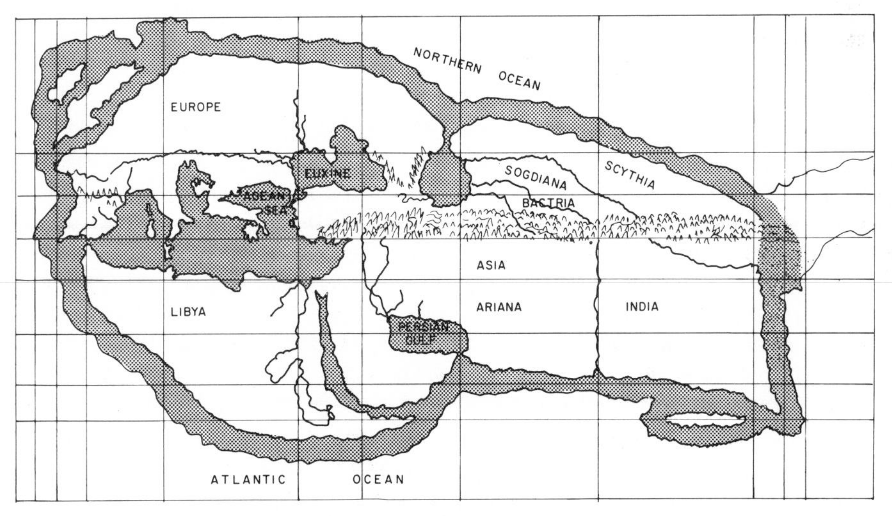

MAP OF THE WORLD ACCORDING TO ERATOSTHENES

Figure 7.17

The existence of the antipodes gave the ancients much concern. Says Pliny: "On this point there is a great contest between the learned and the vulgar. We maintain that there are men dispersed over every part of the earth, that they stand with their feet turned towards each other, that the vault of the heavens appears alike to all of them, and that they, all of them, appear to tread equally on the middle of the earth. If anyone should ask why those situated opposite to us do not fall, we directly ask in return, whether those on the opposite side do not wonder that we do not fall." (*Natural History* 11, p. 162) Pliny is also surprised at "what the vulgar most strenuously contend against," namely, "that the water is forced into a rounded figure." To prove the reality of this phenomenon, he cites the demonstration still popular with us today, that when a glass of water full to the brim has nails added to it, there will be no overflow but "what is dropt in raises up the fluid at the top.... It is from the same cause that the land is not visible from the body of a ship when it may be seen from the mast; and that when a vessel is receding, if any bright object is fixed to the mast, it seems gradually to descend and finally to become invisible." (*ibid*).

Aristotle in his *Meteorology* does, however, postulate an inhabited zone south of the equator that corresponds to the temperate zone of the northern hemisphere. But he does not believe that the earth is inhabited all around. "The way in which present maps of the world are drawn is therefore absurd. For they represent the inhabited earth as circular, which is impossible both on factual and theoretical grounds. For theoretical calculation shows that it is limited in breadth but could, as far as climate is concerned, extend round the earth in a continuous belt: for it is not difference of longitude but of latitude that brings great variations of temperature, and if it were not for the ocean which prevents it, the complete circuit could be made. And the facts known to us from journeys by sea and land also confirm the conclusion that its length is much greater than its breadth. For if one reckons up these voyages and journeys, so far as they are capable of yielding any accurate information, the distance from the Pillars of Heracles to India exceeds that from Aethiopia to Lake Maeotis and the farthest parts of Scythia by a ratio greater than that of 5 to 3. Yet we know the whole breadth of the habitable world up to the unhabitable regions which bound it, where habitation ceases on the one side because of the cold, on the other because of the heat; while beyond India and the Pillars of Heracles it is the ocean which severs the habitable land and prevents it forming a continuous belt round the globe." (Loeb Classical Library, Page 181-183)

But the fully mature, scientific foundations of geography as a full-fledged science were laid by Ptolemy in his great masterpiece. Says Ptolemy with his usual stolid but genuine enthusiasm: "It is the great and the exquisite accomplishment of mathematics to show all these things (re the geography of the earth) to the human intelligence so that the sky, too, having a representation of its own character, which, although it cannot be seen as moving around us, yet we can look upon it by means of an image as we look upon the earth itself, for the earth being real and very large, and neither wholly nor in part moving around us, yet it can be mapped by the same means as the sky....

"But now as we propose to describe our habitable earth, and in order that the description may correspond as far as possible with the earth itself, we consider it fitting at the outset to put forth that which is the first essential, namely, a reference to the history of travel, and to the great store of knowledge obtained from the reports of those who have diligently explored certain regions; whatever concerns either the measurement of the earth geometrically or the observation of the phenomena of fixed localities; whatever relates to the measurement of the earth that can be tested by pure distance calculations to determine how far apart places are situated; and whatever relations to fixed positions can be tested by meteorological instruments for testing shadows (astrolabes and sundials). This last is a certain method, and is in no respect doubtful. The other method is less perfect and needs other support, since first of all it is necessary to know in determining the distance between two places, in what direction each place lies from the other; to know how far this place is distant from that, we must also know how under what part of the sky each is located, that is, whether each extends toward the north, or, so to speak, toward the rising of the sun (the east) or in some other particular direction. And these facts it is impossible to ascertain without the use of the instruments to which we refer. By the use of these instruments, anywhere and at any time, the position of the meridian line can be found, and from this we ascertain the distances that have been traveled." (*Geography of Claudius Ptolemy*. Tr. by E. L. Stevenson, New York, 1932, p. 26) Land or sea travel to be accurately determined must be specified by distances traversed, as well as direction, since the earth is a sphere; such specifications are not easy to be followed, especially on the earth's seas. "But measurement based on celestial observation gives each of these things accurately. It shows how great are the arcs mutually intercepted by the parallel circles and the meridians (i.e., the arcs of the meridians falling between the parallel circles and the equator, and the arcs of the equator and the parallels falling between the meridians); it also shows how great an arc the two places in question intercept on a great circle of the earth drawn through them." (Cohen and Drabkin, p. 165) To accomplish such measurements with accuracy, "it is sufficient to take the circumference of the earth, divided into as many parts as desired, and to show how many such parts of a great circle of the earth there are in each of the several distances examined." This means that it is most convenient to represent earthly distances in degrees of arc rather than such units as miles, kilometers, or stades, which may vary from place to place.

To render this mode of measurement possible, "it has become necessary to compare some straight distance on the earth with the similar arc of a great circle on the celestial sphere, and, obtaining by observation the proportion of this arc to the whole circle, and by measurement based on some given part--the number of stades in the terrestrial distance under this arc--to find the number of stades in the whole circumference." This is the method adopted by Eratosthenes and Posidonius in their approach to the problem. If the center of the earth and the center of the revolving heavens are assumed to be the same, both being "substantially spherical," then "the angles subtended at the center intercept similar arcs on these circles."

With the instruments at hand there was little difficulty in determining the latitude of any place on earth and the position of the sun at noon. Most of the accurate instruments of antiquity were described by the same Ptolemy and were used by him to the fullest advantage. The problem of longitude determination was never satisfactorily resolved in by the ancients, and could not be until the coming of accurate clocks, or chronometers.

Both latitude and longitude are best measured as angles at the center of the earth. Latitude on earth is laid out by planes perpendicular to the axis and cutting it anywhere from the north pole to the south pole, with the plane of the equator in the middle between the two poles. We thus have 90° of latitude from the equator going north and 90° going south. Since the polar or north star is overhead at the north pole, and directly on the horizon at the equator, its elevation at any given spot can be used as a measure of the latitude of the locality.

Says Ptolemy: "Hipparchus alone gave us the elevation of the north pole (hence the latitude) for a few cities of the multitude that must be included in a description of the earth, and indicated places that lie on the same parallels." But Ptolemy realizes that with longitude the task was more difficult. Longitude is the angle at the center of the earth made by the planes of the meridians of any two localities. Such imaginary planes intersect along the earth's axis. While we use today as our prime meridian the one at Greenwich, outside London, it being essential to agree upon one as a reference point, the ancients used the one along the Canary Islands as their zero meridian, and measured angles east of it. West of it was the Atlantic Ocean which went uncharted.

Ptolemy was aware of the fact that distances "east and west," meaning meridianal angles, had not been carefully measured and that they could most easily be obtained from the measurements of times of eclipses in different localities. Eclipses, as we saw, travel eastward on earth because the moon's shadow moves faster than its corresponding spot on earth at any given moment. By knowing the moon's velocity and that of the heavenly vault, or as we would say, by knowing the velocity of the earth's rotation, longitudinal distances can be computed. But Ptolemy was not pleased with the accuracy with which such determinations were made in his day. Says he: "I refer to an eclipse like that observed at Arbela at the fifth hour and at Carthage at the second, from which the distance of the two places from each other eastward or westward could have been determined in equinoctical (equal) hours. For these reasons it would be proper for one who is to make a map of the earth in accordance with these principles to use the data obtained by more accurate observations as the foundation of the map, and to fit in with these data those obtained from other sources, until the positions indicated in the latter data both in relation to one another and in relation to the fundamental data are in accord, in so far as is possible, with the more accurate traditions." In other words, Ptolemy was seeking the highest possible accuracy and was fully aware of shortcomings.

It lay, however, in the very nature of the situation that accurate determinations of longitude could not be made until the final invention of an accurate and dependable clock. Such a clock was finally attained due to the efforts of Huygens, Hooke, Harrison, and other, whose labors culminated around 1750 A. D. The fact is that Ptolemy gives three hours as the difference in the occurrence of the eclipse between Carthage and Arbela. This means that Arbela should be regarded as lying 45 degrees east of Carthage, since one hour is equivalent to 15 degrees of longitude. In reality, the actual difference in longitude is 34 degrees, which is closer to the difference of two hours, as given by Pliny.

Ptolemy devotes much attention to the science of cartography, or scientific map-making. He realizes, as did others before him, that it is as impossible to take the surface of a sphere and represent it accurately on a plane, as it is to take an orange peel and flatten it out. Ptolemy realized he had to resort to inevitable distortion, as our own maps still demonstrate. He decided to retain the lines of latitudes as arcs and the longitudes as straight lines. Also, the further away from the equator, the smaller the lines of latitude per degree of longitude, since the circles get smaller and smaller. On the line of longitude, however, distances per degree of latitude do not undergo any change. "The parallel through Rhodes on which the most numerous measurements of longitudinal distances have been made may be divided in accordance with the ratio it bears to the meridian circle... of approximately four to five measured along equal arcs." This means that at Rhodes, an arc measuring five degrees at the earth's center on a circle of latitude is equal in length to one of four degrees on a line of longitude. Thus, the parallel circle through Rhodes is four-fifths as long as the equator or any great circle on the earth.

First, Ptolemy makes a sphere representing the globe. Next he attaches a rotatable semicircle to its two poles with which to draw meridian lines when necessary. He next divides the movable meridian into 180 parts, or 90 in each quadrant, and does the same to the equator. "Now we shall make our map on the basis of the tables of degrees of longitude and latitude for each of the places to be represented using the divisions on the semicircles, viz., the equator and the movable meridian...we place a mark corresponding to the indicated number of degrees just as we make a star map on a solid sphere." The latter comment would indicate that celestial spheres were in use before well-mapped globes.

Ptolemy was the first to construct several types of projected maps of the inhabited part of the earth. The one here represented is shown as a grid consisting of arcs for the circles of latitude and straight lines for the meridians. This particular map is known as a conic projection and yields a clever mathematical device, which every map ultimately has to be by the very nature of presenting a spherical surface upon a plane. Every map conveys some features accurately and others quite inaccurately. The maps we use today are Mercator projections, named after the great Flemish cartographer, Gerhard Mercator (1512-94) who originated the scheme for the specific purpose of practical navigation. Mercator's map is a central cylindrical projection. Wrap a cylinder around a globe made of transparent material and lighted by a lamp at its center, so that the contours of the globe are projected onto the cylinder. The latter is then unfolded into a flat map that is valuable for navigation in all regions of the globe except in the polar areas.

Ptolemy's conic projection is obtained as follows. Take a conical paper cup and place it inverted over a ball representing the globe. Let the apex of the cone be on the polar axis of the globe, that is, above the pole. The cone will then be tangent to the globe on some parallel of latitude. A light at the center of the sphere will project onto the surface of the cone the globe's grid of lines of longitude and latitude. Under these conditions the projected meridians will be straight lines radiating from the North Pole. "When the cone is then unrolled into a flat map after slitting the cone down one meridian, the meridians will continue to be straight lines converging to the north pole, and the parallels and the equator will be sectors of circles with the north pole at

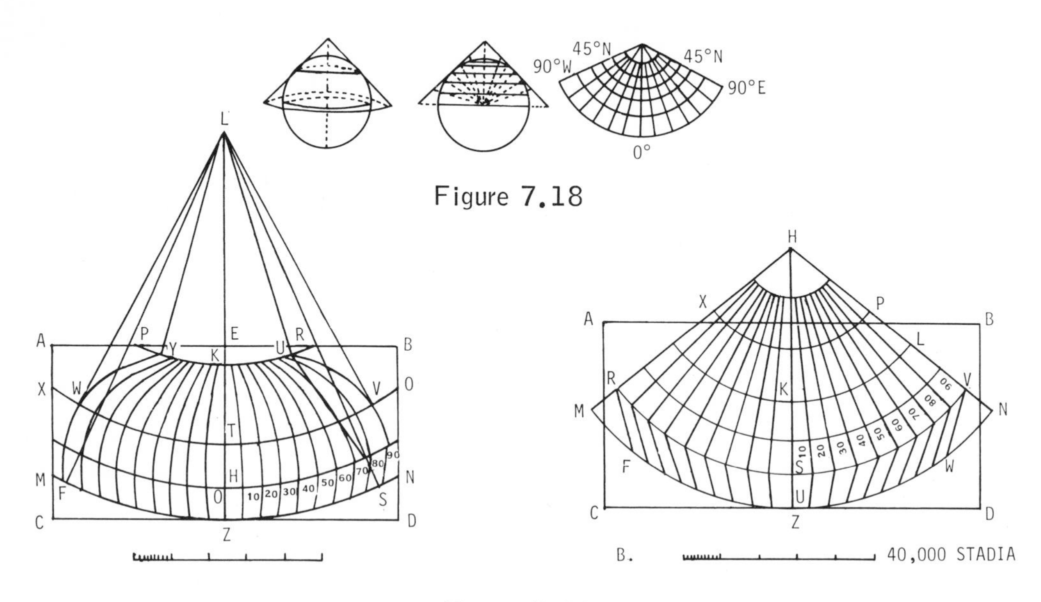

Figure 7.18

Figure 7.19

their center. The spacing of the parallels north and south will increase as we move north and south of the parallel to which the cone is tangent. Thus the scale along the meridians will vary; that is to say, the scale will vary from parallel to parallel. On the other hand, as intersections with any parallel will be equally spaced, the scale on any one parallel will be the same throughout its length." (Fisher, I. and Miller, O. M., *World Maps and Globes,* New York, 1944. p. 52) Figure 7.18 shows a cone tangent to globe at latitude 45° N. Cone is unwrapped at right showing that meridian lines do not converge at pole at the same angles they show on globe.

Ptolemy also gives the following projection, which, he points out, is mathematically more complex but yields more accurate results. For the construction of this map, "we make the meridian lines appear as they do on the surface of a sphere when the axis of vision (the axis of the cone of visual rays emanating from the eye) passes through the center of the sphere and that point of the sphere at which the meridians bisecting its breadth intersect. In this way the opposite boundaries are symmetrical with respect to the vision and are so perceived." (Cohen and Drabkin, p. 174) Figure 7.19 left has "the meridian lines appear as they do on the surface of a sphere", in Ptolemy's words. He finds this projection more accurate than the one on the right, but more difficult. In the one on the right Ptolemy shows a right cone tangent to globe at parallel of Rhodes, 36° N. Meridians are straight lines. Resulting scheme is simple but not so accurate as scheme at left.

Although both of these maps are pioneering mathematical inventions, Ptolemy gives in his Geography twenty-six special maps of various parts of the habitable globe that are actually much simpler; in these maps the meridians of longitude are parallel to each other and are perpendicular to the parallels of latitude. With the appearance of his book, both geography and cartography became full-fledged sciences, in which geometry was applied to spatial projection.

VIII The Search for Theory: The Spheres of Eudoxus

1. The Challenge

No books on the burgeoning science of Greek astronomy have come down to us from the period prior to Aristotle, if we except the *Timaeus* of Plato (427-347 B.C.). Yet, although the latter deals with many astronomical concepts and data of the science, it is mainly a mystical and philosophical work. Only Aristotle's books, *On the Heavens, Metaphysics,* and *Meteorology,* afford us the first authentic recounting of the kind of astronomical thinking that had already, by the mid-fourth century B.C., gained a foothold in the intellectual heritage of Greece.

It is amazing how readily the human mind displays its reluctance to feed exclusively on a diet of facts and how eager it is to comprehend nature by organizing and coordinating raw data into a theoretical generalization. We see this phenomenon take place in Greece as early as around 400 B.C. when Eudoxus (408-355 B.C.), a pupil of Plato, makes his debut on the arena of thought by advancing the first courageous and comprehensive attempt at a truly scientific theory, designed to unify and, roughly, make sense of the impressive store of facts concerning celestial events gathered by that time. His is the first effort of the human mind to devise a generalization based upon reliable physical data and to conceive a scheme which by its simple and logical operations should fully account for all observed phenomena and make verifiable predictions about the future motions of the celestial bodies under consideration. Eudoxus' name will forever be honored in science on many grounds. It is believed that Book V of Euclid's *Elements of Geometry* is his, which means that he brought to perfection the concepts of incommensurability and of irrational numbers. A number is incommensurable, that is, has no common unit of measurement with other numbers or lines, when it cannot be expressed as a ratio of two whole numbers, or integers, as is the case with $\sqrt{2}$. Such numbers were called irrational to distinguish then from the more natural-seeming family or rational numbers which are defined as quotients of two integers, such as 1, 2, 3, 4, etc., or our common fractions. While it was the school of Pythagoras that made the discovery of incommensurable quantities, it was Eudoxus who developed the concept and perfected our knowledge of such numbers. Eudoxus also elaborated the theory of proportion and the highly significant mathematical operation known as the method of exhaustion, which permitted the finding of areas of circles and volumes of pyramids, cones and spheres. He also rendered possible other operations as well and is regarded as one of the giants of ancient geometry.

Our concern, however, is with his theory in astronomy. Again, it should be noted that during the period from Thales to Plato, hence from about 590 B.C. to about 350 B.C., there already appeared some cosmological theories of a most fanciful nature, precisely because much factual observation had been rapidly accumulating. Of that factual knowledge, the harvest in quality and quantity was truly impressive. Such facts and postulations as the source of the moon's light, the sphericity of the earth, the cause of the moon's phases, the cause of solar and lunar eclipses, the obliquity of the ecliptic, a calendar with good approximations of equinoxes and solstices, the divisions of the zodiac, the orbits of the planets with their direct and retrograde motions, the inequality of the seasons, Venus and Mercury as morning and evening stars and the magnitude of their elongations from the sun, the regularity of the risings and settings of the constellations, the movements of the circumpolar stars - these and other astronomical data of prime significance had gained firm recognition. In addition, the irregular paths of the planets, their baffling loops, were noted, and the mystery of their paths were duly taken cognizance of and gloomily pondered over, literally in shame at its definance of sense.

The great challenge of the times was the matter of the planetary loops. We have already seen that the paths of the sun and moon against the stars can be readily mapped. The sun revolves daily together with the starry sphere completing a full circle in 24 hours, while receding leftward, eastward, about one degree each day, thus returning to its original point with a year. When the point of origin is chosen against the stars, the year is called sidereal; when the sun's circuit is measured from equinox to equinox, we obtain the tropical year. The moon acts similarly in its circuit in the sky. It moves eastward daily about 13 degrees and completes its cycle within about 27.3 or 29.5 days, depending against what we view its revolution, the stars or the sun. Such motions, as we saw, the ancients could handle with ease.

The situation was different with the five planets seen with the naked eye - Mercury, Venus, Mars, Jupiter and Saturn. These showed irregularities: Mercury and Venus as inferior or inner planets that remained close to the sun, of one kind, the other three which could be seen in opposition, of another. Mercury and Venus had a rhythm of their own: They appeared for a while as evening stars, then they disappeared from view, and next they appeared as morning stars. As morning stars they moved daily westward against the fixed stars until they reached their greatest distance from the sun, so-called elongation. After this event they swung back, which means they moved eastward toward the sun. For Mercury the greatest elongation can be as far as 28° and for Venus 46°. As evening stars they moved like the moon, eastward toward their greatest elongation, then back again toward invisibility as they lined up in conjunction with the sun. Both Mercury and Venus were given in recorded history different names as morning stars and evening stars, until some brilliant observer recognized their identity. The Egyptians called Mercury respectively Set and Horus, the Greeks Apollo and Mercury. Venus was Phosphorus and Hesperus before their identity was recognized.

The outer planets presented a truly baffling situation, namely, their loops. If Mars is observed against certain neighboring stars on a given night, then a week or two later it will be seen to the left of those stars chosen as markers. It will in fact be seen to move steadily leftward in the sky, meaning eastward. This is called its direct motion. In time it will, however, be seen to halt. This was styled its stationary phase. Its next course was a shift westward against the stars, followed by a resumption of its eastward course. In this manner it could be seen to make a loop each year. This was true for the outer as well as the inner planets. Actual records are shown in Figures 8.1A and 8.1B.

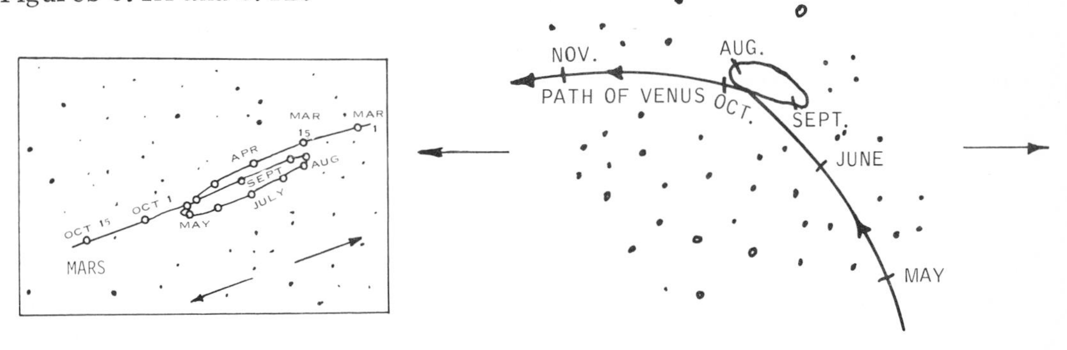

Figure 8.1A Figure 8.1B

It is these loops that disturbed the ancients no end. That the paths of celestial bodies were circular could be seen everywhere and at all times, most directly in the circumpolar stars, but also in the paths of all other stars and of the sun and the moon. It was apparent to all that the circle was characteristic of celestial paths. Aristotle believed he stated a truism when he said that "the circumference of the circle must be a perfect line" and further, "it is an observed fact that the whole revolves in a circle." (*On the Heavens*. p. 159) For this reason such unseemly and outlandish paths as loops had to be explained somehow, and they had to be explained in terms of what was seen and accepted. Similarly, a modern chemist must explain any chemical event, no matter how strance, in terms of atomic forces. And a physicist must explain freezing point depression or boiling point elevation in terms of kinetic theory. It was this kind of challenge that any theory of celestial motions had to face.

Circular motions could be seen elsewhere as well. Certainly the moon describes a circle about the earth. According to Vitruvius, "Aristarchus the mathematician of Samos, by his powerful intelligence, left in his systematic works an explanation of the moon's phases." (Vol. 2, p. 229) All the classical Greek philosophers - Anaximander, Anaximenes, Pythagoras, Xenophanes, Heraclitus, Parmenides, Anaxagoras and Empedocles, had sounder and more intricate schemes of the nature of the world, the fixed stars and the solar system, than the usual brief mention in philosophy textbooks gives them credit for. Because their schemes were speculative and their evidence unknown to us, since all we know about them is from references and quotations left by others, we shall omit them and refer the reader to the excellent study of Greek astronomy by Sir Thomas Heath, *Aristarchus of Samos* (Oxford, 1913), so frequently cited here, and to J. L. E. Dreyer's *History of Astronomy* (Cambridge, 1905).

Mention should be made, however, of the followers of Pythagoras (572-497 B.C.) who enjoyed a great vogue in the Greek colonies of southern Italy and who honored a theory of a central fire. "They say that there is fire in the middle, and the earth, being one of the stars, is carried round the centre, and so produces night and day. They also assume another earth opposite to ours, which they call counter earth, and in this they are not seeking explanations and causes to fit the observed phenomena, but they are rather trying to force the phenomena into agreement with explanations and views of their own and to adjust things. Many others might agree with them that the place in the centre should not be assigned to the earth, if they looked for the truth not in the observed facts but in *a priori* arguments. For they consider that the worthiest place is appropriate to the worthiest occupant, and fire is worthier than earth..." (*Aristarchus* of Samos, p. 95) These few sentences from a text by Aetius and many more cited by Sir Thomas Heath, bear full testimony to the freedom in speculation that prevailed, as well as to the freedom in criticism. Apparently there were more theories by respected scholars entailing revolution of the earth, than there are theories today concerning the origin of the solar system or the birth and death of stars. With Philolaus, a follower of Pythagoras, the theory assumed philosophic status, though being more speculative than data-bound, its message lies somewhat outside our scope.

More relevant is the contribution of Heraclides of Pontus (388-315 B.C.) a pupil Plato and Aristotle. Concludes Heath on the basis of a full study of the sources: "All authorities agree that Heraclides of Pontus affirmed the daily rotation of the earth about its own axis.... Thus we are told of Ecphantus that he asserted that 'that the earth, being in the centre of the universe, moves about its own centre in an eastward direction.'" (p. 251) Of Heraclides relatively much is known from several sources. He was the author of many philosophic works, but also of two lost diaglogues, *On Nature* and *On The Heavens* which seem to have been devoted exclusively to astronomy.

According to Proclus, "There have been some, like Heraclides of Pontus and Aristarchus, who supposed that the phenomena can be saved if the heaven and the stars are at rest while the earth moves about the poles of the equinoctial circle from the west (to the east), completing one revolution each day, approximately; the 'approximately' is added because of the daily motion of the sun to the extent of one degree. For of course, if the earth did not move at all, as he will later show to be the case, although he here assumes that it does for the sake of the argument, it would be impossible for the phenomena to be saved on the supposition that the heaven and the stars are at rest.

"But Heraclides of Pontus supposed that the earth is in the centre and rotates (lit. 'moves in a circle') while the heaven is at rest, and thought by this supposition to save the phenomena." (*ibid.* p. 254)

Heraclides of Pontus made another contribution, basically geometrical in nature which proved to be a valuable steppingstone toward the expanding adventures of mathematical astronomy. After examining the small wanderings of Mercury and Venus east and west of the sun, but never far enough from him to be seen in opposition, that is, on the opposite side of the earth from the sun, Heraclides suggested that these two planets "revolve round the sun as centre." Vitruvius and many authorities of antiquity refer to this theory without either surprise or annoyance, in the true spirit of free scientific inquiry. Says Martianus Capella: "For, although Venus and Mercury are seen to rise and set daily, their orbits do not encircle the earth at all, but circle round the sun in a freer motion." (p. 256)

There can be little doubt that while the field seemed fully ready for a general astronomical theory, the initial conjectures were speculative and tended more to please one's fancy, appeal to the flare for the poetic and grandiose, were akin to the religious cosmologies, and some even spiced with numerological flourishes. They were a step removed from the colorful myths, but perhaps more stimulating and suggestive. With the appearance of Eudoxus, however, the human mind took a step forward which marked a definite turning point in the hitherto speculative thinking.

According to Sosigenes, called the Peripatetic to distinguish him from the Sosigenes who helped Caesar introduce our calendar, who prospered in the second century A. D. and is quoted in the extant writings of Simplicius, the basic problem that faced all astronomers was stated by Plato in the following form: "By the assumption of what uniform and ordered motions can the apparent motions of the planets be accounted for?" This was a true challenge, because the motions of the circumpolar stars and the rising and setting of the sun and moon had established the prevalence of circular motion in the heavens beyond question of doubt. With Aristotle, the circular paths became perfect and divine, before him they were factual data. The existence of the planetary loops were certainly an exception, in whichever light the circle was regarded, fact or perfection.

2. The Scheme of Eudoxus: Its Backgrounds

The desire to explain an exceptional phenomenon in terms of established principles, on the assumption that in the irregular situation these principles were somehow obscured by superimposed circumstances, is at all times a normal phenomenon of scientific thought. It was such a challenge that Plato laid before astronomers, and it soon was duly taken up successfully by Eudoxus.

To begin with, Eudoxus postulated that each planet was located on the equator of a revolving sphere, a conception which was neither wild nor called into being out of the blue. We must recall here the warp and woof of the cultural milieu in which Eudoxus lived. Our concept of force as an abstraction was unknown to the scholars of antiquity and would have been totally repugnant to them had it been suggested. To the thinking world of antiquity, force was a mechanical phenomenon brought about by physical contact producing motion. *Omne quod movetur, ab alio movetur.* "Everything that is in motion must be moved by something," says Aristotle in his *Physics* over and over again. Next, "That which is the first movent of a thing - in the sense that it supplies not 'that for the sake of which' but the source of the motion - is always together with that which is moved by it (by 'together' I mean that there is nothing intermediate between them). This is universally true wherever one thing is moved by another.... Things that are moved by themselves... contain within themselves the first movement, so that there is nothing in between.

The motion of things that are moved by something else must proceed in one of the four ways - pulling, pushing, carrying and twirling. . . . Inhaling is a form of pulling, exhaling a form of pushing. . . . Everything, we say, that undergoes alteration is altered by sensible causes." (Basic Works. p. 342) Further, "Every movent moves something and moves it with something, either with itself or with something else. . . . For there must be three things - the moved, the movent, and the instrument of motion."

Circular motion was regarded by Aristotle as characteristic of heavenly bodies, whereas earthly motion was rectilinear. Phenomena natural to the earthly sphere were unnatural in the heavenly world, and vice-versa, because the two realms were different: their compositions were different, and their laws differed. The motions of the heavenly spheres were caused by a prime mover, a divine force which was somehow physical in nature, though not quite. It manifested itself as the outermost celestial sphere, which was divine and endowed with eternal, divine motion and was somehow responsible for the motion of the other spheres. At other times Aristotle postulated special divine intelligences which moved the individual planets. Both these postulates were rather vague in his mind, it would appear.

Says Aristotle in Book II of his *On the Heavens:* "The world as a whole was not generated and cannot be destroyed, as some allege, but is unique and eternal, having no beginning or end of its whole life, containing infinite time and embracing it in itself. . . . Therefore we may well feel assured that those ancient beliefs are true, which belong especially to our own native tradition, and according to which there exists something immortal and divine, in the class of things in motion, but whose motion is such that there is no limit to it. Rather it is itself the limit of other motions, for it is a property of that which embraces to be a limit, and the circular motion in question, being complete, embraces the incomplete and finite motions. Itself without beginning or end, continuing without ceasing for infinite time, it causes the beginning of some motions, and receives the cessation of others. Our forefathers assigned heaven, the upper region, to the gods, in the belief that it alone was imperishable; and our present discussion confirms that it is indestructible and ungenerated. We have shown, also, that it suffers from none of the ills of a mortal body, and moreover that its motion involves no effort, for the reason that it needs no external force of compulsion, constraining it and preventing it from following a different motion which is natural to it. Any motion of that sort would involve effort, all the more in proportion as it is long-lasting, and could not participate in the best arrangement of all. . . . To sum up, if it is possible for the first motion to take place in the way we have described, then not only is it more accurate to conceive of its eternity in this way, but moreover it is the only way in which we can give a consistent account and one which fits in with our premonitions of divinity. . . .

"It follows that above and below, right and left, front and back, are not to be looked for in all bodies alike, but only in those which because living, contain within themselves a principle of motion. . . . The heaven is alive and contains a principle of motion, so it is clear that the heaven possesses both upper and lower parts and right and left. . . .

"The question must be asked why there are several different revolutions, although we are far removed from the objects of our attempted inquiry, not in the obvious sense of distance in space, but rather because very few of their attributes are perceptible to our senses... Everything which has a function exists for the sake of that function. The activity of a god is immortality, that is eternal life. Necessarily, therefore, the divine must be in eternal motion. And since the heaven is of this nature, i.e., it is a divine body, that is why it has its circular body, which is by nature moved forever in a circle.

"Why, then, is not the whole body of the world like this? Because when a body revolves in a circle some part of it must remain still, namely that which is at the centre, but of the body which we have described no part can remain still, whether it be at the centre or wherever it be.... It follows that there must be earth..." And there must also be fire as the contrary to earth. "The shape of the heaven must be spherical. That is most suitable to its substance, and is the primary shape in nature....

"What is contiguous to the spherical is spherical.... The revolution of the heaven is the measure of all motions, because it alone is continuous and unvarying and eternal.... Therefore the motion of the heaven must clearly be the quickest of all motions.... If herefore the heaven a) revolves in a circle and b) moves faster than anything else, it must be spherical....

"Everything moved is moved by something.... If the mover does not act with constant force, or if the object changes instead of remaining constant, or if both alter, then there is nothing to prevent the movement of the object from being irregular. But none of these hypotheses can be applied to the heaven; for the object of the movement has been demonstrated to be primary, simple, ungenerated, indestructible, and altogether changeless..." (Loeb Classical Library. Cambridge, Mass. 1953. p. 131ff)

Throughout the reasoning of antiquity, force implied a mechanical mover and our somewhat abstract conception of force as energy, our notion of a field of force or lines of force, would appear as totally mystical to the ancients. It was therefore in line with the spirit of the times that Eudoxus could not allow the planets to lie suspended in midair, or mid-space, but had them attached to spheres, not solid and opaque spheres, but celestial and translucent in nature. Says that noted scholar of ancient mathematics, Sir Thomas Heath: "It does not appear that Eudoxus speculated upon the causes of these rotational motions or the way in which they were transmitted from one sphere to another; nor did he inquire about the material of which they were made, their sizes and mutual distances. In the matter of distances the only indication of his views is contained in Archimedes' remark that he supposed the diameter of the sun to be nine times that of the moon, from which we may no doubt infer that he made their distances from the earth to be in the same ratio 9:1. It would appear that he did not give his spheres any substance or mechanical connection; the whole system was a purely geometrical hypothesis, or a set of theoretical constructions calculated to represent the apparent paths of the planets and enable them to be computed." (*Aristarchus of Samos.* Oxford, 1913, p. 196)

Eudoxus' main concern was to advance mathematical schemes and motions that were within the realm of plausibility. To account for the complex motions of the planets, he postulated a sphere that carried a particular planet on its equator, and of course rotated on an axis, but had the poles of this axis embedded within another sphere which rotated on an axis of its own, inclined to the first axis. These two spheres were situated concentrically (that is,

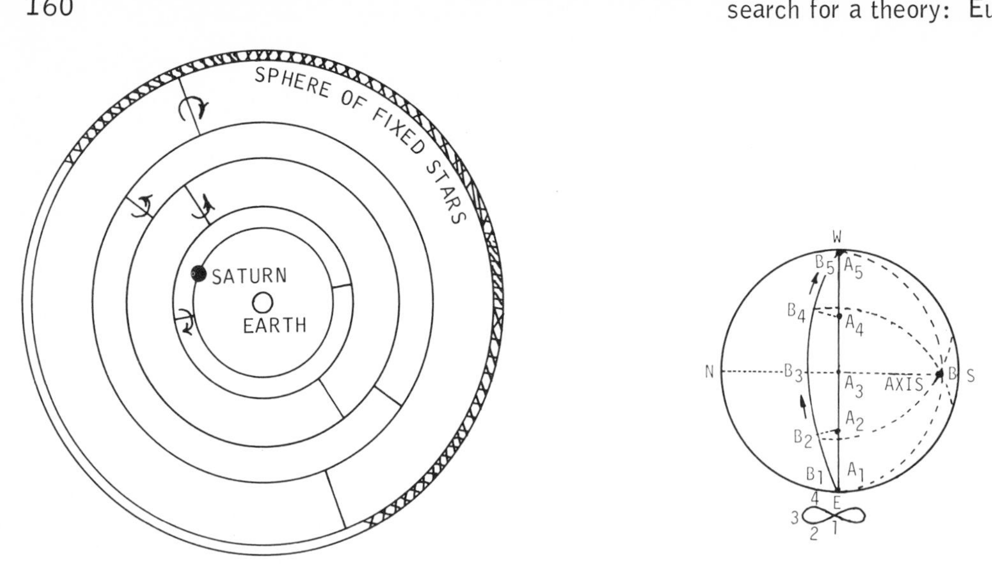

Figure 8.2

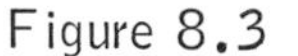
Figure 8.3

having a common center) within a third sphere, in which the poles of the axis of the second were fixed in a fashion similar to the previous arrangement, and its axis fixed again in a fourth one. Each of these four concentric spheres rotated uniformly on its own axis, but each was necessarily endowed with the motions of the spheres outer to it because each outer sphere carried the axis of the next inner one. The innermost sphere carrying the planet had, besides its own rotation, also the motions given to it by the rotations of the three outermost ones. The final goal of all these rotations was to simulate the observed course of the particular planet as it pursued its path in the belt of the zodiac, its different speeds in longitude, meaning along the zodiacal circle, and its deviations in latitude, meaning above and below the sun's orbit, the so-called ecliptic, the scheme served as well to account for the loops with their direct, stationary and retrograde episodes.

His main objective was to account for the irregularities in the planetary orbits, and his spheres acquitted themselves of this task in the following manner. Assume a celestial globe revolving about a horizontal axis as indicated in Figure 8. 3 with the cardinal points as shown. Consider first the path of a point located upon the equator. Its path will appear to an observer such as the reader to lie along the line WE, specifically, along the numbered points A_1, A_2, A_3, A_4 and A_5. Now assume a point north of the equator and follow its path as the globe revolves. The path will then consist of arc B_1, B_2, B_3, B_4 and B_5. It will be seen to lie to the north of the equator; A_1 and B_1 are joined, B_2 is below A_2, B_3 furthest from A_3, B_4 above A_4 and B_5 again joined with A_5. With the continuation of the path a mirror image of semicircle B_1 B_5 will be obtained to the right of the WE line. If the orbit of the B points is viewed from the top, above W, and projected downward, the symmetrical figure of a horizontal 8, namely ∞, as shown in the illustration, will be seen. If we have a sphere with points A on its equator, we will obtain a vertical line for the project of its path, as seen from any point on the plane of the equator. Let us assume sphere one, whose equator is the ecliptic circle, revolving around a suitable axis, NS. By adding to the first sphere a second one whose axis is at an angle to the axis of the first, B in the figure, and whose plane of the equator is therefore at an angle to the ecliptic, we shall obtain upon revolving it an oscillation of all points situated on its equator. Such a revolution will place these points for half a period above the ecliptic (to the left of WA_1) and for another half period to the right (not shown in figure). Such a sphere can therefore be made to account for any planet's motion in latitude. The plane of revolution of the second sphere will be at an angle to the earth's plane of revolution, which is sphere one, whose equator represents the ecliptic. Points on the equator of the second sphere will appear above (to the right) and below (to the left) of the ecliptic. This is motion in latitude.

So much then for the first two spheres, which Eudoxus made to revolve in opposite directions and which together yield the projection of a hippopede, the horizontal figure 8. But to account fully for planetary motion, Eudoxus assumed two more spheres. The outermost one rotated once in twenty-four hours about the celestial poles. Since it held fastened to it in onion shell manner the axes of the inner three, it necessarily carried them along. The next inner one, third from inside, "carries the planet quite regularly along the ecliptic in a west-east direction in the period of revolution of the planet. The motion along the hippopede, which is performed in one synodic period, is superimposed to transform the regular mean movement into the alternation of a long direct and short retrograde path. For this purpose the third sphere has its axis fixed in two opposite points of the ecliptic, and it carries the fourth sphere, contrarily revolving about an inclined axis. Thus all the phenomena are represented: the daily rotation, the opposite revolution along the ecliptic, and the alternation of direct and retrograde motion in a synodic period." (Pannekoek, A. *History of Astronomy*, New York, 1961. p. 110)

The outermost rotated the fastest about the celestial poles, making one revolution in twenty-four hours, going from east to west. This carried the planet along its diurnal revolutions together with the starry heaven. The next sphere, carried along by the first, moved again in uniform motion so as to account for the planet's path along the zodiacal constellations, and in a direction contrary to the diurnal motion of the first sphere. The third sphere with its axis fixed in two opposite points on the ecliptic sought to account for the planet's motion in latitude, meaning above and below the ecliptic. In our terminology, this accounted for the fact that planets revolve in planes that lie at an angle to the earth's plane of revolution and will thus be seen above and below the ecliptic. Finally, the innermost or fourth sphere, revolving in a direction contrary to that of the third sphere, accounted together with it for the irregularity in the actual planet's zodiacal path, hence for the planet's loops, its direct, stationary and retrograde movements. Thus, the planet's path is broken down into several components and each is accounted for by ascribing a sphere to it.

By assigning to each of the spheres a proper direction and velocity, the final outcome was such that the motion of the planet harmonized fairly well with that actually observed in the sky. All told, Eudoxus postulated twenty-six spheres. But it must be borne in mind that a sphere meant to him only a constituent of motion, conceived as we do vectors for a given component force, or a possible clutch of vectors to break down any single force we choose to treat thus. His method was scientifically as sound for his time as the use of unbalanced forces and suitably component vectors is for us today. Neither need be real in a strict literal sense, yet each is a logically consistent symbol, serving a specific purpose.

According to Eudoxus the motions of the sun and moon could be accounted for by three spheres each. The outermost performed the same motion as the fixed stars; the next one revolved so as to have its equator in the ecliptic. The innermost one which carried the planet on its equator, revolved so as to have its equator inclined to that of the ecliptic; "but the circle in which the moon moves is inclined at a greater angle than that in which the sun moves." (*Metaphysics*, Vol. 11, p. 157) Without the concept of force and orbit, the ancients never conceived of circular motion without a mechanical carrier, such as, a spoke or a sphere.

This scheme of Eudoxus was brilliant in the extreme, and constituted the first strictly mathematical scientific generalization serving to organize a complex set of observed phenomena. The scheme was not perfect; it possessed in fact several glaring weaknesses. Its inadequacies were both due to incomplete observations and to the price that frequently must be paid for the advantages of a theory. Nevertheless it fitted the paths of Saturn and Jupiter very well, was satisfactory for Mercury, poor for Venus and out of step entirely for Mars, the troublesome planet whose orbit remained a snag and a challenge until subdued by the genius of Kepler. With regard to motion in latitude, i.e. the planet's motion above and below the ecliptic, the theory of Eudoxus was generally poor.

Calippus, a pupil of Eudoxus, sought to fill these gaps. Again, such an effort is a scientifically sound procedure, since every brilliant theory has weaknesses which a clever adherent may seek to eliminate by improving the original theory. Calippus' book is lost, but the core of his modifications is known to us. He added another sphere to Eudoxus' four for Mars which, as has been pointed out by Aristotle, might well have removed some of the original shortcomings. He also added one each to the sets for Mercury and Venus, two to the three for the sun and moon, respectively, to account for the inequality in their motion in longitude, that is, in the zodiacal circle. In this manner he raised the total number of spheres to thirty-three.

With Aristotle's attitude to physics as distinguished from astronomy, it was not surprising that he should have been displeased with the strictly mathematical manner in which Eudoxus and Calippus handled their spheres. To Aristotle a sphere had to be an actual material carrier just as a force implied a movent that moves by direct contact. The suggestion of a force acting at a distance would appear to him as sheer magic. He was a thoroughgoing materialist and mechanist in the true spirit of the 18th and 19th century materialists. In his *Metaphysics* he summarized the system of Eudoxus and repeated that "the sphere of the fixed stars is that which moves all the other spheres." We shall see later that he distrusted the value of mathematics in physics not because of any prejedice against mathematics, which he regarded highly but because he did not think it useful in physical phenomena. He asserts in his *Metaphysics* that "the first principle and primary reality is immovable... but it excites the primary form of motion," especially of the planets. "It is clear that the movers are substances, and that one of them is first and another second and so on in the same order as the spatial motions of the heavenly bodies. As regards the number of these motions, we have now reached a question which must be investigated by the aid of that branch of mathematical science which is most akin to philosophy, i. e. astronomy; for this has as its object a substance which is sensible but eternal, whereas the other mathematical sciences, e. g. arithmetic and geometry, do not deal with any substance." (Loeb Classical Library, 1935. Vol. 2, p. 155)

Calippus, comments Aristotle, added two spheres to each, the sun and the moon, and one to each of the other planets. And he continues: "But if all the spheres in combination are to account for the phenomena, there must be for each of the other planets other spheres, one less in number than those already mentioned, which counteract these and restore to the same position the first sphere of the star which in each case is next in order below. In this way only can the combination of forces produce the motion of the planets. Therefore since the forces by which the planets themselves are moved are 8 for Jupiter and Saturn and 25 for the others, and since of these the only ones which do not need to be counteracted are those by which the lowest planet is moved (i. e. the moon), the counteracting spheres for the first two planets will be 6, and those of the remaining four will be 16; and the total number of spheres, both those which move the planets and those which counteract these, will be 55." (*ibid.* p. 159)

It would seem that Aristotle regarded the spheres as actual and considered each cause of motion, including the prime mover, as material. And if a sphere caused motion, then such motion was undone when one sphere revolved in one direction and another lodged within it, revolved oppositely. What better way to set apart two such motions and render each independent, than by inserting another sphere, a neutral one this time, in between them, to separate the two motions? To a practical, mechanistic mind, this seems the only logical step.

Other mathematicians soon realized that the theory of Eudoxus suffered from serious shortcomings and omissions. Sosigenes expressed himself as follows on this topic: "Nevertheless the theories of Eudoxus and his followers fail to save the phenomena, and not only those which were first noticed at a later date, but even those which were before known and actually accepted by the authors themselves.... I refer to the fact that the planets appear at times to be near to us and at times to have receded. This is indeed obvious to our eyes in the case of some of them; for the star called after Aphrodite (Venus) and also the star of Ares (Mars) seem, in the middle of their retrogradations, to be many times as large, so much so that the star of Aphrodite actually makes bodies cast shadows on moonless nights. The moon also, even in the perception of our eye, is clearly not always at the same distance from us, because it does not always seem to be the same size under the same conditions as to medium. The same fact is moreover confirmed if we observe the moon by means of an instrument; for it is at one time a disc of eleven fingerbreadths, and again at another time a disc of twelve fingerbreadths, which when placed at the same distance from the observer hides the moon (exactly) so that his eye does not see it. In addition to this, there is evidence for the truth of what I have stated in the observed facts with regard to total eclipses of the sun, for when the centre of the sun, the centre of the moon, and our eye happen to be in a straight line, what is seen is not always alike; but at one time the cone which comprehends the moon and has its vertex at our eye comprehends the sun itself at the same time, and the sun even remains invisible to us for a certain time, while again at another time this is so far from being the case that a rim of a certain breadth on the outside edge is left visible all 'round it at the middle of the eclipse. Hence we must conclude that the apparent difference in the size of the two bodies observed under the same atmospheric conditions is due to the inequality of their distances (at different times)... But indeed, this inequality in the distances of each star at different times cannot even be said to have been unknown to the authors of the concentric theory themselves.... In this respect Aristotle was not altogether satisfied with the revolving spheres, although the supposition that, being concentric with the universe, they move about its center, attracted him." (*Aristarchus of Samos,* pp. 221-222)

We see here the same kind of dissatisfaction with a theory that can occur in our own times, and above all, the same kind of resignation in the acceptance of a prevailing theory simply because it performs a useful function, though fully realizing its partial shortcomings. Perhaps Aristotle's displeasure with the theory served to undermine the definite attraction it wielded to the mathematically inclined. In any case, the scheme of Eudoxus did not long endure.

3. The Flourishing Third Century B.C.

Many new suggestions began to make their appearance. The realization that the earth was not situated at the world's center necessitated the postulation of an eccentric path for the planets. This realization came long after Eudoxus, who apparently was not aware of it, but soon after Euclid who also failed to cite it in the account of elementary astronomy he gives in his *Phoenomena.* Nonetheless, the entire period between Euclid and Ptolemy which encompasses the flourishing four centuries and a half of Alexandrian learning, was full of vitality and novelty. At the very inception of this period stood Apollonius of Perga, who lived between the latter part of the third and early part of the second century B.C. Known as "the great geometer," he was the author of *Conical Sections* and eleven other books on geometry. That period also boasted of Hipparchus, often referred to as the greatest astronomer of antiquity, the man whose works have not survived but whom Ptolemy constantly quotes in admiration as his guide and master.

The period of Eudoxus teemed with robust speculations, some of which were of genuine mathematical stature. Not only the Pythagoreans but Heraclides of Pontus and others had the earth in motion of one kind or another. According to Cicero (*Academica* 11, 39, p. 123), Hicetas of Syracuse "holds that the heavens, sun, moon, and stars, all the heavenly bodies, in short, are at rest, and that nothing in the universe moves except the earth, and as the earth turns and rotates about its axis at very high speed the effect is exactly the same as if the heavens were rotating and the earth at rest." Most famous of these early speculative pioneers was Aristarchus of Samos (310-230 B.C.), "the mathematician," who wrote on a variety of subjects but whose works are unfortunately lost except for his brief *On the Sizes and Distances of the Sun and Moon,* already discussed. He was truly the first to advance the heliocentric theory, as is testified to be Archimedes and Plutarch.

Archimedes (287-212 B. C.), in his famous work *The Sand-Reckoner,* in which he demonstrates how to express any number, however great, even that of the grains of sand on the entire earth, in terms of exponentials, had this to say about the heliocentric speculations: "But Aristarchus of Samos brought out a book consisting of some hypotheses, in which the premises lead to the result that the universe is many times greater than the 'universe' just mentioned. His hypotheses are that *the fixed stars and the sun remain unmoved, that the earth revolves about the sun in the circumference of a circle, the sun lying in the middle of the orbit,* and that the sphere of the fixed stars, situated about the same centre as the sun, is so great that the circle in which he supposes the earth to revolve bears such a proportion to the distance of the fixed stars as the centre of the sphere bears to its surface. Now it is easy to see that this is impossible; for since the centre of the sphere has no magnitude, we cannot conceive it to bear any ratio whatever to the surface of the sphere. We must, however, take Aristarchus to mean this: since we conceive the earth to be, as it were, the centre of the universe, the ratio which the earth bears to what we describe as the 'universe' is the same as the ratio which the sphere containing the circle in which he supposes the earth to revolve bears to the sphere of the fixed stars. For he adapts the proofs of his results to a hypothesis of this kind, and in particular, he appears to suppose the magnitude of the sphere in which he represnets the earth as moving to be equal to what we call the 'universe.'" (Sir Thomas Heath, *The Works of Archimedes.* The Sand-Reckoner. Dover Publications, New York. p. 222)

It is clear from this statement by Archimedes that as a true mathematician he is concerned with an accurate evaluation of what Aristarchus had in mind. We would say today that the radius of the earth is to the radius of the earth's orbit as the radius of that orbit is to the radius of the starry sphere. Mathematically this would not be correct, because it would make the radius of the earth's orbit around the sun a mean proportional. We would then have $a:b = b:c$; $\therefore$ $b^2 = ac$, which we have no way of ascertaining. What Aristarchus probably meant is merely to say that just as the radius of the earth is a very small part of the radius of its orbit, so is the radius of the earth's orbit a very small part of the radius of the starry sphere, which is a literary rather than a strict, mathematical expression.

The references in the literature of antiquity to the heliocentric hypothesis were numerous indeed, indicating wide awareness of its existence. Besides Cicero, such authors as Hippolytus, Diogenes Laërtius, Seneca, Simplicius, and Plutarch refer to it, among others, while Vitruvius, Martianus Capella, and others, referred to the revolution of Mercury and Venus around the sun. Plutarch, for instance, in his *The Face on the Moon* has the following to say: "Thereupon Lucius laughed and said: 'Oh, sir, just don't bring suit against us for impiety as Cleanthes thought that the Greeks ought to lay an action for impiety against Aristarchus the Samian on the ground that he was disturbing the hearth of the universe because he sought to save (the) phenomena by assuming that the heaven is at rest while the earth is revolving along the ecliptic and at the same time is rotating about its own axis. We express no opinion of our own now; but those who suppose that the moon is earth, why do they, my dear sir, turn things upside down any more than you do who station the earth here suspended in the air? Yet the earth is a great deal larger than the moon according to the mathematicians who during the occurrences of eclipses and the transits of the moon through the shadow calculate her magnitude by the length of time that she is obscured." (Loeb Classical Library. Plutarch's *Moralia,* 1951. vol. 12, p. 55) This passage is of interest because it shows that Aristarchus postulated both motions of the earth, namely rotation and revolution, and that as in our day, freedom of speculation was not always welcome. Another point of interest is the reference to Cleanthes. Apparently, it is not only the common man who goes in for persecution of pioneers in novel ideas, but also their learned peers who are so aroused over disagreement with their so well-reasoned defense of a current theory that they seek to resort to force or law-suits in order to suppress opposition.

We have also seen that Heraclides postulated for both, Mercury and Venus, revolutions about the sun, with the sun revolving about the earth. What is interesting about this scheme is that it resembles the scheme of Tycho Brahe which was advanced close to twenty centuries later. Also, while the arguments for the revolution of the earth were wholly untenable and contrary to the evidence and to common sense, the logic behind the revolutions of Mercury and Venus around the sun, could appear to be almost reasonable to the thought pattern of the times. Admittedly the world of antiquity regarded the centricity of the earth as too important to allow two such brilliant planets as Mercury and Venus not to revolve around it but around the sun, which clearly revolved around the earth. But as against this, it may be argued that the view of Heraclides merely required Mercury and Venus to be in epicycles around the sun, which scheme was fully in harmony with prevailing notions. Vitruvius, like many others, refers to this notion without regarding it in a disturbing light. Says he: "The planets Mercury and Venus, with their orbits, encircling the sun's rays as on a centre, retreat backwards and delay their course; thus because of their orbit they delay at the nodes in their course through the signs." (Vol. 2, p. 217)

We may now call attention to the fact that side by side with the idea of the centricity of the sun and the movements of the earth in rotation and revolution, there appeared in the thinking of the times the two intriguing and serviceable concepts of eccentric and epicycle. The arguments cited by Sosigenes against the adequacy of the Eudoxian scheme had much force and demanded theoretical accommodation. Planets did appear to be regularly brighter at certain times than at others, implying that they did not revolve at uniform distances from the earth. Although we know this to be due to varying distances from the earth, nature could just as well have arranged it for these bodies to be subjected to some periodic event, much like sun spots or other expressions of periodicity, and thus account wholly differently for their variations in brightness. However, the attempts to account for possible differences in distance and also for the other irregularities, such as the movements of planets above and below the ecliptic and the apparent differences in their orbital speeds, referred to as variation in longitude, led to the two concepts of the eccentric and epicycle which served well in their function as alternative explanations.

It is on this matter that Heraclides is presumed to have made a major addition to the fertile thoughts of the time. "Departing altogether from the system of spheres, to which the Aristotelian school doggedly adhered, and adopting a system of circles more akin to Pythagorean ideas," he extended the circles he had devised for Mercury and Venus to the motions of Mars. This puzzling planet was brightest in opposition, that is, when opposite the sun with the earth between them, rather than in conjunction, (with the sun between Mars and the earth) when it is nearer the sun. It must therefore be nearest the earth at opposition, which means that it cannot have the center of the earth as the true center of its motion. This led directly to the postulation of the planetary path as an eccentric circle, meaning that the actual path of the planet encircled the earth but that the earth was not at the center. The path will then be represented in the following manner.

Let E be the earth at the center of the universe and let QR be an accentric circle around it with its center at O. The line QR is the diameter of this circle. If we assume the planet Mars to move around the earth along this eccentric circle, then the point Q will represent the perigee of this planet, the point at which it is nearest the earth. At point Q, Mars will be in opposition with the sun at R or on line ER which line also contains O, the center of the eccentric.

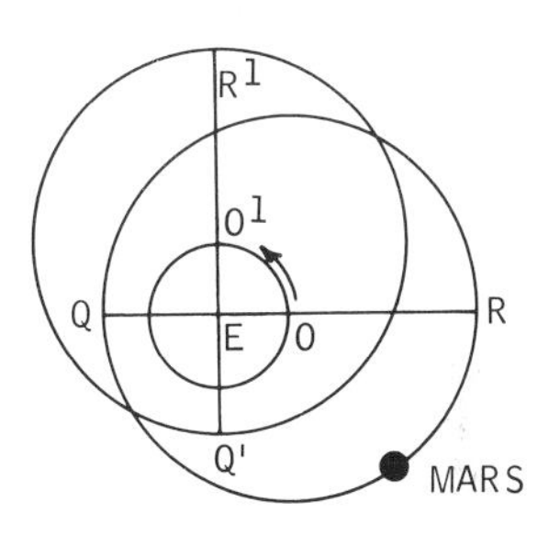

Figure 8.4

Now, it is a fact that Mars is in opposition and brightest in different signs of the zodiac on different occasions in the course of time. This can only mean that the diameter QR shifts its direction by moving around the center E, placing Q all around the zodiac, in time, with point R invariably at the opposite end. This means that O, the centre of the planet's eccentric orbit, will describe a small circle around E, the earth, in a year. It revolves thus always in the direction of the sun. In the figure, circle Q^1R^1 shows what happens when QR has moved counterclockwise 90 degrees.

Now, assume Mars to move uniformly around the eccentric in the *reverse* order of the zodiacal signs, completing a circuit from perigee to perigee. This period will signify one revolution of Mars around the earth. It can be calculated in advance and verified by obervation, that this theoretical scheme is legitimate and we can then proceed to the next step. The distance EO is called the eccentricity and measures the deviation of the position of the earth from the true center of the planet's circle around it. If we choose the length EO in the proper ratio to OR by trial and error, all the observed motions of the planet--its stationary and retrograde positions--can be quite well explained and predicted. Having available past data of Mars' perigees in the various zodiacal signs, it was quite simple to establish the *ratio* of EO to radius OR, but not the *absolute lengths* of these factors. Moreover, the center of the circle QR, the point O, could be made naturally and logically to represent the sun, which also revolves around the earth, E. This seems to have been the original practice. According to Sir Thomas Heath: "The use of ideal points as centres for epicycles and eccentrics was no doubt first thought of, at a

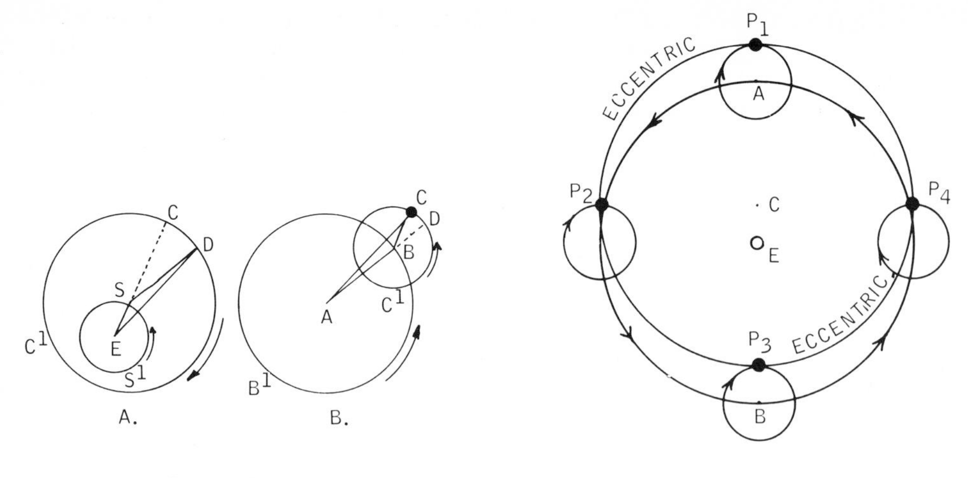

Figure 8.5 Figure 8.6

later stage, by some of the great mathematicians such as Appolonius." (*Aristarchus of Samos*, p. 264) This kind of geometrical representation of a planet's movement is known as the *movable eccentric*.

We may now consider the argument that the same explanation and accuracy of prediction could be attained by means of postulating an epicycle for the path of movement of a planet. Although it is very likely that both theories of the eccentric and the epicycle evolved gradually some time in the third century B. C., it seems reasonable to ascribe the eccentric to Heraclides and the epicycle to Apollonius of Perga. A century later, Hipparchus gave it further elaboration and is believed to have been the first to prove its explanatary identity with the eccentric. With Ptolemy, three centuries after Hipparchus, the epicycle theory reached its full development.

Consider the two diagrams A and B. In A, E represents the earth, S the movable center of the eccentric with the arrow indicating its direction of motion, so that ES is always in the direction of sun and moving in the direct order of the signs. CC^1 is the eccentric circle with S as its center. Line ES produced to C will indicate the position of apogee, or the planet's greatest distance from the earth on its circular path. The planet will be at D, as it moves in the inverse order of the signs. "Angles CSD, or arc CD, reckoned from the apogee in the inverse order of the signs will be the *argument of the anomaly,* or shortly the *anomaly;* the planet will be seen from the earth in the direction ED."

The proof of the equivalence of the two schemes, the eccentric and the epicycle, is shown in Figure 8. 5. Consider first Figure 8. 5B. Let A be the center of the earth. Describe circle BB^1 equal to the eccentric circle of Figure 8. 5A. Draw AB as radius parallel to SD in A. Let B be the center of the epicycle, CC^1, equal to circle SS^1 in the other figure. Continue AB to periphery of epicycle, to D, so that point D is the apogee on the epicycle. Let the angle DBC be equal to the anomaly, or angle DSC in the other figure, but reckoned in the opposite direction, in the direct order of the signs. Let the planet be at C as seen, of course, from A.

Triangles ESD and ACB can be seen to be equal because a) since CBD = DSC, angles ABC and ESD are also equal; AB = SD and BC = ES, and ES is parallel to CB since AB and SD are parallel and angles between these sides are equal. Therefore AC is equal and parallel to ED. This latter means that "the planet will be seen in the same direction and at the same distance under either hypothesis." To bring about this relationship of equivalence of eccentric and epicycle, only two conditions are needed: 1) The radii of the eccentric and the circle housing the epicycle, BB^1, also known as the deferent, must be equal; SD = AB. 2) The anomaly, CSD, in the eccentric, must be equal to anomaly in the epicycle, CBD, though the two angles must be reckoned in opposite directions; in the inverse order in the eccentric, in the direct order in the epicycle.

The identity of the two explanations can best be seen in Figure 8.6. The circle with counterclockwise arrows is described with E as its center. This circle, called the deferent, carries the center of the epicycle upon which rides the planet which revolves in a clockwise direction. The planet makes one revolution on its epicycle in the same interval of time as its center makes one full revolution on the deferent. The positions of the planets are indicated by the numbers.

Now lay off a distance on the unseen line AB equal to the radius of the epicycle. This yields line EC. With C as center describe a circle marked eccentric. It can readily be seen that this circle has on it all the positions of the planet. Now if E is the position of the earth, the path of the planet can be described either way. In either case P_3 is the planet's perigee and P_1 the apogee.

In historical fact, "the Greek mathematicians preferred the epicycle hypothesis to the eccentric." This was so primarily because the epicycle is easily applicable to the inferior planets, Mercury and Venus, as well as to the superior ones, Mars, Jupiter and Saturn, while the eccentric could not at first be applied to the former group. Secondly, "the epicycle hypothesis enabled the phenomena of the stationary points and retrogradations to be seen almost by simple inspection, whereas on the eccentric hypothesis a certain amount of geometrical proof would be necessary to enable the effect in this respect to be understood." Nevertheless, there is a significant, though far from crucial, point of difference between them. In Figure 8.5A, the circle SS^1 may be regarded as the actual orbit of the sun, while the center of the epicycle, point B in Figure 8.5B, cannot be given material significance. But that very limitation of the epicycle turned out to be of great advantage. It taught the mathematicians to think of centers of both epicycles and eccentrics as ideal and abstract points, rather than to follow the natural, but mathematically sterile, instinct of always having some material object at centers or other points of special mathematical function.

4. The Role of a Theory

Greek mathematicians were fully aware that the orbits of the planets could be explained by either one of the theorems, the eccentric or epicycle, or that some planets could be best explained by the former and other planets by the latter scheme. Their thinking was wholly mathematical and was little concerned with devotion to the so-called "true" or "real" orbit, presumably as verified by one transported into the midst of the heavens in observable proximity to the planets. Their thinking was scientifically as mature and sophisticated as is our approach to neutrinos, anti-matter, and the reaction mechanisms yielding solar energy. Says Simplicius in one of his commentaries: "Why do the sun, moon, and planets appear to move irregularly? Because, whether we suppose that their circles are eccentric or that they move on epicycles, their apparent irregularity will be saved; and it will be necessary to go further and consider in how many ways the same phenomena are capable of being explained, in order that our theory of the planets may agree with that explanation of the causes which proves admissible." (*Aristarchus of Samos*, p. 268)

Hipparchus was puzzled over the problem "why on two hypotheses so different from one another, that of eccentric circles and of concentric circles with epicycles, the same results appear to follow." He himself preferred the epicycle theory as "more natural... and yet because he was not sufficiently equipped with physical knowledge, even he did not know for certain which is the natural and therefore true movement of the planets, and which the incidental and apparent." And so the ancients resolved the problem in the same manner we do today in similar situations, which is by sanctioning both theories at once, or one alone at a time, so long as they could account for the observed facts in a consistent geometrical fashion. The one assumption which all agreed upon and which apparently remained unquestioned even by the most sophistic quibbler was, in the words of Geminus, the following: "It is a fundamental assumption in all astronomy that the sun, the moon, and the five planets move in circular orbits at uniform speed in a sense contrary to that of the universe." And so long as the theory of eccentrics and epicycles, either alone or in combination, harmonized the actually observed facts of non-circularity and non-uniformity, with the "fundamental assumption" through clever geometry, the results pleased everybody at all aware of the problem. Such is the search for a scientific theory, and precisely such was the challenge raised by Plato.

The mathematical scholars of antiquity were fully aware of their goal and their methodology. We have the account given by Simplicius of what the great mathematician Geminus has to say on this matter. Said he: "It is the business of physical inquiry to consider the substance of the heaven and the stars, their force and quality, their coming into being and their destruction, nay it is in a position even to prove the facts about their size, shape, and arrangement; astronomy, on the other hand, does not attempt to speak of anything of this kind, but proves the arrangement of the heavenly bodies by considerations based on the view that the heaven is a real *cosmos* and further, it tells us of the shapes and sizes and distances of the earth, sun, and moon, and of eclipses and conjunctions of the stars, as well as of the quality and extent of their movements. Accordingly, as it is connected with the investigation of quantity, size, and quality of form or shape, it naturally stood in need, in this way, of arithmetic and geometry. The things, then, of which alone astronomy claims to give an account, it is able to establish by means of arithmetic and geometry. Now in many cases the astronomer and the physicist will propose to prove the same point, e.g., that the sun is of great size or that the earth is spherical, but they will not proceed by the same road. The physicist will prove each fact by considerations of essence or substance, or force, of its being better that things should be as they are, or of coming into being and change; the astronomer will prove them by the properties of figures or magnitudes, or by the amount of movement and the time that is appropriate to it. Again, the physicist will in many cases reach the cause by looking to creative force; but the astronomer, when he proves facts from external conditions, is not qualified to judge of the cause, as when, for instance, he declares the earth or the stars to be spherical; sometimes he does not even desire to ascertain the cause, as when he discourses about an eclipse; at other times he invents by way of hypothesis, and states certain expedients by the assumption of which the phenomena will be saved. For example, why do the sun, the moon, and the planets appear to move irregularly? We may answer that, if we assume that their orbits are eccentric circles or that the stars describe an epicycle, their apparent irregularity will be saved; and it will be necessary to go further and examine in how many different ways it is possible for these phenomena to be brought about, so that we may bring our theory concerning the planets into agreement with that explanation of the causes which follows an admissible method. Hence we actually find a certain person, Heraclides of Pontus, coming forward and saying that, even on the assumption that the earth moves in a certain way, while the sun is in a certain way at rest, the apparent irregularity with reference to the sun can be saved. For it is no part of the business of an astronomer to know what is by nature suited to a position of rest, and what sort of bodies are apt to move, but he introduces hypotheses under which some bodies remain fixed, while others move, and then considers to which hypotheses the phenomena actually observed in the heaven will correspond. But he must go to the physicist for his first principles, namely that the movements of the stars are simple, uniform and ordered, and by means of these principles he will then prove that the rhythmic motion of all alike is in circles, some being turned in parallel circles, others in oblique circles." (*Aristarchus of Samos*, p. 276)

We have here not only the distinction as understood at the time between physics and astronomy, but also a highly perceptive insight into the meaning and function of a scientific theory. This statement presents a view which would have been completely rejected in the nineteenth century, but is by and large universally honored in our own times. The nineteenth century was an era of mechanistic certainty in which people thought that what they called matter and motion could account for all physical phenomena in nature, and probably biological ones as well. It was also an age in which people believed that they had a firm grip, even a monopoly, on reason, while those who saw things differently or started out with a different set of assumptions were unreasonable. Being the sole possessors of reason, because what was past seemed full of unreason, they further believed that it revealed to them the exact and absolute nature *of reality as it really was,* so to say, and everyone who claimed that they only theorized, though with excellent justification, was a heretic and antiscientific.

Few scientists cherish this naive attitude today but generally tend to agree with the more sophisticated and probably more accurate conception presented by Geminus. The more modern view was imposed upon contemporary science by historic events, by such concepts as the wave nature of matter, the postulation of mesons, photons, neutrinos, antimatter, electron spin, parity and similar creations which exist by virtue of their logical necessity and their value in organizing, coordinating and harmonizing a diversity of data. This is precisely what Geminus wishes to convey in the above passage.

As a scientific investigation of physical phenomena gets further away from the realm of direct experience, the reasoning mind has to rely more and more upon mental constructs which are neither inferior nor superior to facts, i.e. to direct sensory experiences. As a science grows more sophisticated, as in the case with much of modern science, our basic material ceases to be objects of immediate sensory perception but becomes increasingly abstract. Under such conditions it is futile to be concerned over the problem--is the wave nature of an electron real? Does the neutrino exist in reality? By asking such questions we are confusing direct experience with the kind of theoretical postulates that can never be translated or identified with direct experience. Science works perfectly well and productively with both experience and concepts, requiring no caste or rank among them, and is in no way obliged to ask questions impossible of being answered.

The Greek mathematicians were fully aware of the problem stated here by Geminus with remarkable clarity. They were concerned with a theory, a mathematical one, that would account for the data in terms of circular and uniform motions, an assumption which seemed so reasonable to them that they never thought of questioning it. They never stopped to think, so far as we can determine, whether epicycles or eccentrics were real. It is a fact that in time the epicycle theory came to prevail even though the movable eccentric seemed more convenient so far as the sun's path was concerned.

How real the eccentric circle is, can readily be seen from the path of the sun. In *The Elements of Astronomy* by Geminus, we are told that "from the vernal equinox to the summer solstice there are 94 1/2 days. For in this number of days the sun traverses the Ram, the Bull, and the Twins, and arriving at the first degree of the Crab, brings about the summer solstice. From the summer solstice to the autumnal equinox there are 92 1/2 days, for in this number of days the sun traverses the Crab, the Lion, and the Virgin, and, arriving at the first degree of the Scales, brings about the autumnal equinox. From the autumnal equinox to the winter solstice there are 88 1/8 days.... From the winter solstice to the vernal equinox there are 90 1/8 days ... The days forming these periods, when all added together, make up 365 1/4 days, which, as we saw, was the number of days in the year.

"At this point the question arises, why, although the four parts of the zodiac circle are equal, the sun, travelling at uniform speed all the time, yet traverses the arcs in unequal times. The Pythagoreans were the first to approach such questions, and they assumed that the motions of the sun, moon, and planets are circular and uniform. For they could not brook the idea of such disorder in things divine and eternal as that they should move at one time more swiftly, at another time more slowly, and at another time stand still, which last expression refers to what are called the stations, or stationary points, in the case of the five planets. No one would credit such irregularity even in the case of a steady and orderly man on a journey. No doubt the exigencies of daily life are often the cause of slowness and swiftness in men's movements; but when the stars, with their indestructibe constitution, are in question, no reason can be assigned for swifter and slower motion." (Sir

Thomas Heath, *Greek Astronomy,* New York, 1932. Cited by Cohen and Drabkin, p. 118)

In this passage from Geminus, we have a clear statement of the primary moving force in the theoretical structure of Greek astronomy, namely, the axiomatic acceptance of circular and uniform motion, which meant necessarily that any deviation from it had to be explained in a manner consistent with observations, common sense, general knowledge, and stated assumptions. It is to the attainment of this goal that the scientific genius of the mathematicians of the time applied itself.

Geminus, who lived about 250 years before Ptolemy, had already offered a consistent theory of the motion of the sun which was to be little modified in the future. Said he: "If, now, the sun had moved on the circle of the fixed signs (constellations of the zodiac), the times between the solstices and the equinoxes would have been exactly equal to one another. For, moving at uniform speed it ought, in that case, to have described equal arcs in equal times. Similarly, if the sun had moved in a circle lower than the zodiac circle, but about the same centre as that of the zodiac circle, in that case, too, the periods between the solstices and the equinoxes would have been equal. For all circles described about the same centre are similarly divided by their diameters; therefore, since the zodiac circle is divided into four equal parts by the diameters joing the solstitial and equinoctial points respectively, it would necessarily follow that the sun's circle is divided into four equal parts by the same diameters. The sun, therefore, moving at uniform speed on its own sphere (circle), would in that case have made the times corresponding to the four parts equal. But, as it is, the sun revolves at a lower level than the signs, and moves on an accentric circle, as is explained below. For the sun's circle and the zodiac circle have not the same centre, but the sun's circle is displaced to one side, and, in consequence of its being so placed, the sun's course is divided into four unequal parts. The greatest of the arcs is that which lies under the quadrant of the zodiac circle which stretches from the first degree of the Ram to the 30th degree of the Twins, and the least arc is that which lies under the quadrant from the first degree of the Scales to the 30th of the Archer. . . .

"The sun, then, moves at uniform speed throughout, but, because of the eccentricity of the sun's circle, it traverses the quadrants of the zodiac in unequal times." (*ibid.* p. 119)

The situation can be represented follows: (Figure 8.7)

Let C be the center of the circle upon which the sun follows its path around the earth located at E. Let the point V mark the vernal equinox or the position of the sun upon this solar circle on March 21, S the point of the sun's position on the day of the summer solstice, June 22, F of the fall or Autumn equinox, and W the winter solstice. The lengths of the arcs are determined by observation, as stated in the text. The distance EC, called the eccentricity, can then be determined, as well as the line MN and its parts, which designate the points N, on which the sun is nearest the earth, or perigee, and the point M, when it is furthest from the earth, or its apogee. According to Hipparchus, EC = 1/24 of the radius of the circle and the arc VM = 65°30'. Thus the idea of an eccentric circle for the sun's path was successfully established and functioned quite satisfactorily several centuries before Ptolemy. The modern version is presented for comparison. Figure 8. 8.

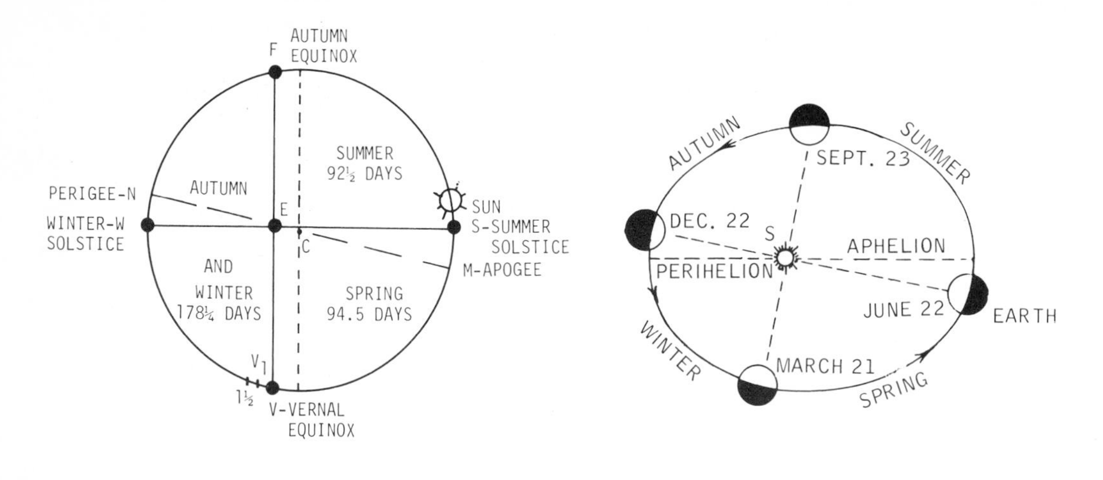

Figure 8.7

Fiqure 8.8

Another significant concept that emerged out of the fertile mathematical mind of those creative times, was the discovery of the precession of the equinoxes by Hipparchus. In comparing the positions of a sample of prominent fixed stars, as recorded by him, with the values of latitude and longitude recorded for them about a century and a half before him, Hipparchus noticed a significant shift in their longitudes, all in a direction opposite to the daily motion of the starry sphere. The shift was only about 1.5°, but it was consistent for all stars. This shift he explained as due to the fact that the equinoctial point showed a regular shift in the retrograde direction of the signs, that is backwards.

To demonstrate: it has already been shown that the path of the sun against the starry sphere across the signs of the zodiac, known as the ecliptic, is at an angle of $23\frac{1}{2}°$ to the equator. This path it will be recalled as seen from any place on earth, runs for half a year below the equator and for another half a year above the equator. The point where this path crosses the equator on the sun's path upward is the vernal equinox, around March 21. Beginning with that day, the sun will be seen anywhere on earth north of the equator, reaching the point furthest north from it on June 22, moving closer to it thereafter, and crossing the equator again on the day of the autumnal equinox, September 22. On this diagram, what Hipparchus observed was that the point of the

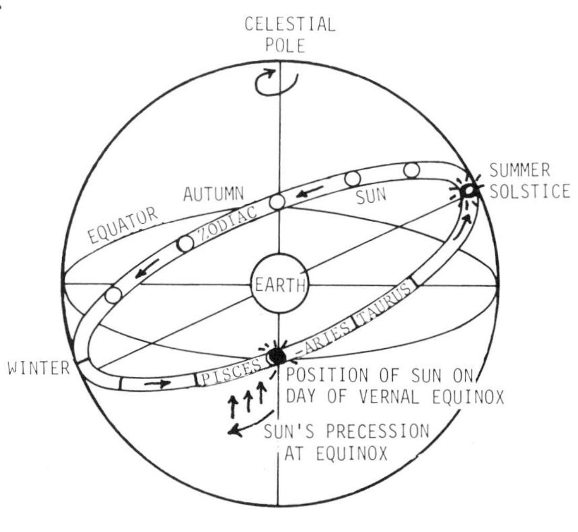

Figure 8.9

vernal equinox shifted to the left, hence as seen from the earth it would mean to the right or westward, about 1.5° every century. In other words, the year of the seasons, or the tropical year, measured from equinox to equinox, is shorter than the sidereal year, or the year measured by observing the sun describe its circle in the sky against the stars. In the latter case the sun will return to the same original point against the starry sphere; in the former the sun will reach the vernal equinox to the west of the initial point by crossing the celestial equator earlier. Hence the tropical year is shorter.

We may conclude that as far back as several centuries before Ptolemy, the scholars of the Greek world were aware of the basic scientific challenge to construct a consistent mathematical reality behind the irregular appearances of the planetary motions. Furthermore, a brilliant, logical and feasible hypothesis had been suggested by Eudoxus to account for these motions. The theory was rooted in mathematics but failed to account for several aspects of the situation. In the persistent attempts to find better explanations to heal the hiatuses left by the Eudoxian scheme, several brilliant conceptions were advanced which possessed valuable explanatory possibilities. If anything, the quest suffered from an excess of explanatory models, because much could be explained by eccentric circles as well as by epicycles; nevertheless, speculation had advanced far enough for Cicero and others to refer to ingenious mechanical models of the entire universe, hence to functional planetaria. Saya Cicero in his *On the Commonwealth:* "Though I had often heard of this famous globe, because of the renown of Archimedes, I was not much impressed by the appearance of the thing itself, because there was another globe, more beautiful and more generally known, also made by Archimedes, which this same ancestor of Marcellus had placed in the Temple of Virtue. But as soon as Gallus began to explain in a thoroughly scientific way the theory of the instrument, I came to the conclusion that the genius of Archimedes transcended human nature. For Gallus told us that the invention of the solid and compact globe in the Temple of Virtue was ancient, and that the first one had been fashioned by Thales of Miletus. Subsequently, Eudoxus of Cnidus, Plato's pupil, as Gallus said, marked on the globe the stars that are fixed in the sky. Many years after Eudoxus, Aratus adopted from him the entire detailed arrangement of the globe and described it in verse, not displaying any knowledge of astronomy but showing considerable poetical skill.

"But Gallus declared that the globe at Marcellus' house, which showed the motions of sun and moon and of those five wandering stars or planets, as they are called, could not be constructed in solid form. All the more remarkable, therefore, was Archimedes' discovery, since he had devised a method of construction whereby, extremely different though the movements of the planets are, the mere turning of the globe would keep them all in their unequal and different orbits. When Gallus rotated the globe, the moon really followed the sun on the bronze globe by the same number of revolutions as are the days it lags behind in the sky. Thus it happened that on the globe there occurred a solar eclipse just like the real eclipse; and also that the moon passed into that tract of space covered by the earth's shadow when the sun [and the moon were on opposite sides of the earth.]" (1929, Columbus, Ohio. p. 119-120) Cicero mentions another model functioning as a planetarium in his *On the Nature of the Gods*. "Our friend Posidonius recently constructed such a sphere.

A single rotation of it produces the same effect on the sun, the moon, and the five planets as is produced in the sky itself on a single day and night." (University of Chicago Press, 1950. p. 260) Other writers make similar references.

However, in spite of this intellectual and mechanical triumph, science still lacked the aid and comfort of a single coherent theoretical scheme that had the power to elicit total acceptance and enthusiastic consensus. This intellectual unity and appeal was supplied by the theory of Ptolemy which was destined to dominate in admiration and loyalty the entire world of learning until the seventeenth century. It was a great theory, the first vast, valid, and magnificent scientific theory which because of its beauty and service, had no competition or challenger until events forced its withdrawal in favor of an offspring wholly in its image, the Copernican hypothesis.

IX The Majestic Theory of Ptolemy

1. Ptolemy's Method

Ptolemy's contribution to the science of cartography is of a magnitude on a par with Galileo's discovery of the nature of motion, Newton's formulations of force and gravitation, the contributions of Michael Faraday, Louis Pasteur, Ernest Rutherford, or other pathfinders. What Ptolemy accomplished was to face up to the basic challenge of map-making, single out its elements, and offer a workable method for their resolution.

The challenge was to spread upon a flat table the curved surface of a sphere. As stated, there is no foolproof way of accomplishing this feat to one's total satisfaction. It can only be resolved at the cost of some compromise, and the idea is to make the cost as small as possible. Let us take two examples of the several methods of which Ptolemy was aware in addition to the one we have already cited, the conical projection.

If you form a cylinder of some flexible plastic material with parallel vertical lines on it around a sphere representing the globe with the circles of latitude and longitude upon it, you can do that so as to have the lines on the cylinder parallel to the globe's polar axis. Consider a line AB on the cylinder grazing the globe at the equator. If you then draw a line along Latitude, La, parallel to the plane of the equator, line DE, you will have a segment CD which can be shown to stand in a known ratio to the corresponding arc CF on the globe. It is therefore possible to have a map with vertical lines of longitude which have a known correspondence, in terms of the geometrical properties of plane and spherical triangles, to the actual reality of a curved surface on earth. Note that such segments as CD will be closely packed and smaller near the pole. But the horizontal distances DG, GH, HI, etc., will be uniformly equal.

Another way of obtaining a compromise projection is to invert a cone over a sphere as shown in Figure 9.2. In this case we can picture a line grazing some circle of latitude north of the equator, since the walls of a cone cannot possible graze the equator.

Let line CB of the cone lie in the same plane as a given meridian circle, as shown in the Figure where line CB grazes the meridian at point D at latitude Lb. Then if MN is a line on the plane of the equator, segment DE can easily be expressed by a known ratio to the arc DF to which it corresponds on the globe. In this manner we can have a conical projection on paper in full and known harmony with the physical reality it represents.

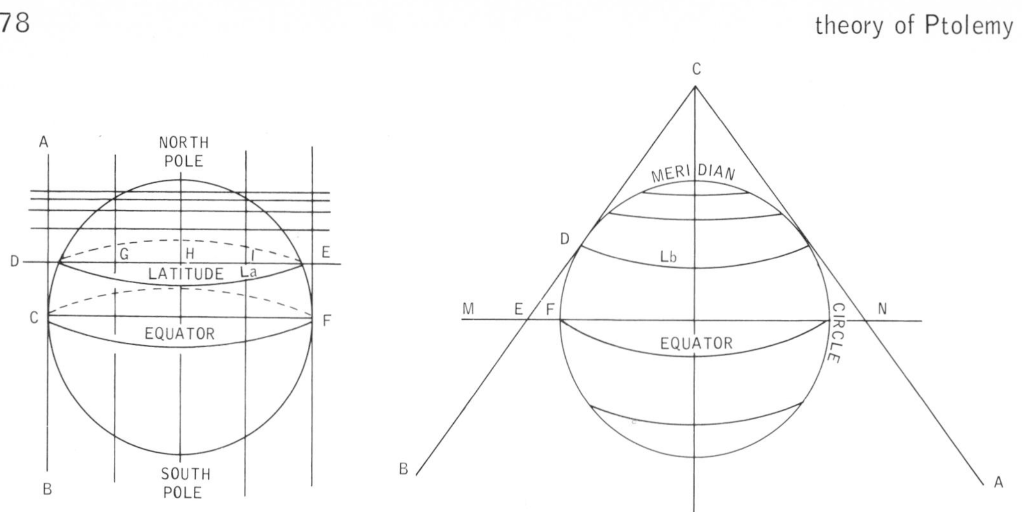

Figure 9.1

Figure 9.2

It so happens that the cylindrical projection yields correct values for all areas on land or sea, although, as stated, it misrepresents some other features. Similarly, the conical projection can be made to preserve distances in latitude and longitude, respectively, though not in the same figure.

Ptolemy's *Geography* brought out the various problems that confront the geographer and cartographer. It went as far as the human mind could go in supplying several mathematical schemes for their solution and provided the needed mathematical language. Ptolemy had inherited many fragments from predecessors and contemporaries and was exceptionally generous in giving them full credit. Were it not for him, we might have known very little about the great contributions of Hipparchus, Marinus of Tyre, and Menelaus.

We have traced the growth of man's awareness of celestial events from its earliest beginnings in awe, curiosity, and worship, to the sophisticated geometrical schemes of Eudoxus and the even more sophisticated criticisms of their shortcomings. We have also seen how there accumulated in the course of several centuries of remarkable intellectual activity within a diversified but none-too-large contiguous culture area, much skill and wisdom in the use of instruments. We have seen the formation of the language of mathematics with which to express much observation and many clever insights and interpretations of laboriously gathered yet still bewildering data. The complex and unifying mathematical synthesis offered by Eudoxus failed to gain universal acceptance within the scientific community of the times. There had, nevertheless, emerged a few new mathematical devices, such as eccentric circles and epicycles that possessed a strong appeal to all those who hungered after a satisfactory generalization with which to comprehend the mechanism of celestial motions. As luck would have it, there arose from the mind of Claudius Ptolemy, who was one of the greatest scientific geniuses of all time, a man on a par with Darwin and perhaps even Newton, a theoretical construction that impressed, and inspired every scientist of stature for fifteen centuries. Moreover, it served as a model for the theoretical generalization which superseded it, namely, the Copernican hypothesis, which in turn proved not only correct in the light of subsequent discoveries, but was instrumental in their coming into being. Without the Ptolemaic theory with its vast intellectual foundation and superstructure, there would have been no Copernican hypothesis.

Little is known of Ptolemy as a person except what can be gleaned from his writings. We know from his own observations of the planets and of a lunar eclipse, the exact times in which he lived. From his references to his predecessors, whom he cites with due honor and credit, Eudoxus, Heraclides, Aristarchus, Apollonius, and above all, Hipparchus, we know that he was a generous and honorable scholar, giving at all times credit where credit was due. Since his great *Mathematical Composition* in thirteen books, better known by its Islamic contraction, *The Almagest,* happens to be the only full treatise on Greek astronomy that has come down to us intact, it is fortunate that Ptolemy was that type of person rather than egotistic, quarrelsome, and grudging. His generous attitude was instrumental in informing us of the work of gifted forerunners of whose efforts we would otherwise be wholly ignorant. His dedication to science was unbounded, and his love for his subject was at all times poetic and impassioned.

Ptolemy opens Book One of *The Almagest* with a Preface which begins with: "Those who have been true philosophers,... seem to me to have very wisely separated the theoretical part of philosophy from the practical." He is not concerned much with the practical, but with "the consideration of the beautiful and well-ordered disposition of things, and to indulge in meditation mostly for the exposition of many beautiful theorems, and especially of those specifically called mathematical." (Great Books, Encyclopedia Britannica Inc., Chicago, Ill. 1952, vol. 16, p. 5)

Furthermore, "Aristotle quite properly divides also the theoretical into three immediate genera: the physical, the mathematical, and the theological." Now, the physical deals with the properties of things that are "corruptible and below the lunar sphere," the theological seeks after God, while the mathematical "seeks figure, number, and magnitude, and also place, time, and similar things." The first two pursuits seem to him conjecture: theology is vague and abstract, and the physical is uncertain "because its matter is unstable and obscure.... And meditating that only the mathematical, if approached inquiringly, would give its practitioners certain and trustworthy knowledge with demonstration both arithmetic and geometric resulting from indisputable procedures, we were led to cultivate most particularly as far as lay in our power this theoretical discipline."

Ptolemy then proceeds to summarize briefly "as many theorems as we recognize to have come to light up to the present.... And in order not to make the treatise too long, we shall only report what was rigorously proved by the ancients, perfecting as far as we can what was not fully proved or not proved as well as possible." And after saying no more by way of introduction, he proceeds to cite on a few pages the established data and hypotheses. "And so, in general, we have to state that the heavens are spherical and move spherically, that the earth, in figure, is sensibly spherical also when taken as a whole; in position, lies right in the middle of the heavens, like a geometrical centre; in magnitude and distance, has the ratio of a point with respect to the sphere of the fixed stars, having itself no local motion at all. And we shall go through each of these points briefly to bring them to mind." He then proceeds to itemize and fortify each of these basic axioms.

Of special interest in his discussion of the axiom "That the Earth Does Not in Any Way Move Locally." After citing the evidence bearing on the complex orbits of the planets, he examines the evidence that compels one to regard the earth as centrally located. Moreover, "the tendencies and movements of heavy bodies are everywhere and always at right angles to the tangent plane drawn through the falling body's point of contact with the earth's surface," and if not stopped by that surface, "they too would go all the way to the centre itself." There is "no 'above' or 'below' in the universe with respect to the earth, just as none could be conceived of in a sphere." Just as fire rises upward, heavy things fall toward the centre. Earth is the heaviest element and can therefore "remain unmoved in any direction by the force of the very small weights" impinging on it.

But Ptolemy is aware, like all other scholars of his day, of the existence of hypotheses contrary to these assumptions. Says he: "Now some people, although they have nothing to oppose to these arguments, agree on something, as they think, more plausible. And it seems to them there is nothing against their supposing, for instance, the heavens immobile and the earth as turning on the same axis from west to east very nearly one revolution a day; or that they both should move to some extent, but only on the same axis as we said, and conformably to the overtaking of the one by the other.

"But it has escaped their notice that, indeed, as far as the appearances of the stars are concerned, nothing would perhaps keep things from being in accordance with this simpler conjecture, but that in the light of what happens around us in the air such a notion would seem altogether absurd. For in order for us to grant them what is unnatural in itself, that the lightest and subtlest bodies either do not move al all or no differently from those of contrary nature, while those less light and less subtle bodies in the air are clearly more rapid than all the more terrestrial ones; and to grant that the heaviest and most compact bodies have their proper swift and regular motion, while again these terrestrial bodies are certainly at times not easily moved by anything else - for us to grant these things, they would have to admit that the earth's turning is the swiftest of absolutely all the movements about it because of its making so great a revolution in a short time, so that all those things that were not at rest on the earth would seem to have a movement contrary to it, and never would a cloud be seen to move toward the east nor anything else that flew or was thrown into the air. For the earth would always outstrip them in its eastward motion, so that all other bodies would seem to be left behind and to move towards the west.

"For if they should say that the air is also carried around with the earth in the same direction and at the same speed, nonetheless the bodies contained in it would always seem to be outstripped by the movement of both. Or if they should be carried around as if one with the air, neither the one nor the other would appear as outstripping, or being outstripped by, the other. But these bodies would always remain in the same relative position and there would be no movement or change either in the case of flying bodies or projectiles. And yet we shall clearly see all such things taking place as if their slowness or swiftness did not follow at all from the earth's movement." (*ibid.* p. 12)

It is important to note here how fair and openminded Ptolemy actually is. Unlike many scientists who indulge in controversy, he does not call the advocates of a theory he rejects by harsh names. He admits that the theory he opposes might even be simpler, but he cannot accept it because its claims are contrary to the evidence as he sees and understands it. To him it seemed perfectly natural that motion belonged more properly to light objects than to a heavy mass like the earth's. Experience proves that to be so; objects on earth when dropped from a height would have to fall behind the point from which they were released, that is westward. If carried by the air, how could they have a motion independent of it? Without our concepts of force and velocity, which were still fifteen centuries removed, and with the notions of matter and motion prevailing at the time, how was it possible for him to reason any differently? The reasoning he did indulge in was in principle as sound, realistic, consistent and scientific as is ours today in the light of our own basic assumptions and concepts of forces, velocities, gravity, and momentum. Should these undergo changes in the future, the people of that era will view us in no different a light, and on the whole with the same amount of sympathy and harshness as we view Ptolemy. They will be as human as we are.

With the summation of his fundamental hypotheses out of the way, Ptolemy proceeds to develop the major basic theorems of plane and spherical trigonometry without using our modern terminology such as sine, cosine, tangent, etc., but employing the relations they stand for. The theorems of plane trigonometry which he develops are for the sake of compiling a Table of Chords, and those of spherical trigonometry are for the purpose of determining arcs, hence angular distances, in various parts of the heavens.

An example of each of these two steps will demonstrate their value. Consider a circle in which AD is a diameter. From point A draw lines AB and AC, which are given in terms of the diameter. Euclid had shown how it is possible to find the length of any side of a polygon in terms of the diameter or radius. He had shown, for example, that the radius of a circle is equal to the side of an inscribed hexagon, and employing the principle of extreme and mean ratios, to find the sides of other polygons. Beginning with these Euclidean rules, Ptolemy develops an extension which is known by his name as the "Theorem of Ptolemy," demonstrated in above diagram and declaring, that the product of the diagonals of a quadrilateral inscribed in a circle, is equal to the sum of the products of the two sets of opposite sides. This means that

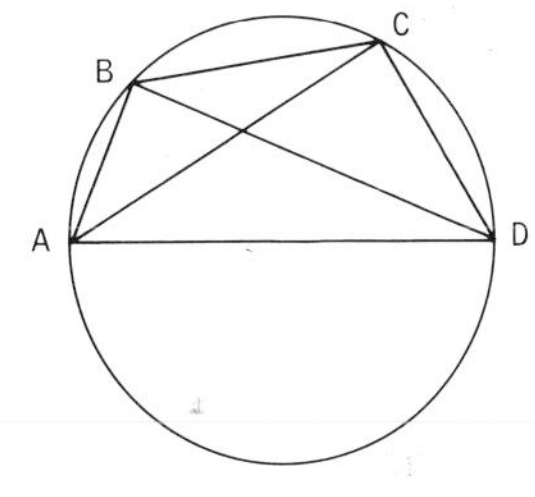

Figure 9.3

$$AC \times BD = AB \times CD + BC \times AD$$

Now, Euclid had proved as much for any quadrilateral, but Ptolemy introduced the valuable modification of making one side of the quadrilateral, here side AD, the diameter of the circle. Since in all his calculations he assigns to the diameter the value of 120 units, he is able to express the lengths of all the other lines as ratios to this length, hence in terms of common units. Now, all lines in a circle are chords, which by definition are any straight lines joining any two points on the circumference. All the six lines in the above diagram are chords and all subtend respective arcs and central angles.

Ptolemy uses his theorem to find the length of line BC when lines AB, AC and of course the diameter AD (120 units) are given. In other words, given the lengths of chords of an inscribed square or hexagon, which is simple enough to calculate, any other chord could readily be found by means of a few simple equations which he elaborated. He then performs the actual task of calculating the numerical values of the chords of all central angles from 0° to 180° at intervals of half a degree, a total of 360 values. Today we can obtain these values in a somewhat simpler fashion, since the chord of 30°, for example, is in our own trigonometric terminology, 2 sin 30/2 = 2 sin 15°. But we must possess a table of the sines of all angles.

Ptolemy next proceeds to extend his method to arcs of circles on a sphere, hence to what we call spherical trigonometry. He does that in order to tackle the practical problems of astronomy proper. For example:

Consider a given locality, in this case Rhodes. The problem Ptolemy poses is: "Given the magnitude of the longest day, how the arcs on the horizon intercepted by the equator and the ecliptic are given." The meaning of this question is as follows. Consider our location in Minneapolis, northern latitude 45°. On September 22, and on March 21, the sun rises true east and sets true west, approximately. These days are equinoxes, equal day and night, twelve hours each. On December 22 the sun rises the farthest south of east, is at noon at its lowest point in the sky, and sets south of west. Conversely, on June 22 it rises north of east, rises to its highest point in the sky at noon, and sets at a point north of west. The question is, if I know the lengths of the longest and shortest days of a given locality, can I determine how many degrees south of east the sun rises on December 21, which angle will also tell me how many degrees north of east it rises on June 22, the two angles being symmetrical about the point of true east. (Figure 9.4)

In the solution of this problem, Ptolemy makes use of a rule known as the "theorem of Menelaus" contained in that author's *Sphaerica,* composed probably toward the end of the first century A. D. Here is the diagram of what is known and what is looked for in the question posed. (Figure 9.5)

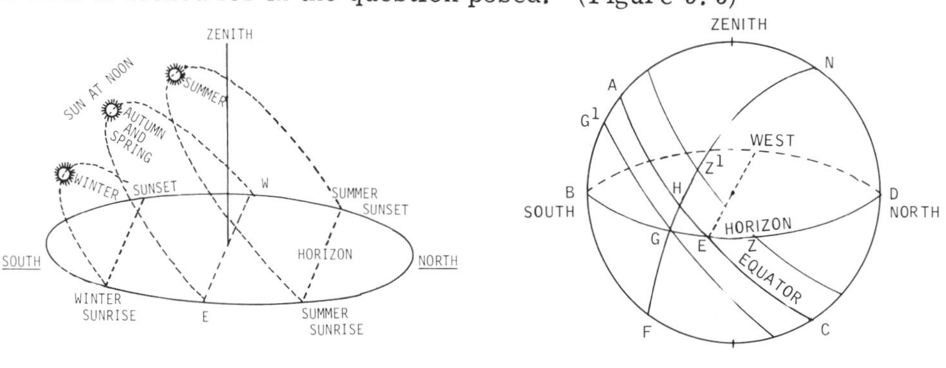

Figure 9.4

Figure 9.5

Let the circle ABCD represent the local meridian, a great circle running through the zenith and the north and south points, and let BED be the eastern semicircle of the horizon, AEC the semicircle of the equator, F a pole, G the point of the winter tropic, meaning the southernmost point where the sun rises on the shortest day of the year at that location. The point E marks true east on the horizon and arc FGH will equal to a quadrant of the great circle through points F and G. It is required to find the arc EG on the horizon, hence the distance from true east to the point of southernmost sunrise which will be equal to the arc to the right of E, extending from it to the summer tropic, the point of northernmost sunrise.

As the sky revolves from east to west, it is evident that points G and H will be on the meridian ABCD at the same time. This means that when point H reaches A on the meridian, the sun rising at G will also culminate, that is be on the meridian circle, hence marking noon, at G^1. An equal arc will bring point H on to the western horizon, not shown, but on the other side of point A. The night hours, again considering the movement of the equator, will consist of twice the arc, CH, (point H is where it is at sunrise) one from the west to C and the other from C to H, "for the sections above and below the earth of the circles parallel to the equator are exactly cut in half by the meridian." In other words, the sun rising at G will describe for its day equivalent arcs to two HA, and the night will last two CH arcs.

Note that "the arc EH is half the difference between the shortest or longest day and the equinoctial day." This means that the longest day, June 21, is longer than March 21 by the same amount as March 21 is longer than December 21. Thus, $ZZ^1 = 2$ EH.

Now the longest day at Rhodes is $14\frac{1}{2}$ equatorial hours; an equatorial hour being $360°/24 = 15°$. The shortest day is $9\frac{1}{2}$ hours. Hence EH = $\frac{1}{2}$ $(14\frac{1}{2} - 12) = \frac{1}{2}(12 - 9\frac{1}{2}) = 1\frac{1}{4}$ hour. On the basis of one hour being equal to the sky's motion of 15°, $1\frac{1}{4}$ hour = $18° \; 45^1$ and the remainder of the arc, HA, equals $71° \; 15^1$ in time, since arc EA is 90° and HA is the difference $90° - 18° \; 45^1 = 71° \; 15^1$.

To find the arcs that are wanted, Ptolemy employs the Theorem of Menelaus, which is:

$$\frac{\text{chord 2 arc HA}}{\text{chord 2 arc AE}} = \frac{\text{chord 2 arc FH}}{\text{chord 2 arc FG}} \cdot \frac{\text{chord 2 arc BG}}{\text{chord 2 arc EB}};$$

Now, angle 2 arc HA is known from observed measurement, and therefore the chord can be obtained from the Table of Chords described above. The same applies to the term in the denominator, 2 arc AE, the terms 2 arc FH, and 2 arc FG (this is FH, 90°, minus GH, the arc of the obliquity of ecliptic, or distance between equator and lowest or highest point of sun on meridian, which was taken as $23°51^120''$ by Ptolemy, about $23\frac{1}{2}°$ today). Two unknown quantities remain, arc BG and arc EB. The other values being known, however, we know the value of the ratio chord 2 arc BG/chord 2 arc EB. Now, arc EB is a quadrant, or a quarter of the circle of the horizon. Therefore 2 arc EB is equal to 180° or a diameter whose numerical value is also known, having been assigned 120 units at the very start. Thus, we are left with one unknown which is readily solved. We find the chord and from it determine arc BG, which turns out to be 60°, and EG is therefore 30°. This means that on December 21 the sun will rise 30° south of east and on June 22, 30° north of east and set correspondingly. At noon on December 21 it will be, of course $23\frac{1}{2}$° south of the equator and on June 22, $23\frac{1}{2}$° north of the equator.

In the very same manner, Ptolemy proceeds with the next proposition: "Now agian, with this given, let it be required to find the height of the pole; that is arc BF of the meridian." In other words, knowing the length of the longest day, what is the latitude of the place. The answer is obtained by the use of the same Theorem. Similarly with the converse. Suppose we know the latitude, which is readily measured as the angle of elevation of the north star, "let it be required to find the difference between the longest or shortest day and the equinoctial day, that is twice arc EH."

In the same Book II, Ptolemy employs this method to obtain all points of information which it can possibly yield to present all data of descriptive astronomy up to latitudes of 84° N. In this section he lays down, as he says, "those things which have first to be completely grasped mathematically concerning the heavens and the earth, and also concerning the obliquity of the sun's path through the middle of the zodiac along the ecliptic and its particular incidents in the right sphere and the oblique sphere for each latitude." (Equator and ecliptic)

2. The Sun and Superior Planets

Book III deals with the theory of the sun, meaning that all available data dealing with the movement of the sun are gathered and a mathematical scheme proposed which gives a rational, scientific and orderly explanation of the rules governing its conduct. Actually, the theory of the sun happens to emerge as the simplest and easiest of all the theoretical constructs for the motions of the planets because the sun is uniquely situated. The sun happens to move in the plane of the ecliptic which is the main reference position for the movements of the other planets and serves as base lines for their superimposed complexities. Moreover, a point should be raised here which many students often overlook. Whether we assume the sun to revolve around the earth or the earth to revolve around the sun, the mathematical theory of the relations between the two bodies is much the same. Hence the overall picture of the sun's motion in the Ptolemaic Theory will be generally identical with that of the earth's motion in the Copernican.

Let us give a brief statement of what Ptolemy accomplished. We know that the sun is seen to complete in a solar year its circular journey across the twelve signs of the zodiac. This path is marked by four key points, the two equinoxes and the two solstices. We saw that the sun's rate of motion in its path is not uniform. (See Figures 8. 7, 8 and 9) Ptolemy cites the values given by Hipparchus as $94\frac{1}{2}$ days for the interval between spring equinox and summer solstice, and $92\frac{1}{2}$ days for the interval between summer solstice and autumn equinox. From these data he obtained an eccentricity of 1/24. "We, too, came to the result that these values are nearly the same today." The apogee can also be calculated from these facts. The major task of the theory of the sun is to account for this non-uniform motion with its forcing the center of the sun's circle out of place.

We have already seen the nature and function of the eccentric circle and of the epicycle. Let us now see the problem Ptolemy faced. The planetary periods recorded by Hipparchus accorded well with the data established for their movements by the Babylonians. Such motions are observed first by the planet's motion against the stars, meaning that the planet makes a circle in the heavens from an initial position against some stars until its return to the exact, same position. This is its sidereal period. But in addition to this, the superior, or outer planets (Saturn, Jupiter, Mars) are observed also in relation to the sun, which in its annual swing around the heavens comes close to them, is in conjunction with them, and then moves away. This is actually the planet's epicycle. Because the planet is in motion eastward against the stars and so is the faster sun, we say the sun overtakes the planet. We term a synodic period the time for the sun to overtake the planet, which is equivalent to a revolution in the planet's epicycle.

Combining the observations of Hipparchus with his own, he found that Saturn made 57 synodic revolutions, meaning epicycles, in 59 years and 1 3/4 days; Jupiter, 65 synodic revolutions in 71 years and a fraction of a day; Mars, 37 synodic epicycles in 79 years and three and a fraction days. "These are the same multiples as used by the Babylonians," says Pannekoek. What these records mean is that, neglecting the extra days, in 59 years counted by an observer on earth, Saturn was shown to have made 57 loops, or epicycles. Therefore, Saturn made 59-57 or 2 sidereal revolutions in that time, 59 years. This gives for Saturn one revolution in $29\frac{1}{2}$ years. Similarly for Jupiter which has only 65 epicycles in 71 years, hence its sidereal period is 7 1/6 = 11.8 years, approximately and for Mars 79/42 or about 1.9 years.

Ptolemy divided the study of the movements of these three outer planets into two phases. He examined first the motion of the center of the planet's epicycle along the deferent, and analyzed next the motion of the planet along its epicycle. In its simplest form this is seen in the case of the sun. The sun moves on a perfect circle and at uniform speed, says his theory, and the circle is an eccentric one. The center of this circle is not in the earth but some distance from it, and the line joining that center and the earth is known as the "Line of Apsides," which joins the perigee with apogee. This line is

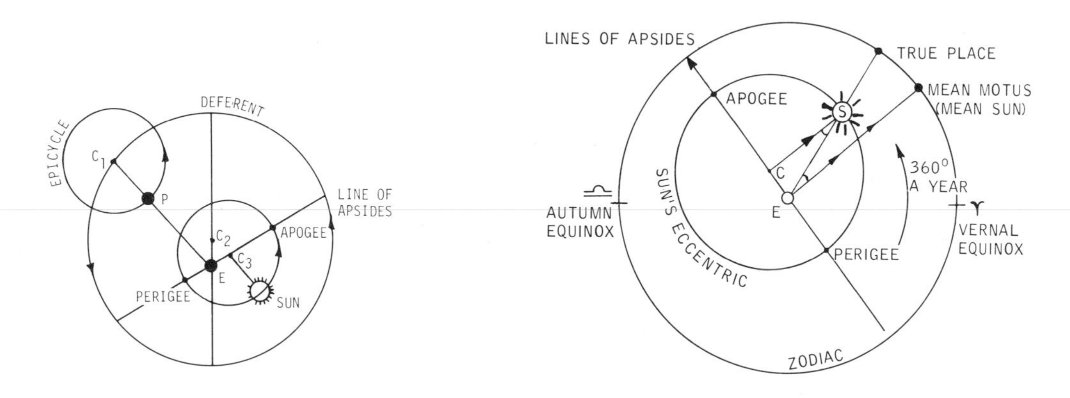

Figure 9.6 Figure 9.7

fixed in the zodiac so that it shifts along with it in the precession of the equinoxes. The distance between the earth and the true center of the sun's circular path is the eccentricity, characterizing the degree of deviation of the sun's path from its use of the earth as its center. As is to be expected from the preceding section, the eccentricity is expressed as a fraction of the ratio of this distance to the diameter or radius. This ratio is important since all ancient measurements of celestial motions are recorded as angles in which the length of the radius is of no importance. With this fraction, such readings assume significance in representing some linear dimensionality.

While the sun's circle has a center off the earth, all its actual measurements are recorded as angular values from the earth. This requires a correction which is best accomplished by establishing a unifromly moving base-line or reference line fixed on earth with respect to which the sun's motion in its path can always be compared. This line which moves uniformly along the ecliptic, like the hand of a clock, is known as the Mean Motus, measured in signs, degrees, and minutes, each sign being 30 degrees. Its starting point is always the First Point of Aries, or the place where the sun is on the vernal equinox, the point of intersection of the equator and ecliptic on the sun's upward seasonal journey. The Mean Motus thus overlooks all regional inequalities in the sun's motion and functions as an average, or what we call today the Mean Sun. The True Sun will be at times ahead of it or behind it, the maximal deviation being $2\frac{1}{2}°$. This maximum deviation from the mean was called by Ptolemy the "Equation of Center."

The mean motus is an abstract standard with which to compare the actual movement of the sun. Ptolemy next introduces a line parallel to it and drawn from the eccentric's center to the sun, so as to have a line moving parallel to the motus but emanating from the center rather than the earth. This line as seen in the diagram serves to locate the "true place" of the sun as seen from the earth by drawing a line from the earth to the actual position of the sun on the eccentric circle.

The term Angle of Anomaly is employed to designate the angle the sun makes with the Line of the Aux. When the sun crosses that line the sun is at its apogee, or furthest distance from the earth. Contrariwise, when the sun crosses the extension of that line at its opposite end, it is at perigee. Mean Anomaly is the name given to the sun's angle with Aux at C, and True Anomaly at E, earth; the difference between these two angles is the Equation of the Center. These terms and concepts complete the so-called Theory of the Sun.

The year begins with the sun at the First of Aries, ♈, on which occasion the Mean Motus and the sun's "True Place" are identical. With the passage of time the Mean Motus moves at a uniform pace while the sun moves ahead, at some months slowly and at other times rapidly. The True Place thus comes to differ from the Mean Motus. The angle Mean Motus - Earth - True Place is the Equation of Center. The sun's orbit is eccentric and the center of that circle can be found by drawing parallels to the Mean Motus through the Sun's observed True Places. The Theory of the Sun is therefore relatively simple, fully accounts for the observed facts, and supplies an unseen, feasible, and appealing geometrical scheme that accounts for the observed facts.

Books IV, V, and VI deal with the data and Theory of the Moon, Book VII with the fixed stars, and the remaining Books, the most original and significant part, with the five planets. The Theories of Mercury, Venus, Mars, Jupiter and Saturn, entail considerable mathematical complexity. Let us consider the three outer planets, which are seen in their sidereal revolution against the stars, and in their synodic or solar epicycles due to the motion of the sun in passing them. We know today that what the ancients called the planet's epicycle, that is, its apparent twist around the sun, is actually due to the *earth's* circular turn around the sun, which makes us think it is the outer planet that performs the twist. Similarly, when we are on a train and the train turns a sharp corner we think it is the houses which turn. Since the planet's epicycle was dependent on the sun's motion, was connected with it, Ptolemy made the radius of the epicycle, C_1P, (Figure 9.6) always parallel to C_3S, the radius of the sun's eccentric circle around the earth, E. On the basis of this assumption, the center of the epicycle can be found when the sun and planet are in opposition. By recording several oppositions, the position of the earth within the deferent circle can be geometrically established.

In practice, Ptolemy found that step difficult to achieve because he noted that C_1 (Figure 9.6) as seen from C_2, the deferent's true center, did not "describe equal angles in equal time." But such uniformity of angular motion was regarded as natural and essential by him and by most geometers and astronomers. Ptolemy, therefore, devised a clever scheme to obtain just such a situation, as we today postulate particles or atomic forces to retain some fundamental principle which we consider indispensable or unimpeachably true.

As can be seen from Figure 9.8 and 9.9, equal angular velocity can be maintained under certainconditions. In Figure 9.8 we have a circle whose center is 0 but which is eccentric with respect to the earth. A celestial body P, such as the sun can be made to have equal angular velocities with respect to the center, 0, with its perigee at G and apogee at C, and be seen from the earth to move at times slowly and at times rapidly, as is the case with the sun. The solar annual motion can be well explained by this eccentric circle and, with respect to an imaginary center 0, the angular velocity can be held constant, angles Θ being equal.

In Figure 9.9 we have another kind of clever device. Here we have a deferent along which the epicycle center, C_1, moves irregularly. The axiom of uniform angular velocity can be saved, and was so saved by Ptolemy, by postulating an equant or "*Equalizing point*", E_1, located at a distance E_10 = OE

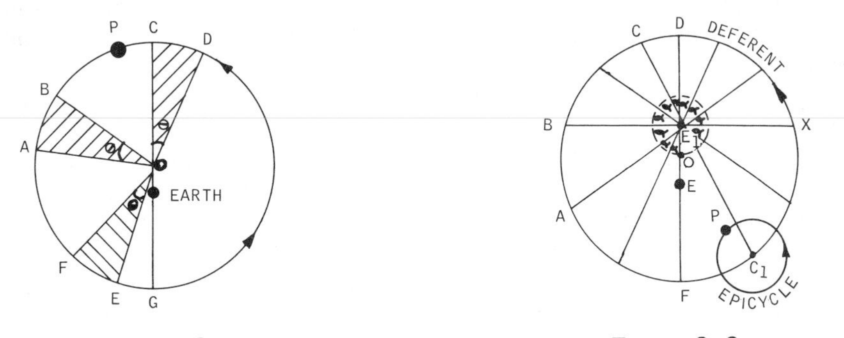

Figure 9.8

Figure 9.9

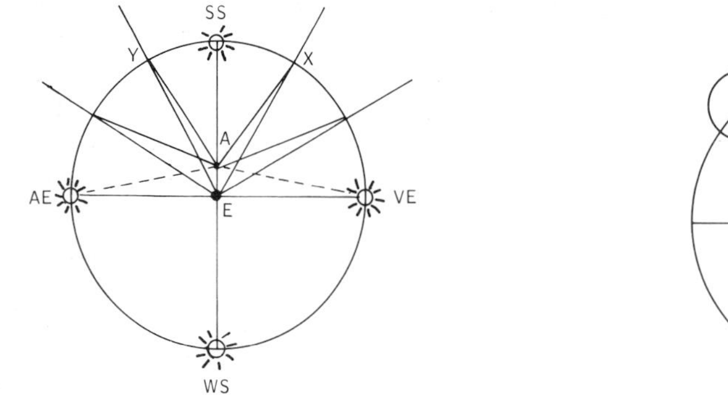

Figure 9.10

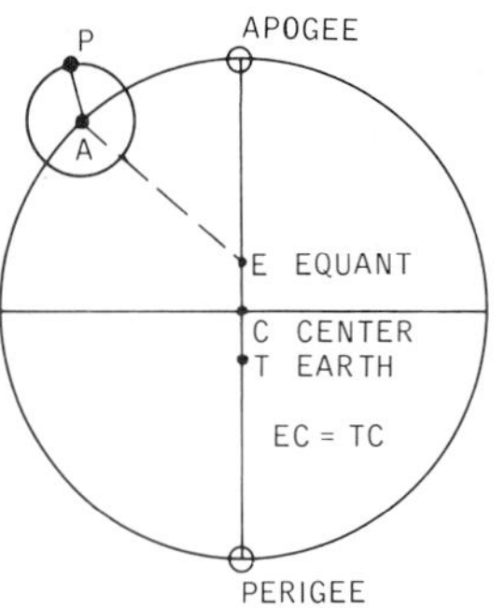

Figure 9.11

from 0, the true center of the deferent circle. The merit of this contrivance is that the angular velocity of the epicycle center can be described as uniform. At the apogee, point D, nearest the equant point, E_1, it appears to go slowly, while at perigee, F, it appears to go rapidly yet the angles (α) at E_1 measure alike. Thus by a trick an axiom is saved, just as in religion the unallowed is permitted by an acceptable pretense or subterfuge. Ptolemy is fully aware of the trick since he merely states: "We found that" by doing this or that the data are nicely and permissively coordinated.

The equant seems to have been contributed entirely by Ptolemy alone. Its actual function can best be seen from the following illustration. Consider the case of the sun, which as already mentioned, does not revolve at uniform speed about the earth. This means that arc VE-SS-AE (Figure 9.10) is greater than arc AE-WS-VE. By the calendar, the former is six days longer than the latter. This would mean that the angle subtended by the Sun at E per day or month would not be uniform. Non-uniform angular motion was wholly unacceptable to Ptolemy and he, therefore, tried to save the situation by postulating uniform angular motion in actuality, though unique circumstances made it appear non-uniform to an observer on earth. This is far from reprehensible, since it constitutes the essence of science. After all, Copernicus also explained the planetary loops as visible appearances of actually unseen motions. Similarly, Ptolemy, loyal to the principle of uniform angular motion, postulated the existence of an equant, or an ideal center, some determinable distance from the earth, the circle's perceptible center, which arrangement could be shown to serve the desired purpose. Starting from VE, the sun moves toward SS and AE. If it were to move 30 degrees every month of equal duration, it could only cover an angle of 180° from VE to AE. If it moves with respect to A, however, it can describe more than 180° and thus account for the longer duration of this period as against the remainder, the tour from AE to VE. What is most important, the sun would then be moving at uniform angular velocity. True, it does not perform its task with E as the center, as it should, but with A, an arbitrarily inserted point. To Ptolemy, this seemed right, nevertheless, since it saved the principle of uniform angular motion. To Copernicus this seemed inelegant and wholly unjustified.

Note in addition that this arrangement explains as well how the angular motion from X to Y, which is uniform with respect to A, will appear as a smaller angle, hence slower, with regard to E and larger with regard to A. This accords with the data, since July and August are long months, the sun moving slowly in that part of the sky, as noted by Kepler's Second Law.

Ptolemy also makes use of the equant in an eccentric circle, as in his equation of the moon. The line of apsides, or the line joining the apogee with perigee, contains the center, C, of a circle about the earth, T, which is also located on the same line. (Figure 9.11) The planet moves on an epicycle of center A which moves along the deferent. E is a point equidistant from the deferent's center with T, earth. Hence EC = CT. The point E has no physical significance. It is a point from which the line EA moves along the deferent circle at uniform velocity, describing equal angles in equal times. Two centers are thus created: E the center of equal motion, and C the center of equal distance. The reason for postulating this ambivalence is the same as the reason for postulating epicycles, eccentrics, or movable eccentrics, namely, that by assuming such a geometrical axiom, the observed data are made to fit the postulated configuration.

Ptolemy's calculations led him to find the values of eccentricities and the positions or directions of the line of the Aux, hence apogee and perigee, of the three planets. As stated this was obtained from several records of past oppositions as well as from his own observations. In this task he employed the method of successive approximations that served his purposes very well.

The next problem that faced him was the job of finding the size of the epicycles, i.e. their radii. This he obtained from taking positions of the planets outside their oppositions and applying again geometric computations by triangulation. The results he obtained are quite accurate. Says the astronomer Pannekoek, "A comparison with modern theory may convince us that this simple structure of circles in space excellently represents the details in the planetary motions which formerly looked so capricious and intricate." (p. 141)

A somewhat different situation is encountered with the inner planets, Mercury and Venus. These planets move around the earth in pace with the sun along a deferent upon which they perform their epicycles, whose elongations east and west of the sun vary and can be observed. By taking the greatest elongation at apogee and perigee of Venus' deferent, he obtained the radius of the epicycle. With Mercury the situation presented serious difficulties. The planet being so near the sun it is not easily or frequently seen and its elongation not reaily measured. Moreover, its orbit is more irregular and Ptolemy had to use an oval orbit for its epicycle center, generated by a combination of circles. The results, though far from satisfactory, constituted, nevertheless, a fairly good approximation in view of the toughness of the problem.

To account for the planet's deviations in latitude, that is, their appearing at times above and at other times below the ecliptic, Ptolemy resorted to a simple but again as usual with him, very felicitous device of introducing small inclinations of the deferent to the ecliptic, and next of the epicycle to the deferent. By means of these two inclinations he could raise the planet above and below the ecliptic to the desired distances. This introduced some real complexities because, as already indicated, Greek physics never allowed a planet to move suspended in space but visualized it as fixed either to a radius or to a sphere. Mathematical though Ptolemy was, he assumed that a planet was actually attached to the epicycle's radius. If this was so, then at different parts of the ecliptic the deviations would appear either north or south of it, respectively. He therefore strained the geometric machinery to insert in it vertical circles that would bring about suitable up and down oscillations to keep the deviations where they were needed to fit the data.

The strange-sounding Ptolemaic terminology was as important to his mode of thought and to his effort at erecting a coherent mathematical system as is the terminology of modern physics to our current needs to understand the nature of the atom. In reality, Ptolemy's theory of the planets rests upon two main angles, the motus, which relates to the position of the epicycle center on the eccentric circle, and the argument, which correspondingly governs the position of the planet on the epicycle. This is understandable enough, since if you have two devices to account for the two motions of the planet, namely its own revolution about the sun and its positional shifts due to the revolution of the earth which carries the observer with it, then you must necessarily have two corresponding baselines with which to designate the motions of each. The Mean Motus and Mean Argument function as angles that increase uniformly with time and can therefore be computed for all times and for the four planets, much like the 24 hours of the day for a railroad time schedule. In addition, however, both of these angles are corrected respectively by the introduction of the True Motus and the True Argument, respectively, which do not increase uniformly but show variability in orbital motion.

3. The Inferior Planets

Equally brilliant and intricate is Ptolemy's treatment of the inner planets. The two planets are made to revolve on an epicycle the center of which can correspond with the apparent position of the sun as seen from the earth, even though the sun is not actually at the epicycle's center. This introduces a simplification because the sun, Mercury, and Venus have the same Mean Motus, since their motions are linked to each other, and therefore employ the same reference point. In reality, the system as a whole acquired so far only three independent guides for motion: the Mean Motus of the sun, to which to refer the irregularity in the sun's annual motion; the Mean Motus of the three outer planets, to serve as reference for them and for the two inner planets; the Mean Argument, which measures the angular relationship of a planet on its epicycle about the sun as its apparent center, measured with respect to a line parallel to mean motus. Given these elements, all other functions can be obtained.

The two celestial bodies, Mercury and the moon, displayed special features requiring unique treatment, both somewhat more complicated than the theories considered so far. To account for the special complexity of Mercury's orbit, Ptolemy introduced a rather intricate scheme in which the center of the planet's eccentric (the center deferent) is taken out of its usual position between earth and equant, and is made to describe a circle about another center on the Line of the Aux, situated as far from the equant as the equant is from the earth. The radius of this circle joined to the center deferent moves in a clockwise direction, while the circling line from the equant which is parallel to and moves with the Mean Motus, revolves in the opposite direction, both at equal speeds so that they merge when in the direction of the Line of the Aux. Further, this movable center deferent has a radius coming out of it which is of fixed length and which is made to describe an oval deferent in place of the usual eccentric circle. Upon this deferent rides the center of the epicycle carrying the planet. By means of these unusually intricate geometrical devices, the epicycle center can be brought significantly far and near the mean center of Mercury's revolution, so as to approximate as much as possible the observed segments of Mercury's path.

Somewhat similar in its unorthodoxy is the scheme for the moon's path. Here both invented points, the equant and center deferent, are made to be fixed at opposite ends of a rotating diameter of a little circle with the earth as its center. Both Mean Motus of the moon and the Mean Motus of the sun are anchored in the earth and can yield the positions of the center deferent and equant. All the other values can then be obtained with their aid. The final paths obtained harmonize quite well with the actual observations in all instances except Mercury, a difficult planet at best.

In the book of Genesis God viewed His creation and found it good. Ptolemy was not so unreservedly pleased with his geometrical edifice. He realized its great complexity and felt obligated to comment: "Let nobody, looking at the imperfection of our human contrivances, regard the hypotheses here proposed as too artificial. We must not compare human beings with things divine.... The simplicity itself of the celestial processes should not be judged according to what is held simple among men.... For if we should look at it from this human point of view, nothing of all that happens in the celestial realms would appear to us to be simple at all, not even the very inscrutability of the first i. e. daily rotation of heavens, because for us human beings this very unchangeableness, eternal as it is, is not only difficult, but entirely impossible." In such words, one of the greatest geniuses of mankind seeks to apologize for the inordinately clever edifice he constructed which, taking geometry at its face value as a mathematical instrument, he employed to perfection so as to inject logic, order and beauty into a jungle of observational confusion.

4. The System in Perspective

Such, then, is the nature of a bold but Herculean construction built on geometry. It is well known to us today that the outcome did not turn out to be the final answer, that the theory did not account too well for all that was demanded of it, and that subsequent schemes, namely those of Copernicus and Kepler, which led to Newton's great synthesis, performed their task far better. Moreover, the subsequent theories expanded their language to generate newer mathematical terms, concepts, and procedures of a nature that not only encompassed and ordered all the known data, and made numerous verifiable predictions, but stood up firmly in the light of the multifaceted expansion of later astronomy and other fields of science having any bearing at all upon its elements and conclusions.

Is Arthur Koestler correct in his statement that "there is something profoundly distasteful about Ptolemy's universe; it is the work of a pedant with much patience and little originality, doggedly piling 'orb in orb...' Ptolemy completed the unfinished job, without contributing any idea of great theoretical value.... It was a monumental and depressing tapestry, the product of tired philosophy and decadent science. But nothing else turned up to replace it for nearly a millenium and a half." (*The Sleepwalkers,* New York, 1959, p. 69) Surely neither the adjective "tired" nor "decadent" can be applied to Ptolemy personally, nor can these terms be applied rightly to an era that produced men like Ptolemy and Galen within a generation. The claim that science in those years was less animated than at other times, is highly questionable. Many believe that century to be the peak of ancient science. What is needed is to understand Ptolemy, not to judge him. Most of his readers to this day are awed and overpowered by his geometrical skill and attainments. Besides, the decadence of Ptolemy's era can hardly explain the inability of sixty generations, fifteen centuries, to substitute a better theory for his.

It is true that as Koestler puts it: "Ptolemy makes it clear why astronomy must renounce all attempts to explain the *physical* reality behind it: because the heavenly bodies, being of a divine nature, obey laws different from those to be found on earth. No common link exists between the two; therefore we can know nothing about the physics of the skies." (*ibid.,* p. 74) Aristotle, in his *Physics, On the Heavens, On Corruption and Generation,* and elsewhere, accepts this idea wholeheartedly, but bases it entirely on evidence and not on inner voices or poetic preference. Where could one see in our earthbound experience uniform circular motion in which no resistance of a medium was to be detected? Consider Aristotle's reasoning concerning the celestial movements as causes of events on earth which he describes as "coming-to-be and passing-away," meaning growth and decay, birth and death. "We have assumed, and have proved, that coming-to-be and passing-away happen to things continuously; and we assert that motion causes coming-to-be. That being so, it is evident that, if the motion be single, both processes cannot occur since they are contrary to one another; for it is a law of nature that the same cause, provided it remain in the same condition, always produces the same effect, so that, from a single motion, either coming-to-be or passing-away will always result. The movements must, on the contrary, be more than one, and they must be contrasted with one another either by the sense of their motion or by its irregularity: for contrary effects demand contraries as their causes.

"This explains why it is not the primary motion that causes coming-to-be and passing-away, but the motion along the inclined circle: for this motion not only possesses the necessary continuity but includes a duality of movement as well." (*Basic Works of Aristotle,* ed. Richard McKeon, New York, 1941, p. 526) The "inclined circle" means the zodiac, the path of the ecliptic, hence the sun's path in heaven. "For the consequence of the inclination is that the body becomes alternately remote and near; and since its distance is thus unequal, its movement will be irregular. Therefore, if it generates by approaching and by its proximity, it - this very same body - destroys by retreating and becoming remote; and if it generates by many successive approaches, it also destroys by many successive retirements.... And there are facts of observation in manifest agreement with our theories.... Thus, from the being of the 'upper revolution' it follows that the sun revolves in this determinate manner; and since the sun revolves thus, the seasons in consequence come-to-be in a cycle, i. e. return upon themselves; and since they come to be cyclically, so in their turn do the things whose coming-to-be the seasons initiate."

Clearly Aristotle weaves here a theory of cause and effect, but it is neither wild nor mystical. It is, in fact, quite realistic and plausible, since, after all, the sun's motion in its orbit, or as we would prefer to put it, the earth's motion in its orbit, is the cause of the seasons and all the "alterations" which are implied.

One can make a good case for the thesis that Aristotle had more evidence for his theoretical explanation of the causes of change in the sublunar world than has Koestler for asserting that "the three fundamental conceits of the new mythology were: the dualism of the celestial and sub-lunary worlds; the immobility of the earth in the centre; and the circularity of all heavenly motion. I have tried to show that the common denominator of the three, and the secret of their unconscious appeal, was the fear of change, the craving for stability and permanence in a disintegrating culture. A modicum of split-mindedness and double-think was perhaps not too high a price to pay for allaying the fear of the unknown." (*The Sleepwalkers,* p. 76) All three assumptions stated above can very well be explained as legitimate generalizations of reality universally honored at the time because they seemed so extremely reasonable and appealing. Indeed, they still seem so to anyone who wishes to put himself in the position of the eager and brilliant minds of those days. It is all in the attitude, really. Koestler is most sympathetic when he chooses, and he does choose to be magnificently sympthetic in his study of Kepler. But he seems harsh on Ptolemy, and the reasons he cites fail to carry conviction. For example, where in any of their writings do either Ptolemy or the equally great Galen display any fear of change, or of anything? Rome, according to most historians, enjoyed the great era of Pax Romana even into the third century A. D. The security of the borders was taken for granted; there was much prosperity everywhere, considerable local or national self government, fairly general honesty in administration, and the highest legal, civic and cultural life ever attained on a wo rldwide scale. Not only does Ptolemy show no signs of fear but he displays only one loyalty and that is to science. The dualism of terrestrial and celestial events was a basic axiom, honored by all. His arguments against the immobility of the earth were thoroughly sound and consistent w ith the prevailing belief-web. His conclusions could not be different from what they were; nor was there a single scholar of the times who wished to disagree with his logic. The circularity of all heavenly motion was a fact. Any other theory, particularly that of Aristarchus of Samos, would have to be regarded as false in the light of the times. How could it possibly have been defended?

The essence of scientific reasoning, it may justly be asserted, consists precisely of this dichotomy, of first having a theory that encompasses the bulk of the data and lays down a foundation for thought about them, and next, of explaining away deviations. Here is what a contemporary scientist has to say on this subject in a current issue of *Science:* "The experiments against which a theory must be tested are not merely those under direct consideration but the ones carried out over the past 50 to 100 years which have given us all-but-absolute, unshakable confidence in a certain structure of fundamental laws: quantum mechanics, relativity, statistical mechanics, the consequences of symmetry, the regular nature of crystals, the bond theory, and so on. I could give you tens of examples of the following general rule: a theory which contradicts some of the accepted principles and agrees with experiment is usually wrong; one which is consistent with them but disagrees with experiment is often not wrong, for we often find that experimental results change, and then the results fit the theory." (Anderson, P.W. Superconductivity. *Science* 1964, vol. 144, p. 373)

In other words, certain fundamental generalizations of deep and extensive reliability are not to be readily discarded or questioned. In the cited case, the contradictory material is a new experiment which seems to testify against established laws. In Ptolemy's case it was some deviations regarded as minor by comparison with the depth and merit of the theoretical generalization regarded as major and unchallengeable. In the former case one waits for new experimentation that will undo the odd, discordant or incomprehensible results; in the latter case one looked for some mechanism that could account for the existence of the odd, discordant, or incomprehensible results. Copernicus used this method in explaining the planetary loops in his heliostatic scheme, Galileo sought to fit the tides into the fundamental law of the earth's rotation, while Kepler on his part tried to coordinate all planetary motions with the principle of magnetic attraction. All of these were daring intellectual efforts, though only the first was crowned by nature with truth or satisfactory applicability. How else can a scientist think except by having a broad theory and then explaining rationally the possible forces or conditions that obscure the theory in some instances? Did Ptolemy really do any more than that?

Let us next consider the charge that "Ptolemy makes it clear why astronomy must renounce all attempts to explain the *physical* reality behind it." To begin with, Ptolemy in the *Almagest* seeks to present a mathematical theory. As has already been pointed out, in considering Aristotle's division of the theoretical pursuit into the physical, mathematical and theological, Ptolemy does not reject the physical explanation because different laws of physics operate in heaven. He rejects physical theory because, as he explicitly says, "its matter is unstable and obscure, so that for this reason philosophers could never hope to agree on them.... And especially were we led to cultivate that discipline, developed in respect to divine and heavenly things as being the only one concerned with the study of things which are always what they are, and therefore able itself to be always what it is - which is indeed the proper mark of a science - because of its own clear and ordered understanding, and yet to cooperate with the other disciplines no less than they themselves. For that special mathematical theory would most readily prepare the way to the theological, since it alone could take good aim at that unchangeable and separate act, so close to that act are the properties having to do with translations and arrangements of movements belonging to those heavenly beings which are sensible and both moving and moved, but eternal and impassible. Again, as concerns the physical, there would not be just chance correspondences. For the general property of the material essence is pretty well evident from the peculiar fashion of its local motion - for example, the corruptible and incorruptible from straight and circular movements, and the heavy and light or passive and active from movement to the center and movement from the center. And, indeed, this same discipline would, more than any other, prepare understanding persons with respect to nobleness of actions and character by means of the sameness, good order, due proportion, and simple directness contemplated in divine things, making its followers lovers of that divine beauty, and making habitual in them, and as it were natural, a like condition of the soul." (The *Almagest*, p. 6)

In other words, the mathematical theory adopted by him, he believes, would actually help theological as well as physical understanding. Its impact on understanding the physical world would be due not to mere incorruptible and circular motion, the chance correspondences, but to intimate causal links between the action of the corruptible (matter), and rectilinear movement, the action of heaviness and lightness upon motion toward and away from the center, and the like. It would seem as if Ptolemy is building bridges here and claiming continuity, or at least harmony, in interaction, rather than postulating different physical laws for the two worlds beyond the general differences which had long since been universally observed and considered established beyond question of doubt.

The fact remains that the Ptolemaic theory maintained itself because it was brilliant, consistent, beautiful in its richness of data and theorems, bewitching in its mathematical ingenuity, in its scope of coordination, and in its unparalleled challenge to the inquiring mind. It possessed no critics or challengers either in the Moslem world, which took it to its culture-hungry bosom for the duration of its bloom, lasting almost for seven centuries. It had no defamers or even reformers during the four centuries or more of its uncontested reign over the Christian world of learning. All this despite the fact that only the keenest philosophical and scholarly minds could grapple with the text and master it; and such minds would be most prone to detect weaknesses or inconsistencies. The work was never popular even among naturalists because of its intricacy. To say that these minds were blinded by some abstract dogma of the sacredness of a circle or fear of something or other, is equivalent to putting one's faith in a formula. Would it not be better and more respectful of learning, to conclude that the scholars of East and West worshipped the *Almagest* because they found it majestic, admirable, and inspiring? They said so, and their conduct verified their words. So why not believe them?

There is another point to be considered. Suppose Ptolemy had decided it was the task of the astronomer to include explanations of the "*physical* reality" behind celestial observations. Precisely what would he do about such a decision? What could he do? What physical knowledge was available at the time? Aristotle's *Physics* might give us one answer and Simplicius' *Commentary on the Physics* might serve to enlighten us further.

Compare Aristotle's study of biology, *The History of Animals,* with his *Physics*. His biological work is a classic of the first order that will serve as a monument to scientific pioneering for many centuries to come. It is experimental in that it reports the dissection of more than 500 animal species, it is perceptive in the selected area of study in that it raises highly significant problems which the subsequent development of the science took into account and fruitfully incorporated into its structure; it is philosophical in that it seeks to classify, coordinate and systematize the vast subject of animal life. It deals with accurate and detailed descriptions of structures and their respective functions, it covers the entire field of animal types, habits and reproduction, it deals with animal habitats and ecology, with animal psychology and effects on man and neighbors. It abounds in ideas, judgments and even some factual statements that turned out to be false. Yet the totality of these errors amount to a miniscule fraction of the true worth of the vast quantity of bold knowledge, originality of thought, and experimental skill and wisdom contained in any chapter of the work, let alone the total. The same could be said about another pioneering work in science - namely, *Enquiry Into Plants* by Aristotle's friend, pupil, and successor as head of the Lyceum, Theophrastus. Even Aristotle's *Meteorology* contains a considerable amount of basic science as well as some experimentation. For example, he states: "I have proved by experiment that salt water evaporated forms fresh and the vapour does not, when it condenses, condense into sea water again." It naturally contains much that is irrelevant.

With Aristotle's *Physics,* however, the situation is altogether different. It is not a pioneering book in science; it does not scan the territory of physics as we know it today, and it has no experimental data of any significance. It is rational, logical, abstract, speculative, and argumentative. It discusses casusality, chance, infinity, change, time, space, matter and form, the void, movement and rest, extension, "whatever is moved is moved by something," the moved, the mover and the immovable. "The immovable first movent is eternal and one," and finally, "the first movent has no parts nor magnitude, and is at the circumference of the world." What Aristotle sought to come to grips with was what we would today call the science of mechanics, and in that quest he failed utterly. The effort was doomed to failure.

Aristotle's *Physics* is a brilliant book as an exercise for the mind. It is full of clever thrusts and intricate logical performances. It gives the mind a good workout and leaves the reader with the feeling that here was a job well worth doing. After finishing it one feels a gratifying sense of mental satiety mingled with fatigue, but no regrets except for the fact that concretely one learned little, that the entire effort was a false lead, and that one labored and sweated to climb the wrong mountain. Not that Aristotle is to blame for this disappointment. The act of blaming is an emotional wasteland in which weak or disturbed minds practice some catharsis which, while beneficial to them, bears no genuine fruit. The fact remains that there was no science of physics and apparently there could not have been one at that time. The work of Archimedes stood alone and led nowhere. Velocity, acceleration, and force were a knotty tangle in the skein which Aristotle called motion and with which he wrestled in vain. He never even came to grips with any phase of the problem. Their clarification lay far in the offing of history with much toil to be expended and frustration to be harvested before being reached. No other wedges seemed available for breaking into the problems of the vast and fascinating horizon. The separation of phenomena within the sublunar world from those in the heavens was not the cause of the sad state physics was in. It was part of the general blockage of progress in that sector of knowledge until time and fortune would deliver unto man some handle with which to grasp a workable tool, some idea with which to pierce the impenetrable, some spark of light with which to discern anything at all in the defiant darkness. None was to show up for centuries to come.

The vagueness concerning the nature of physics, its subject matter, was shared by others besides Aristotle. According to Geminus, cited in Chapter 8, Section 4 above, physical inquiry deals with the substance of the heavens, their force and quality, their coming into being and passing away. Precisely how could any of these items be studied in those days? The answer is - in no way whatever. Moreover, neither Geminus, nor Simplicius, nor Aristotle, nor Ptolemy, ever consciously rejected the physical nature of the heavenly bodies. Aristotle even treated the spheres as if they were real and manifested earthly properties, for which reason he inserted additional spheres as insulation against mutual impact. Only the element of which they were composed was different, which is indeed still valid today. We even go further and say that not only are the stellar temperatures and the state of matter in them vastly different, but the very reactions occurring there are nuclear or of plasma type. Surely, these are of a totally different genre from the chemical reactions on earth. Furthermore, the ancients studied sizes and distances where possible, and used arithmetic and geometry because those methods seemed best suited. Their minds had no other means of approach. In the realm of physics, the most brilliant minds stood baffled and helpless in facing the concepts of force, movement, and energy, the existence of which they instinctively perceived but for the study of which they could muster neither tool, nor design, nor perceive the vaguest glimpse how any aspect of these problems was to be tackled. But "geometry and arithmetic" did present fascinating pathways for inquiry, with many gratifying returns. Those were the uncharted roads that the geniuses of the time pursued, and the fruits of their efforts proved worthy in many ways.

Had they struggled to apply the concepts and procedures of physics as understood at the time, the effort would have been as sterile as is much of Aristotle's physics from the viewpoint of scientific progress. It is only by keeping out the physical principles, causes and forces, and by choosing mathematics as their sole tool, that in part Eudoxus, but especially Ptolemy, succeeded in erecting the first great theoretical edifices of science, thereby pioneering in the realm of theory-construction. The Ptolemaic theory proved monumental in its mathematical grandeur. In spite of its complexity and inaccessibility even to hardened students, it managed to dominate the field of thought even for a century or so after the appearance of the work of Copernicus, its first challenger. It suffered no dramatic rejection after the debut of Tycho Brahe's clever compromise, and bowed out of the arena of science only by the onslaught of time and its cohorts of new tools, new discoveries, and new vistas.

5. Two Functional Ptolemaic Models

In his book the *Almagest,* or *Mathematical Composition,* Ptolemy describes a model, or an instrument, which he calls the *armillary sphere,* or *armilla,* ring in Latin. It has remained unchanged in the intervening eighteen centuries, which is a record for any complex apparatus of this nature and can be as functionally useful today as it ever was in his day or in the subsequent ages. A working model of it is shown in Figure 9.12. In teaching descriptive astronomy it is still most helpful. Together with the Ptolemaic model shown in Figure 9.13, it should be available in every relevant arsenal of demonstrations at both high school and college level in our own day.

The armilla consists of a series of rings. The outermost one (A) is graduated into 360°, is fixed to the base and represents a graduated local meridian. The instrument is placed so that this outer ring is in the true North-South plane, the meridian. Within it, ring B sits snugly, free to rotate. All the rings to be seen inside B are attached to it so that by revolving B, all the others revolve with it. Ring B has two axes built into it. One axis, located unseen on the third inner ring marked C is affixed where the two letters C are inscribed. This axis contains only this ring and no other; the ring is used entirely as a marker, or alidade, as will be seen below. The second axis embedded in ring B is seen in the diagram and is affixed to ring B where the two letters B are inscribed. This axis carries two rings, one perpendicular to the other, D and E. These two are firmly attached to each other, as is shown by the angular attachment, n. These two rings also carry a wire circle, r, firmly attached. On the same axis BB there sits an inner graduated circle within which there is the last ring, G, which turns snugly within F and carries two sights on it, for locating celestial bodies.

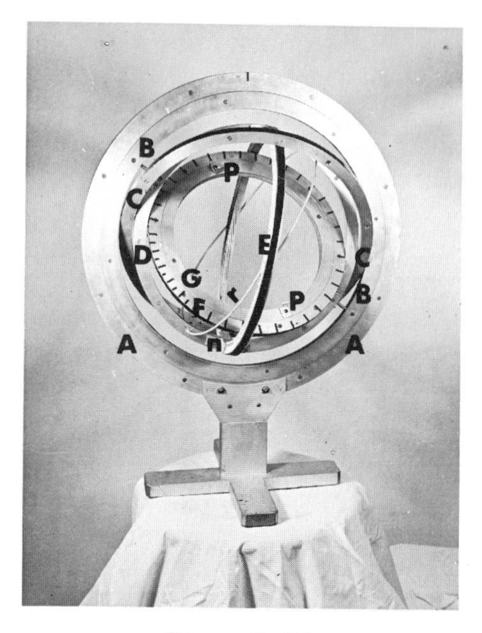

Figure 9.12

By placing this armilla so that A is in the plane of the meridian, one then rotates B until the upper end of the axis it carries points to the North Star, hence to the angle of the local latitude read off on ring A. The armilla in the diagram is adjusted to latitude 45° N, with the North Star at left. The instrument thus placed represents the sphere of the sky with the celestial axis precisely where it should be for the local horizon. The wire ring, r, is the celestial equator, and ring E is the band of the zodiac on which are engraved the names of the signs, each of which is graduated to the number of days in its month. Ring C is an indicator and can be turned freely against fixed D and E. If the date is unknown and the sun is shining, ring C is rotated against the inner set of rings until it lies in line with the sun, that is until the shadow of one semicircle of it falls upon the other half, which means that the ring lies in a plane perpendicular to the disc of the sun. With this achieved, the date can be read off from the graduated scale on the zodiacal sign of ring E on which the shadow falls. The shadow can be at two spots, 180° or six months apart, but the proper day can be readily chosen. The date can in this manner be obtained from a knowledge of the sun's position in the sky, regardless of hour of day. Conversely, knowing the date, one can determine the latitude of the place.

Rings F and G can revolve inside D and E; they function to locate any celestial body besides the sun. The moon, planet or star can be sighted through the two sights, p, on the inner ring and the elevation above the equator (declination) and arc along the equator from the vernal equinox (right ascension) readily determined.

The armilla is a replica of the sky related to all the observer's diagnostic markers, such as, his horizon and latitude. It is a working model more efficient in teaching the student the elements of descriptive astronomy than lectures and more effective in bringing home to him the continuity of the chain of genius and search that characterizes the species man.

There is another kind of model which seems to serve as the best approximation to the numerous references to working "spheres", celestial replicas, or planetariums, which occur in Cicero, Plutarch and others here cited. These celestial representations are still useful in teaching; it is only because the prominent altar places in modern sciences have been occupied by nucleons, atomic models, orbits, spins, parity, spectra, RNA, molecular or crystal structures and the like, that observational astronomy lost its old appeal and is even slighted by lovers of the sky. Yet, the young student of science can gain much from its use.

The models of the Ptolemaic System here shown differ little from Ptolemy's armillary sphere. The quadrant in its base marked off in angles in the lower right of the diagram shows the angle of inclination of the celestial axis, hence of the earthly axis, and refers to the latitude of the place of observation, here the complement, 33° N. The earth is the sphere in the center, E,

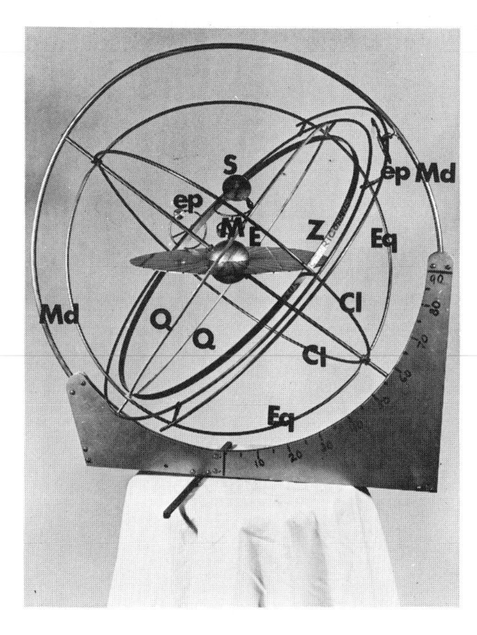

Figure 9.13

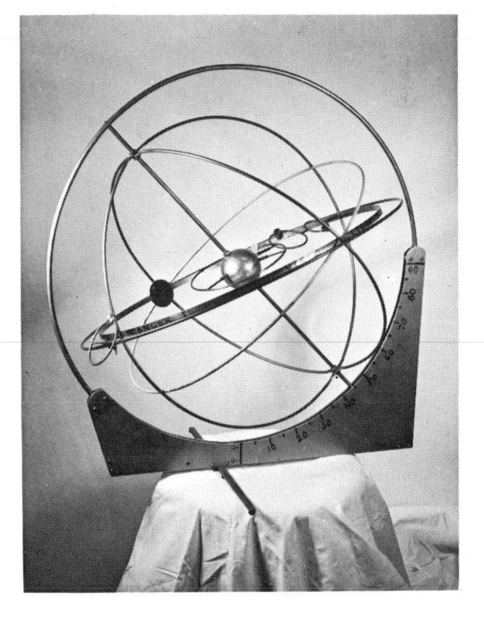

Figure 9.14

and is much larger than proportions demand. The zodiacal signs are seen on the broad band, Z, and the two rings parallel to it are the deferents of two superior or outer planets, Mars and Jupiter. These are seen on their epicycles, ep, riding their respective deferent circles. The celestial equator, Q, can be seen perpendicular to the axis; the circular disc around the earth is the local horizon. The sun is marked S; and the line containing the centers of the epicycles of Mercury and Venus with their respective epicycles can also be seen. The epicycles are marked V and M. Md marks the local meridian. Cl designates the colure which is the circle marking the solstices, while Eq marks the circle going through the vernal and autumnal equinoxes.

This model is a full replica of the sky with all the geometrical aids which the astronomer supplied for better understanding. By turning the central axis, with its celestial poles to the vertical position, we obtain the sky for the earth's horizon at the north pole. The North Star is overhead and the sky revolves as it would at that locality. By placing the sun where it belongs for a given day on the zodiacal ring, the local situation with respect to day and night is fully reproduced. The same is true for any horizon. Place the axis at latitude of 30° N and the sky of Cairo, Egypt, is reproduced. The exact place of sunrise and sunset on any day of the year is automatically observed, the height of the sun at noon, the hours of daylight and sunlight. For the planets the model cannot function as beautifully, but can nevertheless be made to be of some aid.

The horizon can be replaced with the moon as seen in Figure 9.14. With the proper inclination of the lunar orbit, eclipses can be demonstrated and predicted.

In his *Almagest,* Ptolemy devotes the entire Chapter 3 of Book VIII, to a full description of a celestial globe as if to find a well-ordered home for his first published catalogue of fixed stars contained in it. The catalogue lists 1022 stars, with positions in relation to the ecliptic and equator, and their magnitudes. Little wonder that celestial globes anteceded terrestrial ones, even though the southern stars could not be known until the voyages of discovery crossed the earth's equator. More of the southern sky could be known than of the earth west of Gibraltar to China.

X Astronomical Theories in the Middle Ages

1. Christianity Digresses but Soon Returns to Science

Toward the middle of the fourth century A. D., the Roman Empire had become officially Christian, and toward the end of the fifth (476 A. D.), it succumbed to barbarian domination. While paganism and its cultural institutions persisted for a while, side by side with Christian thought, its vigor was declining, and Christian ideology, goals and values soon became the sole intellectual currency of the western culture area. Interest in the vast scientific heritage of the ancient world began to lag and soon vanished almost completely. Plato's ideal realities, Aristotle's four causes together with Apollonius' conic sections and Ptolemy's epicycles, were all relegated to the dark recesses of the steadily declining pagan limbo, and the bright minds of the times devoted their resuscitated exuberance to the new philosophic horizons of divine mercy, the concept of salvation, the brotherhood of man, rebirth in Christ, the meaning of sin and ressurrection, and other appealing abstractions of this calibre which were destined to occupy the fertile minds and channel the culture's creative thinking for more than a millenium.

The early patristic writers, the founders of Christian theology, were familiar with science. Men like St. Basil or St. Augustine (354-430) were cognizant of the scientific wisdom of antiquity, but they knew it mostly as a shadowy memory to be quickly dismissed and forgotten. Others like Lactantius derided anything secular or scholarly, unless it dealt with Scriptural lore. The story of creation as sketched in the few poetic sentences of the book of Genesis was sufficient and necessary truth for them, and the other incidental references to science or nature scattered throughout the various scriptural books were equally final and sacred. The end of free inquiry in natural philosophy is normally assigned to the year 529 A. D., when the Emperor Justinian closed all schools of pagan learning in Athens.

In spite of general rejection of science, there were a few exceptions that sufficed to keep alive a spark of the old learning. The end of the sixth century saw the appearance of a work by Johannes Philoponus on the *Creation of the World* and of commentaries on several books by Aristotle. Early in the seventh century there appeared a work in the nature of a schoolboy's encyclopedia called *Etymologies,* or Origins, by Isidore of Spain, Bishop of Seville (died 636), a high church dignitary, and of another work by him entitled *On the Nature of Things*. While neither of these works attained the scientific excellence of its precursors in the days of Greek and Roman vitality, they are worthy repositories of some secular knowledge in a world growing less and less interested in it. Another popular encyclopedia by Rabanus Maurus (776-856) also served to keep science alive. Early in the eighth century there appeared a more or less summary of Pliny's *Natural History* from the pen of the Venerable Bede (672-735), a highly admired and widely known monk from England. The next century, the ninth, saw the appearance of another popular book on science that achieved wide acclaim, and which also summarized the science of antiquity, including the sphericity of the earth and planetary orbits. Popular encyclopedias continued to be issued all along and since all books were written in Latin, they found widespread reception.

While the small flame of science and secular learning struggled feebly to keep itself alive in Christendom, relatively strong centers of culture prospered in the non-Christian world of the East, such as, Antioch, Edessa, and particularly Jundichapur, and in other cities. These efflorescences of scholarship were due mainly to the influx of Nestorians, a heretical, scholarly Christian sect that felt obliged to leave the evergrowing authoritarianism of the new faith, and of the educated Jews and pagans who chose to leave their old homes in search of freedom to pursue their lives. By 750 A. D., the city of Baghdad was founded and soon became a center in which Greek learning fused with some influx from Hindu sources. Subsequently it came to flourish with great vitality under Moslem rule. One soon finds Syriac and Arabic versions of the works of Aristotle, Euclid, Ptolemy, Pliny, Archimedes, Philo of Byzantium, Hero of Alexandria, Galen, and other stars of the Greco-Roman firmament in many centers of learning which sprang up all at once out of nowhere. These centers produced remarkable efflorescences of scholarship and considerable creativity in a variety of scientific fields. During the tenth century A. D., in the wake of the spread of Moslem power across northern Africa into Spain, the universities of Cordoba, Granada, Seville, and other great Moorish centers became pivotal seats of learning and intellectual cauldrons of productive thinking.

To the Moslem universities of Spain scholars from Western Europe made continuous and prolonged pilgrimages for the discovery of the substance of their famed learning and for its immediate translation. It was in this manner that the twelfth century came to be known as the century of the translators and the thirteenth the century of Western growth and maturity. Into Latin were translated first the valuable works by outstanding Moslem scholars who had published excellent summaries of ancient authors; for example, Rhazes (died 924) on medicine, Alhazen (965-1039) on optics, Avicenna (980-1037) on medicine and physics, Alpetragius (12th century) on astronomy, and Averroes (1126-98) on physics and astronomy, to be followed in rapid succession by the rendition into Latin of the original works of Aristotle, Euclid, Archimedes, Hero of Alexandria, Ptolemy, Hippocrates, Galen, Celsus and the other classical authorities. By the thirteenth century, most of the wisdom of antiquity was firmly established in Europe, in its universities, monastaries, and courts. The thirteenth century boasted such encyclopedic minds as Albertus Magnus, Robert Grosseteste, Roger Bacon, William of Auvergne, and others whose concern with natural science ran broad and deep.

This triumphant return of science brought with it a universal recognition of the beauty and majesty of Ptolemy's mathematical construction that went hand in hand with a reluctance on the part of scholars everywhere to cherish it as a functional working hypothesis. Ptolemy stood in the physical sciences as an Olympian god to be unquestionably worshipped on a par with Hippocrates in the medical field. But while Hippocrates could be easily read and admired by any student of medicine, Ptolemy's *Almagest* was of a far different mettle. Admired though it was by every learned man from its first appearance until the early eighteenth century or thereabouts, the original work was not read by many and was fully mastered by few. Ptolemy's general scheme was known, but mainly from such summaries as that of Alpetragius' (Al-Betrugi) *Liber Astronomiae,* or the one by John of Hollywood, known as Sacrobosco, and entitled, *The Sphere.*

The Ptolemaic system was too mathematical, too abstract. The human mind prefers a model, a scheme, upon which constructions can be hung to the mind's facile satisfaction. It wants to relate an abstract generalization to real phenomena, to the elements of one's daily experiences, to the only laws and aspects of nature that one has direct knowledge of. And the Ptolemaic theory did not make room for any of these conveniences. Ptolemy in his text is thoroughly remote and mathematical, and he regarded the overall scheme as a convenient device for accurate calculation and prediction rather than as an explanation of the actual operations of the machinery. He often begins a particular section with: "Let us imagine a circle," proceeds to the next one, then the next one, and continues to build scheme upon scheme. The same is true of his commentators, such as Proclus, who remarks at the end of his work on Ptolemy, as Dreyer points out, that both "epicycles and eccentrics are merely designed as the simplest way of accounting for the motions, and in order to show the harmony which exists among them." (J. L. E. Dreyer. *A History of Astronomy.* New York, 1953, p. 201) There was no way in which the simple, direct, and mechanistic mind of medieval man could possibly visualize the mean motus, line of apsides, epicycle, equant, and deferent, operating in a specific, functional manner. And so the system was honored and respected, much as a Latin prayer was by a simple but pious peasant.

What the Middle Ages became strongly dedicated to, was the system of Aristotle. Aristotle's approach to reality was that of a practical man planted on hard ground, but endowed as well with vision and understanding. Although he later became the symbol of the speculative mind that becomes enveloped in its own net without regard to nature or experimentation, this stereotype for Aristotle is most tragic. Man's tragedy on earth is not so much Man's Inhumanity to Man, as man's *misunderstanding* of man. The latter is the cause, the former merely one of its outward expressions. When man misjudges another person's motives or acts, his actions will accord with his evaluation of the situation. Such action may often appear to us as inhuman, but not so to him. He is merely acting out of misjudgment which led him into fear or anger. The same is true of scholars. False evaluation will lead to false condemnation.

2. The Aristotelian Faith in Sensory Empiricism

Aristotle, had he lived after Ptolemy, could never have accepted Ptolemy's mathematical world as sufficient in itself, any more than he could accept

Plato's. He was far too practical a scholar, too rooted in common sense. As we saw, he could not even acquiesce in the scheme of Eudoxus in its original form, because his practical mind told him that although spheres were essential, they could not just revolve in concentric array without affecting one the other. (How else will the celestial bodies maintain themselves in space?) They need partitions to keep each independent of the other. His thoughts ran along similar lines on every subject his mind dissected. Mathematics appeared as a servant, a tool, to Aristotle, but not so to Plato, or Pythagoras. To them she was a goddess to be worshipped, an underlying truth which governed all existence much as ground water governed the fertility of the soil.

In Book II of his *De Caelo* (On the Heavens), and also elsewhere, Aristotle develops his theory of the celestial motions, almost exactly 500 years before Ptolemy. To begin with, Aristotle reiterates the concept of the four elements-earth, water, air and fire, of which our world, the sublunar, is composed. "Now all motion in space is either straight or circular or a compound of the two, for these are the only simple motions, the reason being that the straight and circular lines are the only simple magnitudes. By 'circular motion' I mean motion around the centre, by 'straight' motion, up and down. 'Up' means away from the centre, 'down' towards the centre. It follows that all simple locomotion is either away from the centre, or towards the centre or around the centre." (Loeb Classical Library. 1953. Book I, 2. p. 11)

Besides having absolute faith in reality, Aristotle was obsessed with love for reason. Logic to him means comprehension of the truth beneath a confusing surface, the generalized actuality of what we observe, so as to describe nature realistically and objectively. Unlike Plato, he did not seek to add meaning, insight, or vision to a situation, but viewed it coldly and impersonally. After reasoning about the elements and their motions, he states: "From all these premises, therefore, it clearly follows that there exists some physical substance besides the four in our sublunary world, and moreover, that it is more divine than, and prior to, all these... Motion which is natural to one body is natural to another... Thus the reasoning from all our premises goes to make us believe that there is some other body separate from those around us here, and of a higher nature in proportion as it is removed from the sublunary world.... If, then, the body whose natural motion is circular cannot be subject to growth or diminution, it is a reasonable supposition that it is not subject to alteration either... It is eternal, ageless, unalterable and impassive.... The argument bears out experience and is borne out by it.... There is in it something divine.... This truth is also clear from the evidence of the senses, enough at least to warrant the assent of human faith; for throughout all past time, according to the records handed down from generation to generation, we find no trace of change either in the whole of the outermost heaven or in any one of its proper parts. It seems too that the name of this first body has been passed down to the present time by the ancients, who thought of it in the same way as we do, for we cannot help believing that the same ideas recur to men not once, nor twice, but over and over again. Thus they, believing that the primary body was something different from earth and fire and air and water, gave the name 'ether' to the uppermost region, choosing its name from the fact that it 'runs always' and eternally." (*ibid.* p. 25)

With intricate logic, never deviating from what he regards as experience and reality, Aristotle then proves that "it is impossible for an infinite body to revolve in a circle. Neither could the heaven if it were infinite.... Also, neither a sphere nor a square nor a circle can be infinite, and without a circle there cannot be circular motion." Hence the heavens are finite, not infinite, and "there cannot exist an infinite body... there cannot exist an infinite weight... an infinite lightness.... All bodies that occupy a place are perceptible. Therefore, there is no infinite body outside the heaven. Nor, however, is there a finite. Therefore, there is no body at all outside the heaven.

"Further, all the worlds must be composed of the same bodies, being similar in nature. But at the same time each of these bodies must have the same potentialities, fire, and earth, and the bodies betwen them... It must be natural therefore for the particles of earth in another world to move toward the centre of this one also, and for the fire in that world to move toward the circumference of this. This is impossible, for if it were to happen the earth would have to move upward in its own world and the fire to the centre; and similarly, earth from our own world would have to move naturally away from the centre, as it made its way to the centre of the other, owing to the assumed situation of the worlds relatively to each other." (*ibid.* p. 71)

The world is one and unique, eternal, indestructible, and ungenerated. Objects that have form are subject to diversity. The fact that the world has form may lead one to assume that there are many worlds. Yet this is not so. The world is finite and there can be no bodies outside the heaven. "It is obvious then that there is neither place nor void nor time outside the heaven." All this is established with intricate logic, advancing with great caution and accuracy from conclusion to conclusion, each step sound and closely tied to nature, yet each leading further and faster into delusion and irrelevance, from our point of vantage. The fault lies not with Aristotle, but with Reason as a method for venturing too far beyond the data, and with the ambivalent nature of analogy which, though leading to many wonderful discoveries, may also, on occasion, lead soundly astray. Reason, after all, is like a small dinghy which is most valuable in quiet inlets and baylets, but dangerous in open and rough seas.

Having established the nature of matter and the physical foundation of the world, Aristotle proceeds to examine the nature of the heavenly bodies. Circular motion, unlike up or down, has no opposite. Generally speaking, it is the existence of opposites which causes action and reaction, aging, decay, and change. Their absence brings about stability, inaction, and changelessness. Celestial bodies are divine, and since "everything which has a function exists for the sake of that function," the heavenly bodies whose function is eternal motion, "by nature move forever in a circle." No part of such a divine body could remain still; "it follows that there must be earth, for it is that which remains at rest in the middle... The shape of the heaven must be spherical - that is most suitable to its substance, and is the primary shape in nature." Heaven, being divine, must be perfect, and the circle is perfect and so is the sphere. "The place of the sphere among solids is the same as that of the circle among plane figures." Words and phrases properly ordered and uttered can make out an excellent case for these assertions within the temple of Reason, presumably based on evidence.

"Again, the revolution of the heaven is the measure of all motions, because it alone is continuous and unvarying and eternal, the measure in every class of things is the smallest member, and the shortest motion is the quickest, therefore the motion of the heaven must clearly be the quickest of all motions." It is constant, unaccelerated, and unretarded. "Everything moved is moved by something" except the outer heaven. "Each star consists of the body in which it moves. . . . whose nature it is to move in a circle. . . . The heat and light which they emit are engendered as the air is chafed by their movement." The stars, that is, the planets "do not roll. Whatever rolls must turn about, but the moon always shows us its face (as men call it). Also, they are immobile and only the heavens move." The theory that the planets make music as they are moved around the earth "shows great feeling for fitness and beauty, but nevertheless, cannot be true. . . . The questions of their order, their relative positions. . . and their distances from one another, may best be studied in astronomical writings where they are adequately discussed. One characteristic is that their movements are faster or slower according to their distances." Since the motion of the planets is in a direction opposite to the outer heaven, the further from it the planet is, the faster is its motion. The stars are spherical "and the moon can be shown by the evidence of sight to be spherical. . . . If, then, one of the heavenly bodies is spherical the others will clearly be spherical also."

The proof of the world's being ungenerated and indestructible occupies Aristotle for many pages, as does his reasoning in denying its infinity and the possibility of the existence of a multiplicity of worlds. His approach here summarized gives us a lucid picture of the strength and weakness of his method. His manner is that of a sophisticated modern scientist. It is based solidly upon the sensory data of common experience as well as upon the kind of syllogistic speculative logic that has a powerful appeal to the thinking practical man, who is neither a mystic nor irresponsible, neither poetic nor romantic, but a true seeker after theoretical generalization built upon a solid foundation of facts. The difficulty does not lie in his reasoning, but in all reasoning to some extent, since it lies in the nature of reason that it can never be free from intellectual goals, significances and values, from similies and parables acceptable at the time. Relationships and challenges which mean nothing today, baffle, bother and bedevil the mind of the period, until they are properly organized and happily arranged; aspects of a problem we would never dream of seeking to resolve, seem vital enough to the thinkers of that day to demand argument upon argument until laid to rest in the overall scheme of things in irreproachable security.

We have already seen that Aristotle (in his *Metaphysics*) embraced the system of Eudoxus and attempted to give it his stamp of realism by adding spheres. In *Meteorology* and other works, Aristotle discusses other celestial and terrestrial phenomena such as clouds, dew, rainbows, comets, earthquakes, halos, mock suns, etc., in such a naturalistic and intellectual manner that it is no wonder his writings held the attention of the brilliant scientific minds of the world for well nigh two millenia, and his name towered unshaken in awe and respect. The Church honored him, after some initial opposition, because the minds of cultured men were obliged to honor him; scholars studied him because his ideas were irresistible and rewarding.

3. Ptolemy's Hypotheses

In the struggle for survival upon the arena of ideas, Ptolemy's complex and abstract mathematical scheme simply stood no chance against the lure of the Aristotelian outlook which was realistic and physical in its construction and was based upon principles and operations that seemed sound to the men of the time. Its popularity with the scholars of the Middle Ages was universal, while the *Almagest* was respected, but unread. Moreover, as if to face the situation and seek some compromise with it, there came to the fore another work of Ptolemy, about the authenticity of which there has been some doubt, and which was entitled *Hypotheses of the Planets*. Its author claims it to be a summary of the *Almagest*, but it is that in Book I only. Book II, which contains the major message of the work, presents a theory which differs widely from that offered in the *Almagest*.

The model presented in the *Hypotheses* is truly a compromise, in that it takes the pure mathematics of the *Almagest* and gives it the flesh and blood of a physical substructure. The upshot of this effort is that the final model is as realistic as Aristotle's (Eudoxian) spheres with their naturalistic substructure of earthly forces and concrete motions. The Ptolemaic epicycles and eccentrics are fully honored in this new scheme, but they are cleverly rendered palatable to the simple pseudo-mechanistic, reality-bound mentality of the medieval scholar. The epicycle ceases to be a mathematical fiction, but becomes a little solid sphere rolling along not on its deferent, but in a space between an inner sphere encompassed by the deferent, or eccentric, and an outer sphere similarly called into being. In other words, every circle is a sphere and every epicycle is a small sphere between two large ones, much like balls in our roller-bearings. The medieval texts represented the scheme thus:

The outermost deferent, or eccentric circle, revolved and communicated its motion to its closest inner epicycle sphere, carrying the planet. This small sphere, in turn, rolled along with the motion of the contiguous inner eccentric sphere, and so further inward until the lunar sphere upon its deferent around the center of all, the earth. It was this picture of the heavens that the great Moslem astronomers, Al Fargani and Al Battani, advanced in their works which became the West's own widely read popularization, *The Sphere of Sacrobosco*. The latter continued to guide the learned world in edition after edition far into the seventeenth century, accompanied with commentaries by numerous scholars of stature.

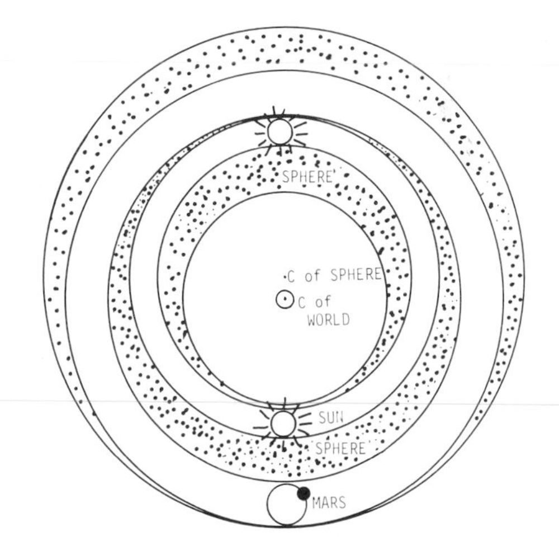

Figure 10.1

The adherence to a physical model of the motions of the planets on their spheres, readily led to a conceptualization of the actual distances between all of the planets. So strong was the desire for a physical model of the motions of the heavenly bodies that in spite of their worship of Ptolemy and his disembodied mathematics, astronomers welcomed workable additions to it of physical schemes. This could readily be done in the following manner. Since all measurements consisted solely of angles of motion, only relative ratios of the radii of epicycle and deferent could be established, as well as quantity of eccentricity. Assume, however, that nature is economical and that it allows no voids in space so that shpere touches upon sphere and permits all the necessary freedom of motion for each. This can be rendered possible only if the apogee of the innermost sphere touches upon the perigee of the next sphere and so on outward, as shown in the illustration.

Each shell is here thick enough to contain its respective planet at perigee when it is nearest the earth, and at apogee when it is furthest. Allowing no intervening spaces, the entire planetary scheme can be correctly mapped out, since the ratios of deferent radius to epicycle radius is known for each planet. Although there is no mathematical or theoretical scheme for tieing the distance of one planet to another, the scheme of juxtaposing the nearest point of approach of an outer planet against the furthest point of removal of the inner one, renders the total scheme coherent. To crown it all, knowledge of the innermost radius, namely the distance of the earth to the moon, renders the entire scheme numerically calculable. Radius can be added to radius so that the dimensions of the entire system can be known.

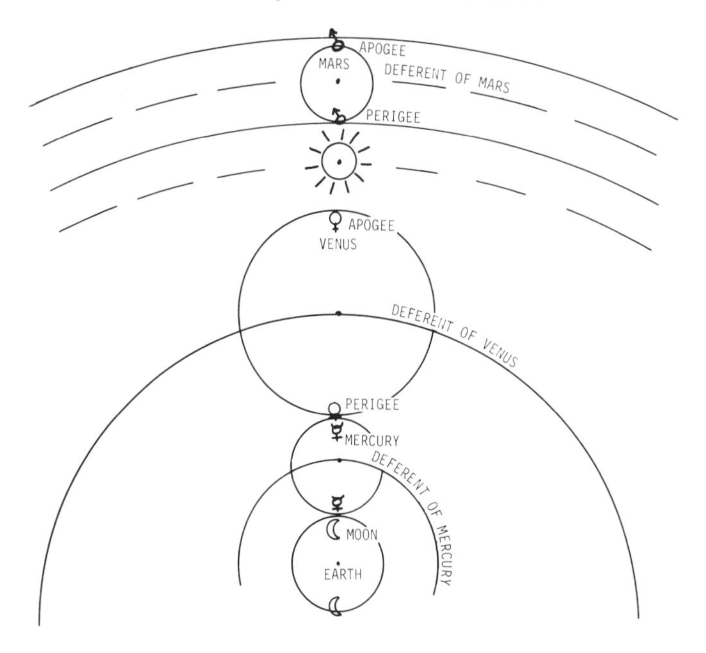

Figure 10.2

Thus did Aristotle's mode of approach win a double victory. His simple scheme won the field in the first place, and the Ptolemaic system was seldom presented as such to the public in its basic *Almagestian* form, but rather as expounded in the *Hypotheses* within a realistic, mechanistic, Aristotelian setting. For example, the most widespread popularization of Ptolemy's *Almagest* was *The Sphere of Sacrobosco.* "Within two centuries after invention of the printing press, Europe was covered with literally hundreds of editions of commentaries on Sacrobosco's *Sphere.* Virtually all of these texts, which increased with the years, used without qualification the machinery of planetary motion set up by the second Ptolemaic system. As late as 1581, such an erudite mathematician and astronomer as Christopher Clavius entitled his scholarly book on astronomy a *Commentary on 'The Sphere' of John of Sacrobosco,* and utilized the planetary machinery of the second Ptolemaic system.... From 1581 until the last independent edition of 1611, the frequently reprinted *Commentary* of Clavius stood as the most influential textbook on astronomy known to Europe." (McColley, Grant. "Humanism in the History of Astronomy" in *Toward Modern Science,* Vol. II, ed. R. M. Palter, New York, 1961, p. 143)

Copernicus was, no doubt, correct when, in his Dedication to Pope Paul III of his classic, *On the Revolutions of the Heavenly Spheres,* he declared: "Mathematics is intended for mathematicians." Non-mathematicians and perhaps even some mathematicians love a model, a working, visual scheme with which to perceive a complex theoretical explanation. When at a given time the genius of man can only provide a mathematical explanation of data, the scholarly community as a whole will not rest until it has devised some scheme which is material and tangible and can serve as a skeleton upon which to hang ideas. The question is, should this skeleton be taken literally? Should one at any given time believe in the truth of a postulated, theoretical scheme? Clearly the answer cannot be an unequivocal "yes," because in this instance, the Aristotelian-Ptolemaic scheme proved untenable. Nor can the answer be an unequivocal "no," since there is a reality and there are celestial bodies in motion, else our retinae would not respond to their light. It is therefore reasonable that there be a configuration conceived by man which agrees precisely with what exists in nature. But how are we to know that we have reached concordance between a theoretical conception and nature's actual design which is beyond sensory interception? There is always the possibility that some imaginative mind will in the future conceive a different model, a better scheme for what had previously been regarded as firmly established or as a highly probable one. To seekers of the absolute, this may be disturbing indeed.

4. Ptolemy vs. Copernicus: Dead End vs. Expanding Horizons

From the very beginning of its career as a recognized and respected theory, the system of Ptolemy, as already mentioned, had an ambivalent existence. It was highly respected by the pioneering Moslem mathematicians who introduced it to the West, and though found wanting here and there, managed to remain aloof from efforts at modification either by them or by the later Christian scholars. It was never really warmly accepted. Every brilliant astronomer sought to bypass it after paying tribute to it, and either yearned to restore the physical mechanism of Aristotle, or devise one on his own along similar lines. A most conspicuous Moslem critic was Al Betrugi, better known as Alpetragius, who wrote of his teacher Ibn Tofeil as follows: "You know that the illustrious judge Abu Bekr Ibn Tofeil told us that he had found an astronomical system and principles of the various movements different from those laid down by Ptolemy and without admitting either eccentrics or epicycles, and with this system all the motions are represented without error." (J. L. E. Dreyer. *Planetary Systems,* p. 264) No such work by Ibn Tofeil is available, but Alpetragius developed the theory on his own in a work on the planets.

Alpetragius' system is largely Aristotelian and physical. It is based upon Eudoxian spheres-within-spheres carrying the planets upon an equator. The outermost of the ninth sphere is the prime mover which, as with Aristotle to whom he consistently refers as the Sage, has intrinsic motion which it transmits to all the other spheres that it encompasses. But he produces one modification: All motion is from east to west unlike the case with Aristotle who endows the prime mover with east-to-west daily motion but the planets with direct or west-to-east additional movement. Alpetragius rejects the latter, and makes the prime mover's sole motion suffice by attributing a characteristically slower movement to each planetary sphere, thus accounting equally well for their various direct motions. The *primum mobile,* or *prime mover,* makes a complete revolution in less than 24 hours. The next inner sphere, the eighth, which carries the stars, is a bit slower and completes its revolution in 24 hours; every progressively innermost planet is progressively slower and takes longer to complete its revolution, the spheres of the moon taking the longest, nearly 25 hours.

Alpetragius was aware that the planets moved in latitude, which meant that the axis of the sphere had to bend away from the pole of the ecliptic so as to raise or lower the planets. He was also aware that the orbital velocities of all planets were not uniform but were fast in some regions and slow in others. This meant they showed variation in longitude. To account for these deviations, the eighth, or starry sphere, was made to have two motions; one in longitude to account for precession in which the equinox is not in the same place each year but precedes its previous position by a small amount. Its second motion was that of having the pole of the ecliptic describe a small circle around some particular mean position, "thereby producing the supposed oscillation or trepidation of the equinoxes."

This statement refers to a peculiar belief that found its way into ancient and medieval astronomy which began with the discovery of precession. As already mentioned precession implies that the point where the ecliptic and equator cross, shifts about a degree westward every century, a fact first discovered by Hipparchus. This discovery proved to be correct and of prime significance. But, says Dreyer, "It is very remarkable that so important a discovery should not have become universally known; and yet we find that precession is never alluded to by Geminus, Kleomedes, Theon of Smyrna, Manilius, Pliny, Censorinus, Achilles, Chalcidius, Macrobius, Martianus Capella. The only writers, except Ptolemy, who allude to it are Proclus, who flatly denies its existence, and Theon of Alexandria, who accepts the Ptolemaic value of one degree in a hundred years, but who tells the following strange story about it: 'According to certain opinions, ancient astrologers believe that from a certain epoch the solsticial signs have a motion of 8° in the order of the signs, after which they go back the same amount; but Ptolemy is not of this opinion, for without letting this motion enter into the calculations, these when made by the tables are always in accord with the observed places. Therefore we also advise not to use this correction; still we shall explain it'.... The idea of these people was, therefore, that the longitude of a star increased for 640 years (1° in 80 years) and that it then suddenly began to decrease and went on doing that for 640 years, and then equally suddenly took to increasing again." (*ibid.* p. 204) The year 158 B.C. was singled out as the year in which a change of direction occurred.

This belief that the point of the equinox oscillated back and forth about 1° in a century, proved to have no foundation in reality, was not mentioned by Ptolemy, and yet maintained itself for many centuries. And a special motion was assigned to the oscillation of the eighth starry sphere, with the ninth negotiating precession, and the tenth being the prime mover.

The inner seven spheres referred to the seven planets, the moon, Mercury, Venus, the sun, Mars, Jupiter and Saturn. To account for the shifts of a planet north and south of the ecliptic, or its motion in latitude, each respective sphere was made to wobble by having its pole describe a little circle around a mean position, thus moving the planet, located on its equator, up and down with respect to the ecliptic. It also accounts for the inequalities in longitude, that is for the unequal speeds of the planet in its orbit since, like the earth, each planet moves rapidly in some parts of its orbit and slowly in other regions. Al Betrugi correctly noted that these small circles made by the axis of each sphere were related to the synodic (solar) periods of the planets, meaning, a planet's period of revolution around the sun, in our terminology. Thus, he observed that the pole of the sphere of Venus "makes five revolutions in eight years less 2 1/4d + 1/20, lagging 1 5/8 revolutions in one year; and Mercury 145 revolutions in 46 years and 1 1/30d. It is curious that Alpetragius alters the order of the planets, placing Venus between Mars and the sun, because the defectus (lagging) of Venus is smaller than that of the sun. He also says that nobody has given any valid reason for accepting the usually assumed order of the planets, and that Ptolemy is wrong in stating that Mercury and Venus are never exactly in line with the sun;... and as they shine with their own light they would not appear as dark spots, if passing between us and the sun. That they do not receive their light from the sun is proved, he thinks, by the fact that they never appear crescent-shaped." (Dreyer, p. 266-7)

We see how beginning with Eudoxus, we pass on to the reforms of Aristotle and continue with the modifications of Al Betrugi in the attempt to devise a physically workable scheme of the celestial machinery. This was done quite naturally within the physical concepts of the time, as already stated. Al Betrugi seeks to correct some lacunae left bothersome by Aristotle, namely, deviations in the planet's path north and south of the ecliptic, and longitudinally, that is, in different regions of the orbit. While the variations in brightness were not really accounted for, enough improvement was introduced to render the corrections acceptable for a while.

But then, early in the sixteenth century, it was bruited about that one, Niklas Koppernigk, or Nicholas Copernicus of Prussia, had revived the old scheme of Aristarchus of Samos in a most ingenious manner. Absurd though his speculation appeared at first, the new theory was nevertheless based on much knowledge, was complex, challenging, and worthy of acquaintance. Copernicus was not known for any other work in his lifetime. He had written at the behest of a friend, a Canon of Cracow and secretary to the King of Poland, a criticism of the work of an astronomer of Nürnberg, Johann Werner, who in 1522 published a small treatise entitled *On the Motion of the Eighth Sphere,* the one assigned to the presumed oscillation of the equinoctial point, or trepidation. Copernicus apologizes humbly in his essay but nonetheless offers conscientiously his criticism of Werner, and as luck would have it, the entire argument happened over a non-existent event. Copernicus accepts trepidation in his great work, points out some small error in the chronology and insists that the oscillation is most rapid in one region of the little circle made by the motion of the pole, whereas Wener had claimed it was most rapid in another region.

There has been much debate whether Copernicus was Polish or German. This unprofitable battle of words is best answered by A. Koyré who points out that Copernicus lived at a time when Poland was an empire rather than a nation in our sense. In a medieval empire, nationalities, or groups speaking different languages, were united by a common political entity, the Res Publica. These linguistic groups lived together relatively amicably, with considerable intermarriage. "Were Copernicus asked 'Are you Polish or German?' he certainly would not have fully understood the question but would have probably answered that he was Prussian, meaning a citizen of Toruń, a good Catholic, a cannon of the Cathedral of Frauenburg in Warmland and therefore a subject of the King of Poland. Being a scholar, he would have spoken Latin in his scientific correspondence and works, but in any intercourse with commoners and princes, he would have employed the vulgate, Polish at Cracow, German at Frauenburg or Heilsberg, and no doubt, Italian at Padua or Bologna." (*La Revolution Astronomique.* Paris, 1961, p. 20)

It is not uncommon to encounter in history an intense controversy in which two scholarly and brilliant minds battle passionately over the merits of a theory, using strong language, spiced with flashy sarcasm and rhetoric, only to have history wipe away the whole issue, much as a sudden onrush of the tide levels castles in the sand over which children had fought for hours. Such seems to us now the Werner-Copernicus controversy. Copernicus' treatise was in manuscript form, apparently intended for circulation only among friends. In all likelihood he did the same in circulating a summary of his forthcoming work, which summary he titled, *Commentariolus,* or a brief sketch. It was no doubt composed before the main work, and served as pilot study of the fuller opus, giving a brief presentation of its major points.

The Copernican theory is generally regarded as the beginning of modern science and as the dawn of the new era. The phrase Copernican Revolution has been accepted as a fitting designation for its place in history, although it is by now generally admitted that the core of the revolution came afterward. The great work of Copernicus is entitled *On the Revolutions of the Heavenly Spheres,* which mode of carrying the planets was still adhered to by him throughout, as are circles and major and minor epicycles, of which there are more than in Ptolemy's *Almagest*. This was the price paid by Copernicus for his rejection of the equant and eccentric. Copernicus' book is fully in the Ptolemaic tradition in thought, outlook, purpose, axioms, methodolgy, and mode of expression. It did contain a few all-important elements of novelty which served as wonderful seeds for rich germination in the future.

What were Copernicus' motives for introducing his novel scheme? To begin with, it is essential to bear in mind that Copernicus was no revolutionary rebelling against authority, condemning and demolishing old ideas, defiantly seeking to replace them with his own superior, more truthful, or more accurate theory. Ptolemy remains the unquestioned authority. In arguing against Werner, Copernicus writes: "Now since Ptolemy based his tables on fresh observations of his own, it is incredible that the tables should contain any sensible error or any departure from the observations that would make the tables inconsistent with the principles on which they rest." (Edward Rosen. *Three Copernican Treatises*. Columbia University Press, New York, 1939, p. 97) In his dedicatory preface to the Most Holy Father, Pope Paul III, Copernicus gives some indication of his reasons for presenting his new ideas. His own statement reads: "But perhaps Your Holiness... will be eager to hear from me what came into my mind that in opposition to the general opinion of mathematicians and almost in opposition to common sense I should dare to imagine some movement of the Earth. And so I am unwilling to hide from Your Holiness that *nothing except my knowledge that mathematicians have not agreed with one another* in their researches moved me to think out a different scheme of drawing up the movements of the spheres of the world. For in the first place mathematicians are so uncertain about the movements of the sun and moon that they can neither demonstrate nor observe the unchanging magnitude of the revolving year. Then in setting up the solar and lunar movements and those of the other five wandering stars, they do not employ the same principles, assumptions or demonstrations for the revolutions and apparent movements. For some make use of the homocentric circles only, others of eccentric circles and epicycles, by means of which however they do not fully attain what they seek. For although those who have put their trust in homocentric circles have shown that various different movements can be composed of such circles, nevertheless they have not been able to establish anything for certain that would fully correspond to the phenomena. But even those who have thought up eccentric circles seem to have been able for the most part to compute the apparent movements numerically by those means, they have in the meanwhile admitted a great deal which seems to contradict the first principles of regularity of movement. Moreover, they have not been able to discover or to infer the chief point of all, i. e. the form of the world and *the certain commensurability of its parts*. But they are in exactly the same fix as someone taking from different places hands, feet, head, and the other limbs - shaped very beautifully but not with reference to one body and *without correspondence to one another* - [italics mine] so that such parts made up a monster rather than a man. And so, in the process of demonstration which they call 'method', they are forced either to have omitted something necessary or to have admitted something foreign which by no means pertains to the matter; and they would by no means have been in this fix, if they had followed sure principles. For if the hypotheses they assumed were not false, everything which followed from the hypotheses would have been verified without fail; and though what I'm saying may be obscure right now, nevertheless it will become clearer in the proper place." (*On the Revolutions of the Heavenly Spheres*. Great Books. Vol. XVI, p. 507)

Clearly, he feels that the Ptolemaic system lacks a basic unity of organization, or cohesion, which his own, he thinks, does contain. Copernicus also suggests that the Ptolemaic theory did not explain all the data satisfactorily and that discrepancies grew with the centuries. But he does not make much of this explicitly, perhaps because he realized that his own system was still far from perfect. It would seem that his reasons were those of any creative mind, namely, that he conceived a new and more gratifying conception.

There are two features of the Ptolemaic system which should be stressed. First, Ptolemy was interested in a mathematical construction, and cared little about the physical reality of the system. One cannot enter into another person's mind, but he was apparently pleased with the abstraction and cared little for the model, just as some minds function reversely. Second, a careful study of his book reveals that Ptolemy really did not offer a unified system in his *Almagest*, but a mathematical treatise on celestial phenomena. He examined his data, he geometrized the paths of each planet, he loved his material and accepted the symbol of a divinity attached to each planet. He viewed each planet as an entity and not as a member of a family held together by some natural bonds. This is frequently overlooked by the modern student, who finds it difficult to isolate a planet from the solar family. For Ptolemy the main reality was the earth and the heavens around it. The planets were there and so were the stars. There were also comets and clouds and rain and fog and a host of other natural phenomena. They were all parts of nature worthy of study. An epigram constituting a four-line motto preceding his *Almagest*, probably represents his character well. "I know that I am mortal and ephemeral, but when I scan the crowded circling spirals of the stars I no longer touch the earth with my feet, but side by side with Zeus, I take my fill of ambrosia, the food of the gods." He worked out the path of each planet with the best mathematical accuracy he could muster.

With the Copernican theory, this feature undergoes a radical change. Copernicus gave rise to a system, presented to the reader in his usual modesty. His postulation of an arrangement in which all the planets were made to circle around a point near the sun, or loosely around the sun, combined with the sun's stationary position and the earth's becoming one of the planets, gradually evolves into a significant springboard for novelty. That springboard was promptly exploited by Kepler to attempt to bind all the celestial participants into a coherent functional system, which was a bold and noble idea. It was promptly taken up by Newton and fashioned it into his magnificent structure.

If Copernicus revolutionized astronomy, purged it, or reorganized it, these performances were not done dramatically or consciously. He merely enriched it with a bold idea which had previously been much too cavalierly dismissed. In terms of the biblical aphorism of the stone spurned by builders, Copernicus showed that not only need that stone not be spurned, but on the contrary, if employed as a keystone, could render possible the erection of a beautiful as well as serviceable unified structure. Little did he surmise that the structure he so warmly but modestly defended as a reasonable scheme or as a real model, would in time become the very center and foundation of a mighty metropolis. And one may well claim that his work was in time transformed into a potent foundation not necessarily because of Copernicus' genius, as was the case with Newton, but because of the pivotal fertility of his concept, the vast possibilities of the nature of the idea he suggested which struck nature in such a vulnerable spot that its future impact could not be of any other kind but revolutionary.

Since everyone is familiar with the Copernican scheme, it is only necessary to point out the exact nature of the transition from the old theory to the new one, and the immediate impact which that transition effected. Copernicus added few new data and no new basic concepts except his boldness, his skill as mathematician, and his will to take the earth's rotation and revolution in dead earnest. Copernicus also approached the subject with no new instruments. His method was a rearrangement of Ptolemy's data, which he employed almost exclusively, and to which he added a few of his own. For example, Ptolemy gives the values, later employed by Copernicus, for what he calls "cycle of anomaly," meaning the period of a planet's loop or epicycle, and also for a planet's "revolution in longitude," meaning the full circular path of a planet as it starts from any given initial position against the fixed stars, up to its return to that same initial place. Such a cycle marks a revolution in longitude, measured in terms of angles of circular motion in completing 360 degrees. Ptolemy also gives the times in earthly "solar years" which it takes each planet to complete the total trip against the starry sphere, hence the total time it takes a planet to start from any initial position and move eastward until it returns to the starting point. This latter figure will, for the outer planets, be equivalent to the sum of the cycles of anomaly (epicycle time) and the "revolution in longitude," thus comprising the planet's total circular journey against the fixed stars. (Figure 10.3) It comprises the time for its circular longitudinal motion plus the time it takes in running its epicycles. For the inner planets, Mercury and Venus, the times for "revolution in longitude" will be the same as the time for the epicycle, since epicycles are the only paths these planets are seen to pursue.

In Ptolemy's system, all measurements of planetary positions were of angles. Before the availability of the telescope, it was impossible to observe planetary parallaxes, and the respective distances of any of the planets from the earth could not be measured. Only planetary motions could be measured, and only the two kinds, namely, motion in longitude, and motion in

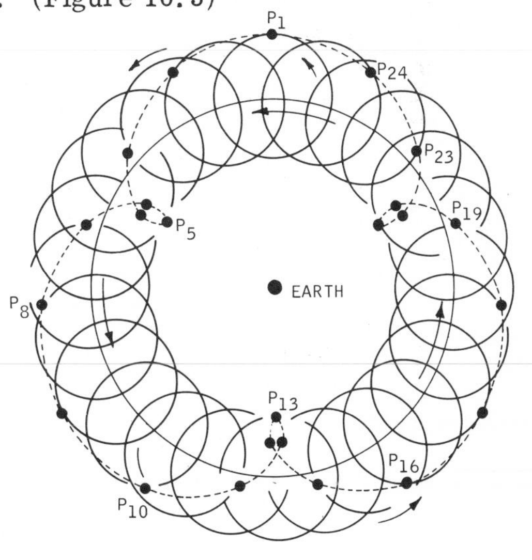

Figure 10.3

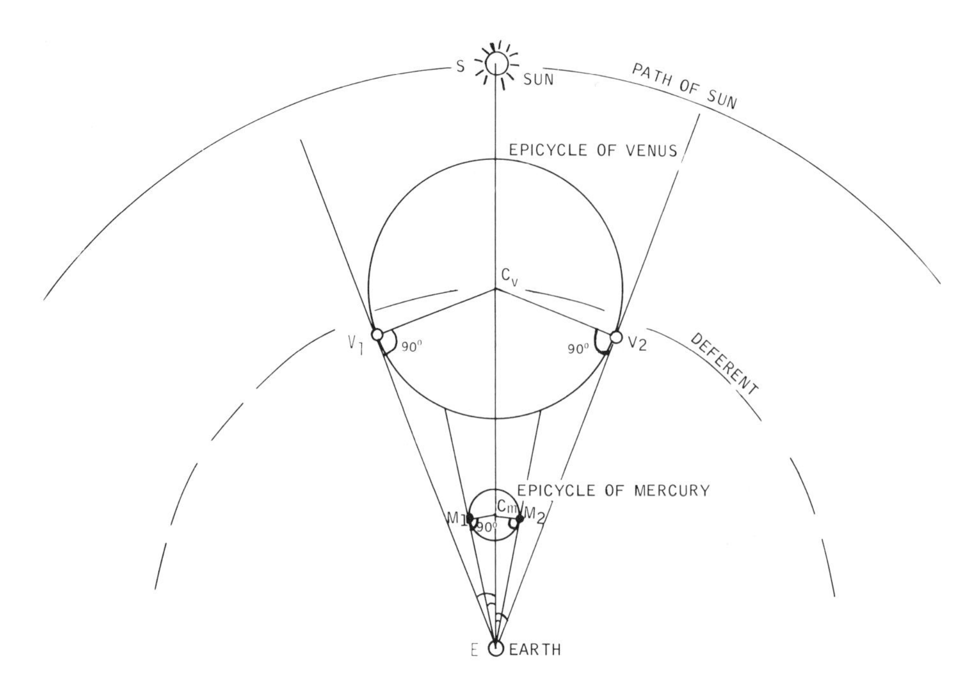

Figure 10.4

latitude. The ecliptic was the chosen base line. No distances from the earth to any planet could be obtained. What Ptolemy did succeed in obtaining was a value for the length of the radius of each respective epicycle on the assumption of its deferent radius having in each case a value of 60 arbitrary units, which means that all epicycle radii were given in terms of sixtieths of their respective deferent radii.

By relatively simple reasoning it can be shown why the Ptolemaic theory was incapable of relating the distances of the family of planets but could adequately relate the radius of each epicycle to the radius of the deferent for each planet separately. Consider the following diagram. Venus makes a larger epicycle than Mercury because it can be seen to have a greater elongation from the sun. By elongation is meant the angle of the planet's furthest distance from the sun as measured actually in the sky. (Figure 10. 4)

In our diagram, V_1V_2 describe the epicycle of Venus and the planet's position at its greatest elongations as evening star and morning star, respectively. Join V_1 and V_2 with the center of the epicycle. Join E to V_1 and V_2. Angle V_1EC_V is equal to 46°; the angle of greatest elongation of Venus is here seen to the left of the sun in the sky, which means it is seen after sunset in the southwest. It can never be seen there further than 46 degrees from the sun. At V_1 the angle must be a right angle because the line EV_1 is tangent to the circle. Hence C_VV_1 is to C_VE as the sine of 46 degrees, which yields the fraction 0. 72. But this ratio is the ratio of the radius of the epicycle of Venus to the radius of its deferent, which is all the measurement can yield. The same can be done with the epicycle of Mercury, and since Mercury comes only 22 degrees away from the sun as evening star and as morning star, we obtain the ratio of its epicycle radius to its deferent by the same reasoning as above, and the value of 0.37. It can readily be seen that the Ptolemaic system has no means of relating the distances of the two planets. The epicycles of Mars and the other planets are found in a similar fashion. Each planet stands alone as a celestial body in a certain relation to the earth and sun without any bonds to its brethren.

Ptolemy assumed next that the planets moved on their epicycles in the same direction as did their center on the deferent. This was a common feature of all the planets; had Ptolemy assumed the epicycle to be real, his scheme might have laid claim to being a system. But he did not view epicycles as physical, and the common direction of motion remained therefore a mere coincidence, fitting the data quite well, so that the fastest motion of a planet occurred when it was in apogee, when the epicycle's center and planet move in the same direction. (Figure 10.5)

Copernicus took the same data and obtained the same results with his scheme of all the planets' spheres pursuing actual revolutions in the same counterclockwise direction, with the sun near the center. At P_1, planet is in apogee with respect to the earth and at P_2, planet is in perigee. The fastest motion of P with respect to E occurs when planet is at P_1, or apogee because earth and planet move then in opposite directions. The same will be true for the inner planets. For Copernicus all planets must revolve in same direction. (Figure 10.6)

Once Copernicus postulated that the earth was merely another planet and revolved around a common center situated near the sun, every observed epicycle of an outer planet became the equivalent of an earth's revolution about the sun, hence a solar year. Saturn had about $29\frac{1}{2}$ epicycles in its total orbit of $29\frac{1}{2}$ years, Jupiter about 12 in twelve years, and so forth. As the earth makes one turn about the sun, it merely appears to us that the outer planet, which the earth overtakes because planets nearer the sun revolve faster than those farther out, makes that circle which we on earth are actually making. For Mercury and Venus, the inner planets, the same applies. What we on earth see as an epicycle, or cycle of anomaly, represents these planets' circle around the sun.

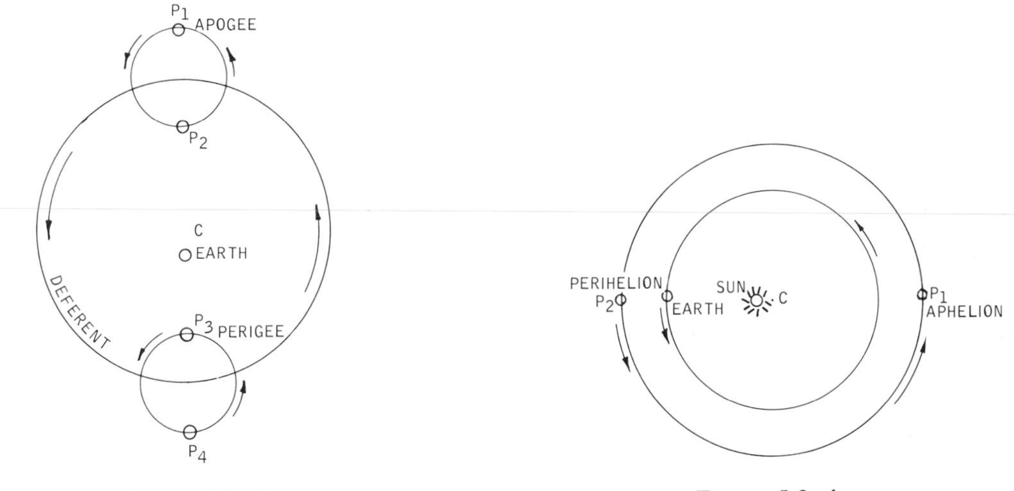

Figure 10.5

Figure 10.6

Further, once Copernicus laid down his scheme, two amazingly impressive and beautiful properties of planetary conduct, wholly impossible under Ptolemy's theory, came to the fore and could not but impress astronomers, regardless of the seeming absurdity of his actual system from an experiential point of view. Specifically, it became possible to determine, 1) the periods, or times, of revolution of the planets about the sun, and 2) the relative distances of these planets from the sun.

Let us see how the first was accomplished. Consider the case of Venus. This inner planet makes, according to the Ptolemaic theory, five cycles of anomaly, or epicycles, in nearly eight solar years. In Copernican language, it makes five revolutions about the sun while the earth makes nearly eight. We know that Venus moves faster than the earth because it moves in the same direction, and must complete a cycle in less time. It overtakes the earth five times, having five perigees. But while Venus is revolving in her orbit, the earth, too, is revolving about the same center. Now, Venus is seen to overtake the earth five times, while the earth revolves as well, making in the same period nearly eight revolutions. This must, therefore, mean that Venus actually makes five more revolutions than the earth, or 13 revolutions in eight solar years. This must be so because when Venus is overtaken by the earth, starting out as they both do from a conjunction, EV, the inner planet V must complete one full revolution before it can overtake. Hence the duration of a Venus period about the sun is p-Venus/p-Earth = 8/13, or Period of Venus = 8/13 x Period of Earth. The period of a planet's revolution about the sun is inversely related to its number of revolutions in a given time. The more revolutions a planet makes per year the smaller is its period. Now 365.25 x 8/13 = 232.72. The time being less than full eight years, the period has only 225 days. By the same method it is found that Mercury completes 145 cycles about the sun while the earth makes 46. Since Mercury passes the earth 145 times, it makes 191 revolutions to the earth's 46. Its period is therefore 365.25 x 46/191, or about 88 days.

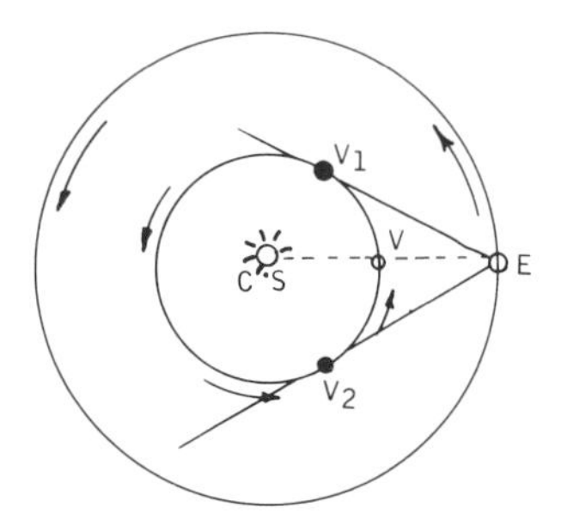

Figure 10.7

For an outside planet the reckoning is similar. Mars, for example, makes 42 revolutions in longitude, and 37 epicycles in close to 79 solar years. This means that the earth revolves more rapidly than Mars, and overtakes it 37 times since the epicycle represents a reflection of the earth's single turn about the sun and occurs when the earth passes Mars in opposition. When Mars is at Mc, in conjunction, the planet is in line with the sun and on his side, and therefore unseen. It is in opposition when E is at E_9 and Mars at M_9. S, E_9, and M_9 are then in line, Mars crosses the south meridian at midnight, and both planets E and M are then in opposition and nearest each other. It is in this position that an epicycle makes its appearance. Since the earth makes 37 more revolutions than Mars' 42 every 79 observed solar years, the figures add up just right, since 42 + 37 = 79. Thus 79 earthly years = 42

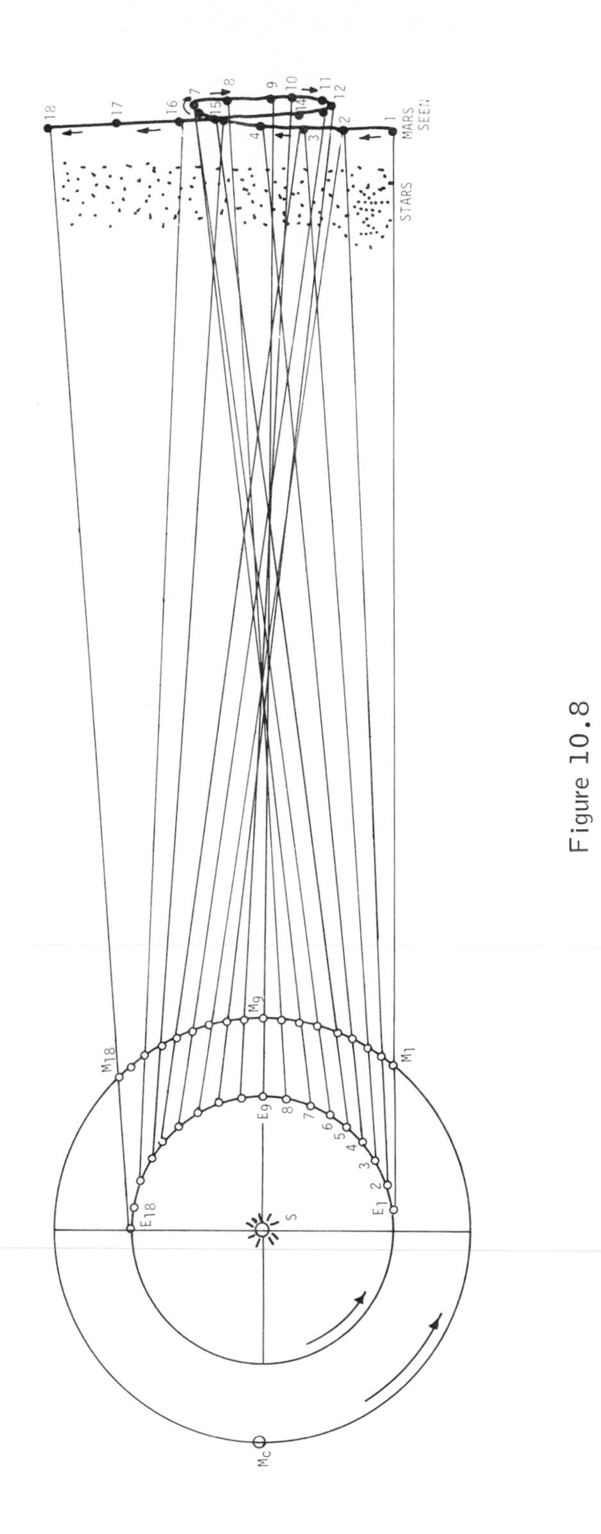

Figure 10.8

Martian cycles, and one revolution of Mars = 365.25 x 79/42, or roughly 687 days [p-Earth/p-Mars = 42/79] or 79 x 365.25 = 42 x Mars year. (Figure 10.8)

So much for the periods. Now as to distances. Again, using Ptolemy's figures, Copernicus makes a simple calculation. According to Ptolemy, the radius of Venus' epicycle is 43 1/6 parts to 60 parts for the radius of the eccentric, the distance between the earth and the sun. The radius of Mercury's epicycle is 22 1/2. In the case of Venus and Mercury, the radii of their epicycles represent their respective distances from the sun, while the radius of the eccentric in these cases is actually the sun's distance from the earth, or the earth's from the sun. If the earth's distance to the sun is put at 60, the mean distance of Venus will be 43 1/2 and that of Mercury 22 1/2.

With the outer planets, the situation is reversed. The epicycle's radius is the earth's mean distance from the sun, while the eccentric's radius represents the planets' mean distance. For Mars, Ptolemy gives the value 39 1/2 for the radius of its epicycle, on the basis of its eccentric being 60. This means that if the earth's mean distance to the sun is 39 1/2, that of Mars is 60. In other words, E to S/M to S = $39\frac{1}{2}/60$; ∴ M to S = $60/39\frac{1}{2}$ [E to S]. Since we have put the distance Earth to Sun at 60, the distance Mars to Sun = $60/39\frac{1}{2} \cdot 60 = 3600/39\frac{1}{2} = 91.14$. The radii for Jupiter's and Saturn's epicycles being given by Ptolemy as $11\frac{1}{2}$ and $6\frac{1}{2}$ respectively, their corresponding distances from the sun, or radii of their eccentrics, will equal 313.04 and 553.84, respectively, on the assumption of distance of earth from sun being 60 parts. Clever and approximate though these calculations are, they remain disjointed. (Eccentric and deferent are used interchangeably.)

With the two simple deductions from his postulated scheme, Copernicus presented science with two wholly new sets of data - the times of revolution of each planet, and the respective relative distances of all planets from the sun. These were fascinating and stimulating conceptions which led Johann Kepler to some of his noblest cogitations *(e.g., The Cosmographical Mystery)* and dramatic consequences, his Third Law.

By some strange quirk of fate, Copernicus' heliostatic (sun stationary) scheme resulted in a poorer fit for the data of Mars' orbit than that obtained from Ptolemy's scheme; and yet, it was precisely this very difficulty, or apparent failure of the theory, that led Kepler to grapple with the problem and discover the elliptical orbit of the planet. It came into being because Copernicus was left with the task of accounting for two planetary anomalies, or irregularities, that of unequal velocities in orbit, or the anomaly in longitude, and the irregularity in the planets' drift north and south of the ecliptic, or inequality in latitude. Having cast out Ptolemy's equant, which troubled him most as "appearing to contradict the first principles of regularity of movement," and Ptolemy's eccentrics, Copernicus had to call upon his own kind of epicycle and eccentric to account for the observed data. A look at these two ways of tackling the same problem will help us see the differences and similarities between the two systems.

Consider the orbit of Mars in the Ptolemaic system without benefit of epicycle, since in Ptolemy's scheme the orbit of the epicycle's center on the deferent corresponds to the planet's path about the sun (or mean sun) in the Copernican system. In Ptolemy's scheme only the epicycle's center need be employed. (Figure 10.9A)

C = Center of equant
B = Center of eccentric circle or deferent
A = Earth
E = Mars at Apogee
D = Mars at perigee

$$AB = BC = 6 \text{ if } BE = BD = 60. \therefore \frac{AB}{BE} = \frac{6}{60}$$

Since Copernicus used the decimal system, we shall convert Ptolemy's figures to the same scale. If AB = BC = 1000, then AC = 2000; then if BE = 10,000; AE = 11,000, and AD = 9000. If we draw line FG perpendicular to diameter ED, then F and G will represent the positions of Mars at the quadrants of Mars' period, midway between perigee (D) and apogee (E), on the right and left sides of the diagram. (Figure 10.9A) Now AF represents the distance of Mars from the earth at its quadrant positions; its length can be easily determined from the known values. $FC = \sqrt{10,000^2 - 1,000^2}$ by Pythagorean theorem of $\triangle BFC$. Hence, considering $\triangle AFC$ we obtain $AF = \sqrt{FC^2 + AC^2}$; $\therefore$ $AF = \sqrt{(10000^2 - 1000^2) + 2000^2}$.

So much for Ptolemy. Now consider the same phenomenon as Copernicus saw it. (Figure 10.9B)

A^1 = Mean sun, i.e. average position of sun
B^1 = Center of eccentric circle, or deferent for Mars
C^1 = Point on diameter and on line joining positions of planet at quadrants

Mars rides on epicycle in same direction as its center travels on deferent. Let radius of deferent $B^1 1$ or B^1G^1 or B^1F^1 = 10,000 and $A^1B^1 = 3/4\ A^1C^1$ = 3/4 (2,000) = 1,500. Let radius of epicycle = 1/4 of distance A^1C^1 = 1/4 (2,000) = 500. Assume planet to travel on epicycle at same velocity as epicycle's center revolves on its deferent. In other words, each makes one revolution in one and the same time. The planet is shown in Figure 10.9B during such a cycle. Point 1 is the aphelion, or point of furthest distance from sun, A^1;

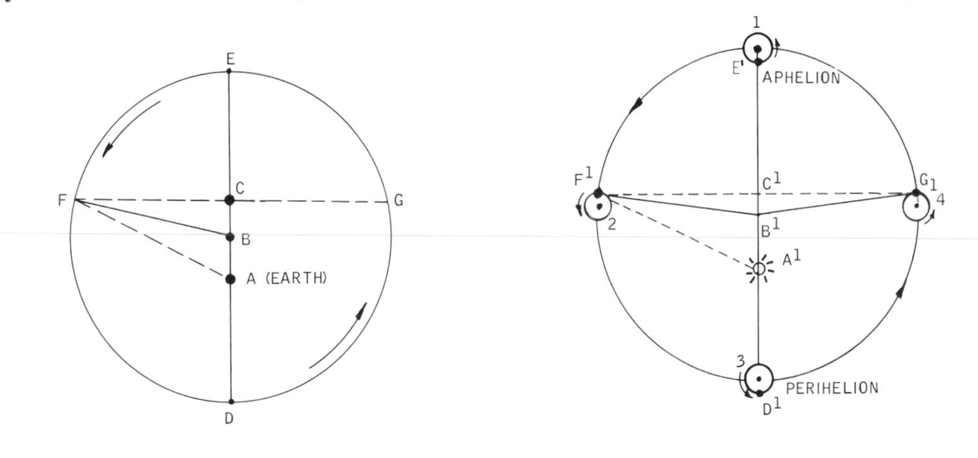

Figure 10.9A

Figure 10.9B

point 3, perihelion. The scheme as here represented shows the planet to be at E^1 and D^1, respectively, at those positions. The distances from mean sun to the planets are the same as in Ptolemy's scheme: $B^1 1 = 10,000$; $B^1E^1 = 9,500$; $A^1E^1 = 11,000$; $B^1 3 = 10,000$; $A^1 3 = 8,500$, and $A^1D^1 = 9,000$. At the quadrants, the planet also will necessarily occupy the same positions, F^1G^1 being perpendicular to E^1D^1 and crossing it at C^1; $C^1D^1 = 11,000$; $C^1E^1 = 9,000$, and $C^1A^1 = 2,000$, exactly as in the Ptolemaic scheme. The different values of B^1A^1 from BA is of little importance because this distance has no physical meaning. However, one significant difference does emerge. In the Ptolemaic scheme, FA, the distance of Mars from earth at quadrants, equals, $\sqrt{(10000^2 - 1000^2) + 2000^2}$, while F^1A^1, its equivalent in the Copernican scheme, which is the distance of Mars from the mean sun at quadrants, equals $\sqrt{(10000^2 - 500^2) + 2000^2}$, which makes it considerably larger than its corresponding Ptolemaic value. This means that "the orbit of the planet in the Copernican system bulges at the quadrants of the periodic time compared to that of the Ptolemaic. The appearances here favor the Ptolemaic system, as Kepler points out. But even the Ptolemaic system does not draw the planet in enough at these quadrants. This is one of the dilemmas which led Kepler to conjecture an elliptical orbit as worked out in the *Commentaries on Mars* and later in the *Epitome*. It is easy to see (from the value of the equants) why Mars should be the planet chosen. For of all the planets it has the largest eccentricity, and the discrepancies would be most manifest." (The *Almagest,* by Ptolemy. Volume 16, Encyclopedia Britannica Great Books. 1952, Appendix B p. 476) It would seem that with some geniuses, even their errors may lead other geniuses to make brilliant contributions.

We are now in a position to summarize the precise nature of Copernicus' contribution to astronomical theory. He says in his dedicatory epistle to Pope Paul III, that there were far too many contradictory theories in the field. Above all, Copernicus took exception to Ptolemy's use of the equant, which he regarded as an artificial scheme for obtaining uniform angular motion. What Copernicus wanted was to return to "the first principles of regularity of movement," which to him apparently meant a single center for the deferent with uniform angular movement around it. Otherwise he retained and respected most axioms and principles honored by Ptolemy. Circular motion as the basic path was honored because obviously the facts demanded it. Deferents and epicycles were retained because how else could one account for the obvious irregularities in longitude and latitude? Such irregularities were recognized because, by and large, the planets circle the earth, at uniform and at irregular rates, which have to be explained.

The basic change which Copernicus introduced into astronomical speculation consisted in taking seriously the old but spurned idea of the earth's rotation and revolution. Copernicus also realized that such an idea could correlate or identify the two deferents of the inner planets corresponding to earth years, and the epicycles of the three outer ones, also corresponding to earth years, and with one stroke discard them by giving them new meaning as aspects of the orbit of the earth around the sun. Their existence rendered Ptolemy's scheme cumbersome and disjointed. His own scheme, Copernicus opined, possessed beauty, logic, economy, and consistency, which it obviously did, through the introduction of as much order and elegance as was conceivable at the time.

To be somewhat more specific, in the Ptolemaic scheme every planet, whether inner or outer, revolved upon an epicycle whose center revolved in turn on a deferent. On the basis of the data, Ptolemy had the centers of the epicycles of Mercury and Venus firmly located on a line joining the earth and the sun, and seemed totally indifferent to the peculiarities of such a unique situation and to the temptation to seek some kind of physical meaning for it. (See Figure 10.4) V_1 and V_2 are points of the planet's greatest elongation or greatest angular distance from sun, $CvEV_1$ or $CvEV_2$ measuring about 45° or 46°: Once this angle is known, the ratio of C_VV_1 (radius of epicycle) to C_VE (radius of deferent) is 43 1/6: 60, or 0.72, according to Ptolemy. As seen from the earth, the final path of Venus is necessarily quite involved. (Thomas S. Kuhn. *The Copernican Revolution*. Harvard University Press. 1957, p. 65)

Here another innovation was introduced by the Copernican system and held out much appeal to students of astronomy. While the Ptolemaic theory never achieved relating the distances of the planets to each other, the system of Copernicus permitted the determination of all planetary distances from the sun, from the earth, and from each other. To the enterprizing this was a speculation which was literally out of this world. Once the major hypotheses were granted, the attainment of this relationship was a direct logical step. Because the distance of the earth to the sun by means of solar parallax was still uncertain, planetary distances could not be established in an absolute sense, but their determination on a relative scale was calculated by Copernicus with little effort and much beauty.

All one has to do is examine the Ptolemaic setup in Figure 10.4 and view the same situation in the Copernican configuration as is done in Figure 10.10. Here too the two inner planets, Mercury and Venus, as well as one outer one, Mars, are shown. The two inner ones are placed at their points of greatest elongation as in Figure 10.4. Angles SEM and SEV are known, namely 22° and 45°, approximately. It is not necessary to know the exact distances because by assuming SE, the distance of the earth to the sun, to be equal to 1, one can readily obtain a relative scale of the distances of all the other planets to the sun. On the same basis of reckoning as used previously, we find the ratio SM to SV. Thus SM/SE = sin 22° = .375, and SV/SE = sin 45° = .707. Since SE = 1, by agreement, the distances to the sun of Earth, Venus and Mercury are in the ratio of 1 to .707 to .375.

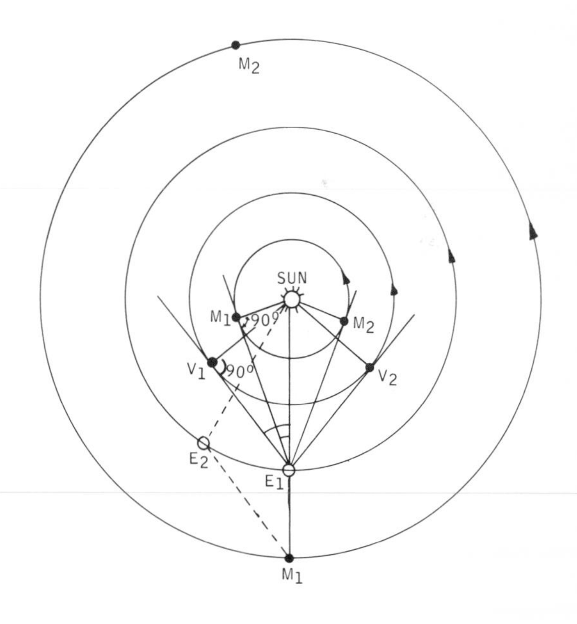

Figure 10.10

With the outer planets the approach is somewhat different. Mars circles the sun in 687 days, the earth in 365.25. Begin the calculation with these two planets as in the above figure, which means when they are in opposition, SE_1M_1. On that occasion Mars crosses the meridian exactly at midnight. One year later the earth is back again at the same place as measured against the stars, while Mars will be at M_2. But 687 days after the earth left E_1, Mars will be back at M_1 while the earth will be at E_2 since it would take $730\frac{1}{2}$ days for it to get back to E_1 the second time. By connecting S with M_1 and E_2 as shown, we obtain a triangle in which all angles can be known; E_1SE_2 is known from knowledge of the earth's orbit and $E_2M_1E_1$ is known by observation. The ratio SE_2/SM_1 can then be found, and since SE = 1, the value of SM in relation to SE becomes known. In this fashion the relative distances of all the planets in terms of SE are established.

5. Further Copernican Advantages

The equant is a typical device of sheer mathematical purity. It is so pure and disembodied that no physical foundation could possibly be conceived for it. Ptolemy never thought his calculation or model required a physical base; even those of his followers who thought they did, never really attempted to supply one. This absence might have been the reason for the equant's rejection by Copernicus. Copernicus' mind obviously tended toward some kind of physical basis for the planetary family, because after daring to take seriously the rotation and revolution of the earth, he suddenly realized that he could thereby do away with two deferents and the three major epicycles of the outer planets. An event of this revolutionary significance could not be fortuitous, he must have opined, and therefore must have meaning. Hence the growth in his mind of a hidden realization that he was dealing with a real mechanism, an actual performance. Vitiating this image was Copernicus' insistance on placing the center of the revolving planets at a point in space near the sun, namely, the center of the earth's revolution which remained an imaginary, vacant place. The reason for his doing so was simply his belief that a planetary orbit, actually a planetary deferent, since the concept of orbits does not appear in its full meaning until Kepler, must be a central circle rather than an eccentric. However, in spite of his being victimized by this concept as much as Ptolemy was by his eccentrics, Copernicus was nonetheless able to realize that he could easily dismiss the equant as gratuitous and inelegant.

The same may be said about a few other ideas which Copernicus was in a position to advance because of his new conception. Consider the case of gravity. If the earth were the center of the world, then obviously gravity meant the tendency of heavy bodies, "earth" and "water", to move toward it. But now that the earth was no longer at the world's center, the mind was open for new ideas. Copernicus was able to state: "I myself think that gravity or heaviness is nothing except a certain natural appetency implanted in the parts by the divine providence of the universal Artisan, in order that they should unite with one another in their oneness and wholeness and come together in the form of a globe. It is believable that this affect is present in the sun, moon, and the other bright planets and that through its efficacy they remain in the spherical figure in which they are visible, though they nevertheless accomplish their circular movements in many different ways. Therefore, if the Earth, too, possesses movements different from the one around its centre, then they will necessarily be movements which similarly appear on the outside in the many bodies; and we find the yearly revolution among these movements." (*On the Revolutions,* p. 521)

The abandonment of one basic assumption and the introduction of another can lead to the opening up of new vistas, new concepts and new insights. Often the new concept is simply forced upon the mind, as is the case here with gravity as a necessary property of all celestial bodies. Conversely, it enables the mind to see certain past explanations as total absurdities and contradictions. In the same chapter (Ch. 9, Bk. I) Copernicus exposes the weakness in the Ptolemaic order of the planets and their distances from the earth. And the more elements of the Ptolemaic system he examines, the more inconsistencies and clumsiness he finds in it, and the stronger grows his feeling that his theory is real, firm, reasonable, and sound. "Furthermore, how unconvincing is Ptolemy's argument that the sun must occupy the middle position between those planets which have the full range of angular elongation from the sun and those which do not is clear from the fact that the moon's full range of angular elongation proves its falsity " (p. 523) Copernicus refers here to the fact that Mercury and Venus have limited elongations, that is are not seen to wander further from the sun on their epicycle than 22° and 45°, respectively, while the outer planets have infinite elongation in their circular orbits. The moon, however, though nearest the earth, also has infinite elongation, but is surely no outer planet. This, too, could clearly be explained only if the earth revolved around the sun with the moon as its faithful companion.

Besides, continues Copernicus, what cause can astronomers offer for their belief that Mercury and Venus "do not also make longitudinal circuits separate and independent of the sun, like the other planets?.... Therefore it will be necessary either for the Earth not to be the centre to which the order of the planets and their orbital circles is referred, or for there to be no sure reason for their order and for it not to be apparent why the highest place is due to Saturn rather than to Jupiter or some other planet." His meaning is that there really is no good reason for the Ptolemaic assumption of planetary sequences in the heavenly space; the sequence generally accepted is purely arbitrary. Nor is there a reason for Mercury and Venus to be uniquely tied to the sun. In his system, the order of the planets makes sense and hangs together in perfect consistency. Copernicus must have been fully aware of the fact that Ptolemy never claimed compulsive faith in his planetary sequence. Says Ptolemy: "First, then, concerning the order of their spheres, all of which have their positions about the poles of the ecliptic, we see the foremost mathematicians agree that all these spheres are nearer the earth than the sphere of the fixed stars, and farther from the earth than that of the moon; and the three - of which Saturn's is the largest, Jupiter's next earthward, and Mars' below that - are all farther from the earth than the others and that of the sun. On the other hand, the spheres of Venus and Mercury are placed by the earlier mathematicians below the sun's, but by some of the later ones above the sun's because of their never having seen the sun eclipsed by them. But this judgment seems to us unsure, since these planets could be below the sun and never yet have been seen in any of the planes through the sun and our eye but in another, and therefore not have appeared in line with it; just as in the case of the moon's conjunctive passages, there are for the most part no eclipses.

"Since there is no other way of getting at this because of the absence of any sensible parallax in these stars, *from which appearance alone linear distances are gotten,* the order of the earlier mathematicians seems the more trustworthy, using the sun as a natural dividing line between those planets which can be any angular distance from the sun and those which cannot but which always move near it. Besides, it does not place them far enough at their perigees to produce a sensible parallax." (*The Almagest,* IX, 1. p. 270, Great Books, vol. 16)

This is a most revealing paragraph because it is typical of Ptolemy the person, the man of thought and of science. Observe how meticulous it is, how critical, how cautious in its claims and mode of analysis. He is never argumentative, belittling of others, or insistent upon the truth or obligatory acceptance of his own hypotheses. He never veers from the path of scientific reason at its purest level. Equally worthy is the fact that he specifically disclaims any coherent theory, any positive assertion about the order of the planets, or any scientifically secure method of determination of that significant item. He puts his faith in the only sound proof there is - namely, measurements of the angle of parallax. Only such angles can determine linear distances. All other means of arranging the radii of the circling planets in order of their lengths are necessarily conjectures. Similarly, when Copernicus proposed his scheme for the order of the planets, he might have realized it was of a conjectural nature. It seemed, however, so appealing and harmonized so well with every aspect of the data that it simply could not be doubted. Copernicus could well exclaim as did Lothar Meyer, the great chemist, in his elation with Canizzaro's clarification of Avagadro's hypothesis: "The scales fell from my eyes, uncertainty vanished, and in its place came a feeling of calmest assurance."

It is easy to observe that every person who advances a new theory or defends an old one feels much the same way. Every believer feels the same about his faith. Unfortunately there is no objective way of distinguishing between error and truth by the intensity of feeling. Belief in the truth of one's faith or the reality of one's postulated scheme constitutes a psychological reaction like pain or joy, love or hate, and cannot be fully subject to reason or judgment, though it can be influenced by them. It is an inevitable facet, a concomitant of hypothesizing, of theorizing. Just as an impassioned singer of sad songs cannot but feel genuinely sad while performing, and experience real joy if the song be joyous, so, too, a great scientist who elaborates a brilliant theory, especially one which rings up one conquest after another, as did the Copernican theory, cannot but grow ever stronger in his conviction that the scheme he postulates is real and true. And since it is man that is the eager consumer, sole judge and generator of ideas, and the source of all definitions as well, it may well be best to define reality and truth in terms of these human experiences. On this basis, Copernicus believed his scheme to be true, although he is scientist enough to be far less dogmatic about it than his later followers who possessed more data that corroborated the theory. His language is always a model of humility; only on rare occasions does he fall into the strictly human trap of considering rotation and revolution as objectively "real". Quite naturally, as more and more confirmative vigor accumulates from a variety of related and even unrelated fields, facts in the truth of a theory or model must necessarily grow stronger.

Typical of Copernicus' attitude is his opening paragraph of Book VI, the last one in his classic. Says he: "We have indicated to the best of our ability what power and effect the assumption of the revolution of the Earth has in the case of the apparent movement in longitude of the wandering stars and in what a sure and necessary order it places all the appearances.... Accordingly by means of the assumption of the mobility of the Earth we shall do with perhaps greater compactness and more becomingly what the ancient mathematicians thought to have demonstrated by means of the immobility of the Earth." (*ibid.* p. 813) This is the essence of his total approach standing as a mute reminder of Copernicus' own attitude.

What impelling powers did the Copernican hypothesis have to render it preferable over the Ptolemaic either in its pure or modified forms, or over other theories advanced by contemporary astronomers, particularly the one by Tycho Brahe? The answer is - none besides the intangible power of appeal. Seen from the vantage point of our times, one can only say that once the mind found itself free to accept it, then the theory acted like a healthy seedling in a fertile soil. It grew in vigor and fruitfulness, and one became attached to it more and more the longer one studied it and compared it to the opposing theories.

We might best conclude this chapter with a thoughtful evaluation of the Copernican contribution by A. Pannekoek in his *History of Astronomy,* (New York, 1961, p. 198): "Thus, the new world structure, notwithstanding its simplicity in broad outline, was still extremely complicated in the details. This, on first impression, gives to Copernicus's book a strange and ambiguous character. In the first chapters a new world system is proclaimed and explained which subverted the foundations of astronomy, brought about a revolution in science and in world concept, and for many centuries made the name of Copernicus a war cry and a banner in the struggle for enlightenment and spiritual freedom. Then, on studying the later chapters, we feel completely transferred into the world of antiquity; on every page his treatment shows an almost timidly close adaptation to Ptolemy's example. Nowhere the breath of a new era, nowhere the proud daring of a renovator, nowhere the symptoms of a new spirit of scientific research!

"In reality, however, the contrast is not so great. The first chapters also breathe the spirit of antiquity. We have already seen this in his arguments on the earth's motion; they belong entirely to ancient philosophy. Copernicus did not consider his work as a break with the ancient world concept but as its continuation, and he appealed to ancient precursors. Through the desire to lean upon venerable authorities, the struggle between adherents and opponents in the years that followed was carried on under the names of 'Pythagorean' and 'Ptolemaic' world systems respectively. It all remained within the realm of ancient science; Copernicus was wholly a child of the Renaissance.

"The astronomers of the sixteenth century regarded the addition of all those complicated circular motions as a refinement of the old theory. Copernicus was highly esteemed among them as one of the foremost astronomers, the man who had improved and replaced Ptolemy. This, however, was only on account of the details and the improved numerical values; his heliocentric system was considered an ingenious theory but was not accepted as truth. His numerical values were the basis of new astronomical tables computed by the Wittenberg mathematician Erasmus Reinhold. These tables, which Reinhold, in honour of his patron the Duke of Prussia, called the 'Prutenic Tables', soon superseded the Alfonsine tables in use until that time."

6. An Interesting Speculation that Missed

Among the theories competing with the Copernican, there was one which could not be eaily dismissed, namely, the scheme of Tycho Brahe (1546-1601), generally regarded as the greatest medieval astronomer before the discovery of the telescope. Tycho was a pathfinder in a direction different from that pursued by Copernicus. His forte was mainly the gathering of reliable and continuous data about as many celestial events as he could possibly single out for study. In the mind of a scientist of Tycho's magnitude, the gathering of observations necessarily lead to ideas and hypotheses. No wonder Tycho published several works of major theoretical or conceptual significance. In his book, *Progymnasmata,* he describes the first fully-studied new star. It had made its sudden appearance on the night of November 11 near the edge of the Milky Way in the constellation Cassiopeia and remained visible until early 1574. Tycho was prepared for careful measurement of the location of that star because in the observatory which his patron, the King of Denmark, had built for him, he greatly improved the known astronomical instruments of his day by increasing their sizes, their stability of construction, their graduations, as well as the methods of sighting. He introduced the custom of continuous nightly readings, and of determining the range of errors of each instrument and its limits of accuracy. He also made allowances at all times of atmospheric refraction in determining the true positions of celestial bodies. Employing the new refinements, a quadrant of 19-foot radius and a celestial globe 5 feet in diameter, Tycho found that the new star showed no parallax, was therefore not sublunar but celestial in origin.

This was a significant conclusion the impact of which grew in vigor with time and depth of comprehension. Although Pliny reports that Hipparchus had observed a nova, the Aristotelian notion of the immutability of the heavens as compared with generation, corruption, and death in the sublunar region of the earth, remained unchallenged throughout antiquity and the Middle Ages. But after Tycho's study of the Nova of 1572, the old dogma could no longer reign unchallenged, or even remain in a state of subdued dormancy. Tycho's findings acted like a slow poison eroding away its very vitals. As one historian puts it: "Although he (Tycho) himself never fully accepted it, the mutability of celestial substance had thus been definitely demonstrated." (A. C. Crombie, *Medieval and Early Modern Science,* Vol. II, 1959, Garden City, New York, p. 179)

Tycho drove another wedge into the established belief-web of astronomical thought, and perhaps also without realizing the historic impact of his deed. Employing his superior instruments and incomparable skill as observer, he was fortunate in 1577 to have at his disposal a comet visible for a considerable length of time. Tycho followed faithfully the movements of the comet against the background of the fixed stars and published his findings. These proved conclusively that the comet showed no parallax and was beyond the sun, hence was part of the planetary family. Of greater significance, however, was that the comet's path in space was such as to cross freely several planetary spheres, if such existed. As Kepler repeatedly stresses, these postulated spheres were not solid, as had been assumed, and probably do not exist. In discussing planetary orbits, Tycho was the first to suggest that they were not circular, but in all likelihood oval.

In his study of comets, Tycho again struck a telling blow at the old belief pattern in astronomy. The Aristotelian notion prevailed that comets were vapors of exhalations generated reactions on earth, which then rose heavenward as vapors do, but on approaching the upper regions near the sphere of fire were ignited and burned away for various durations. They were sublunar in origin. Seneca in his *Natural Questions* discusses Aristotle's view on comets among many others and comes to a different conclusion. Says Seneca: "Our Stoic friends, therefore, are satisfied that like trumpet meteors and beams, and other portents of the sky, comets are formed by dense air.... The comet, according to this account, pursues its fuel just as fires do.... I do not agree with my school here, for I cannot think a comet is a sudden fire, but I rank it among Nature's permanent creations. First of all, everything that the atmosphere creates is short-lived.... Fire cannot possibly abide securely in a volatile body, nor can it keep its place so persistently as does a fire that Nature has fixed never to be dislodged.... If it were a wandering star (i.e. planet), says some one, it would be in the zodiac. Who, say I, ever thinks of placing a single bound to the stars? Or of cooping up the divine into narrow space? These very stars, which you suppose to be the only ones that move, have, as every one knows, orbits differing one from another. Why, then, should there not be some stars that have a separate distinctive orbit far removed from them.... Do you suppose that in this great and fair creation among the countless stars that adorn the night with varied beauty, never suffering the atmosphere to become empty and sluggish, there are only five stars that are allowed to move freely, while all the rest stand still, a fixed, immovable crowd? Should anyone here ask me: Why, then, has their course not been observed like that of the five planets? My answer to him shall be: There are many things whose existence we allow, but whose character we are still in ignorance of.... Why should we be surprised, then, that comets, so rare a sight in the universe, are not embraced under definite laws, or that their beginning and end are not known, seeing that their return is at long intervals? ... The day will yet come when the progress of research through long ages will reveal to sight the mysteries of nature that are now concealed. A single lifetime, though it were wholly devoted to the study of the sky, does not suffice for the investigation of problems of such complexity. And then we never make a fair division of the few brief years of life as between study and vice.... You say a comet is not a star, because its form does not correspond to the type, but is unlike other stars.... Nature does not turn out her work according to a single pattern; she prides herself upon her power of variation." (Seneca, *Natural Questions. Physical Science in the Time of Nero.* London, 1910, pp. 194ff.)

For reasons which might have led to a true as to a false hypothesis, Seneca came to regard comets as part of the celestial family beyond the sublunar world. He disagrees with Aristotle on that point and is lucid in his reasoning. Neither his contemporaries nor his successors adopted his view. They supported instead the Aristotelian theory of the terrestrial origin of comets. Tycho restored the neglected view of Seneca but did it on a far more scientific basis. Among other things, this innovation of Tycho's helped in the further weakening of the grip of the Aristotelian philosophy.

Tycho's next great contribution to the undermining of the ruling belief-web of the astronomical scientific lore was his postulation of a planetary theory that like that of Copernicus resembled a model suggested in antiquity by Heraclides of Pontus. Tycho's theory is of special interest because it represents a clever innovation devised by a bold, creative mind which happens to be in perfect concordance with the accepted beliefs of the culture. It is not an act of cowardice nor a compromise springing out of appeasement. It is a genuine product of critical thought. His major point was that the stationary position of the earth was a reality and all arguments to the contrary were far from proven. No one, not even Copernicus, for whom he had the highest praise, had answered Aristotle's contention that if the earth revolved around the sun, the stars whould show parallax displacement - which they did not. Neither was it conceivable that the heaviest of bodies, the sluggish earth, should wander lustily through space, while the tenuous, ethereal heavens stood still. Nor was it observed that stones dropped from a tower fell far from its base. And since the magnitude of stars were attributed to their volumes, hence diameters, the absence of any trace of stellar parallax in the course of a year must be taken to mean that the stars have volumes of dimensions that would render them bigger than the postulated orbit of the earth around the sun, which was an absurdity that could not even be thought of in polite scientific society. That they might be at infinite distance from the earth was a hypothesis that never entered anyone's mind, and if it did, was rejected as quickly as the putative enormous volume of some stars.

Realizing, however, that the revolution of all the planets around the sun, not only Mercury and Venus, as some of the ancients had speculated, was plausible and mathematically permissible, Tycho proposed in 1588, only 45 years after the appearance of Copernicus' theory, a scheme of his own. He came upon it, he says, "as if by inspiration". In his judgment, it combined all the merits of the Copernican hypothesis without going contrary to faith, observation and common sense. (Figure 10. 11)

As can be seen from the illustration, Tycho retains the Earth, E, at the center of the universe, which ultimately means nothing else than that he retains it as the observer's platform and has the sun circle it daily. Tycho describes his system in his book on the comet of 1577. Dreyer gives the following summary of Tycho's scheme: "The earth is the center of the universe, and the center of the sun and moon, as well as of the sphere of the fixed stars, which latter revolves round it in twenty-four hours, carrying all the planets with it. The sun is the center of the orbits of the five planets, of which Mercury and Venus move in orbits whose radii are smaller than that of the solar orbit, while the orbits of Mars, Jupiter and Saturn encircle the earth. This system accounts for the irregularities in the planetary motions which the ancients explained by epicycles and Copernicus by the annual motion of the earth, and it shows why the solar motion is mixed up in all the planetary theories. (This alludes to the circumstance, which had appeared so strange to the ancients, that the period of the motion of each upper planet, in its epicycle, was precisely equal to the synodical period of the planet, while in the case of the two inferior planets the period in the deferent in the Ptolemaic system was equal to the sun's period of revolution.) The remaining inequalities which formerly were explained by the eccentric circle and the deferent, and by Copernicus by epicycles moving on eccentric circles, could also, in the new hypothesis, be explained in a similar way. As the planets are not attached to any solid spheres, there is no absurdity in letting the orbits of Mars and the sun intersect each other, as the orbits are nothing real, but only geometrical representations." (J. L. E. Dreyer. *Tycho Brahe.* New York 1963 p. 169) The system could indeed explain everything and Tycho promised to do so but never did.

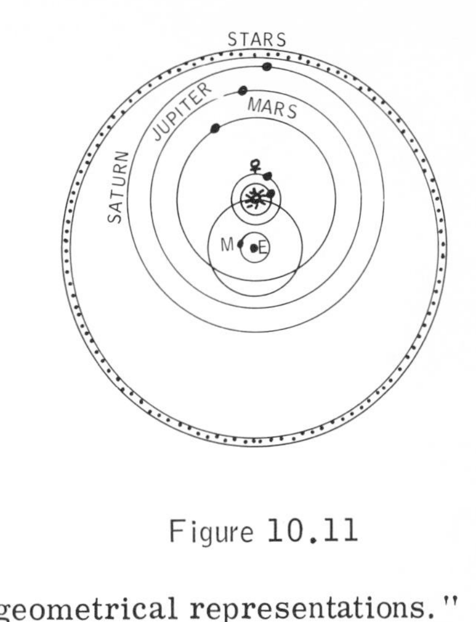

Figure 10.11

We thus find during the seventeenth century, three cosmological theories competing in the marketplace of ideas for public acceptance through intellectual natural selection. The Copernican theory won decisively long before the century was up, even though for awhile it seemed that the Tychonic system might carry the day. Within his lifetime and for a considerable time after his death in 1601, Tycho Brahe enjoyed a practically unchallenged reputation as the greatest living astronomer. His system won many adherents; it catered to the search for a model better than Ptolemy's, and offered one that was simpler and more physical, and did it without invoking unpleasant, absurd or unprovable elements of the kind one discerned in the scheme of Copernicus. But events in science pursued their own course and final victory went to the Copernican scheme. The ideas that seemed so impossible grew steadily in "truth" and stature, gained slowly more credence and in time gained the status of reasonableness and reality.

XI Technology and Instrumentation in the Middle Ages

1. The Vast Technological Progress of the Middle Ages

As in antiquity, we find the same relationship prevail in the Middle Ages between the efforts of scientists in search of a theory for the comprehension of natural phenomena and the labors of practical men at finding solutions to challenging problems. Both activities proceed simultaneously and virtually independently of each other. This has been true throughout all history until the culmination of fertile union between the two activities under the aegis of modern science, beginning with the eighteenth century.

Unfortunately, some scholars and laymen alike helped to establish and maintain the fiction that the medieval period was an age of darkness and superstition, of cultural destitution, of blind worship of authorities and a horror of critical questioning prevailing in the enlightened present. Furthermore, over this vast slough of stagnation presided the Church, armed with the ruthless club of the Inquisition, whose armed minions controlled all thought and blocked all science and progress. In reality, however, this general picture in its pristine purity is probably as accurate as contemporary Marxist or Soviet portrayals of America.

That for many centuries Christian Europe was a theocratic culture is of course a fact. But it is also a fact that our notions of government and of individual rights and freedoms had not yet come into being then, and that people's ideas were of the kind that made a theocratic state as necessary and reasonable as was the rule of Moses to the ancient Hebrews or that of Vercingetorix to his fellow Gauls. Medieval man lived his life and pursued his activities according to the laws of God as interpreted by the Church, and he saw his goals of virtue, faith and salvation in the only light and wisdom he knew, namely, those of the Gospels and their annointed servants. Medieval society was built upon this foundation, and to some extent upon its secular concept of the nature of man and society. The outcome of this outlook was the mental complex we know under the general name of the medieval culture-web with its values, goals, and institutions.

Different as these were from our own, and strange and uncouth as they may seem to us, they were nonetheless components of an actively growing, economically advancing and culturally rather avid and even aggressive society. Medieval technology, engineering, crafts, commerce and exploration were far from wallowing in the stagnation which nineteenth century thought had generally attributed to it. Although all these activities were extensions of ancient skills and practices, considerable novelty began to make its appearance already at the very start of that era. The disturbed conditions within the Roman Empire during the final centuries before its fall in 476 A. D., forestalled perhaps the exploitation of many valuable labor-saving machines. Certain it is that for several centuries after the fall, there was chaos and deterioration until the precocious attempt at order by Charlemagne around 800 A. D. Some opportunities apparently began to present themselves by the tenth century for the effective application of many inventions which had been available in antiquity but remained unused in the chaotic years after the fall.

By the tenth and eleventh centuries Europe emerged from its doldrums. In the year 1086, the Domesday Book, the equivalent of England's national register, recorded an astonishing 5624 watermills in that country for the milling of corn, as compared to fewer than 100 functioning there during the previous century. This was no isolated phenomenon, since similar expansion occurred in Central and Western Europe, as noted in their respective chronicles. From the tenth to the twelfth century Europe underwent a true industrial revolution either simultaneously or a little prior to the wave of translations from the Arabic, with its revival of interest in the scientific literature of antiquity. The more familiar industrial revolution of the 18th century was no unique phenomenon but merely another spurt of a similar nature under different circumstances. It was apparently only part and parcel of a continuous process that reached impressive proportions when it did, but had been in a stage of gestation since about the tenth century, when Europe had apparently settled down to the growth and development of her future nations.

Our past belittlement of medieval technology was due primarily to our legitimate enchantment with the scope, beauty, and utility of the achievements of modern science. As a result of our enthusiasm for its onrush, everything that preceded it was declared to be either ignorant groping, outright perversity, or oppressive superstition from whose murderous grip the mind of man could only be released by radical surgery and denunciation. The primitive "Me-virtue, Thou-villain" complex, was applied to the growth of science as smugly as it had always been applied to the political and social disciplines, and with similarly regrettable results.

Recent studies paint, however, an entirely different picture. No sooner did Europe recover from the Germanic disturbances and pull out of the confusion and economic unrest wrought by the periodic assaults of the Viking raids and Moslem invasions, than serious signs of bold measures to raise economic efficiency and productivity could be discerned. This in itself was a sign of the presence of economic sophistication, evidenced by a growing tendency to overcome latent resistance to change in the use of tools and in work habits.

Power obtained from water turbines was soon put to many uses, a notable sign of economic vitality. Such power was exploited for pumping water to higher elevations, the working of presses for the extraction of oil, grinding pigments, fulling cloth, and various labor-saving operations in the tanning and papermaking industries. The conversion of rotary water power into reciprocal motion and the introduction of such ingenious and revolutionary devices as driving wheels, cranks, complex gears, and cams, marked as significant a rise in relative efficiency as did perhaps steam power or electrical gadgets in later times. Trip-hammers were introduced in fulling with far-reaching consequences to the expansion of the English cloth trade during the thirteenth century, and forge-hammers in the fourteenth with a comparable impact upon metallurgy. The thirteenth century also saw the conversion of wind and water power into the movement of grinding stones, as well as the operation of saws and lathes. By the end of the thirteenth century all of these industrial inventions which could vastly increase productivity were known. If employed on a large scale they could be effective in a manner resembling the industrial expansion of the nineteenth century. One should not, however, be led to believe that machine technology of even minor dimensions had actually spread far and wide. Treadmills were still mostly driven by men and beasts, and primitive labor at most tasks was still ubiquitous; pumps were still operated by manpower, the breaking of stone for cobbles was still done by hand, and crude tools prevailed in every trade and craft. But power machinery had come into being and was utilized perhaps as much as all new tools ever are, that is, spottily and sparingly at first.

Agriculture was the first to feel the impact of the new trend in labor-saving techniques. Already the ninth and tenth centuries saw the invention of a new method of harnessing horses and the use of the nailed horseshoe, two measures which enabled the exploitation of the horse for heavy draft labor. The plough, that basic agricultural tool, also underwent some improvement. While the coulter, ploughshare, and wheels had made their appearance in antiquity, the mouldboard which served to turn over the cut sod, and the ground-wrest, which cleared the bottom of the furrow, were introduced in the eleventh century. Minor but continuous improvements were also made in harrows and rakes, in harvesting implements, in the art of threshing and winnowing, and in virtually every farm operation. Hand mills for flour were provided with treadles operating double-throw cranks. The new plough made it possible to till river-bottom lands and rendered cross-ploughing superfluous. Its use required more draught power, which led to pooling of oxen by peasants. This in turn led to the formation of the medieval cooperative peasant community, the manor. Rotation of crops and of fallowing every third year became widespread and resulted in heightened agricultural efficiency.

The need for greater draught power brought the horse to the plough, which increased the cost of feeding since oxen thrive on cheap hay while horses require grain. The step had to be taken, nevertheless. New crops entered Europe as a result of Moslem influence, particularly rice and citrus fruit in Spain and Italy. These required irrigation which method spread to Italy and Southern France, where viticulture, the cultivation of grapes, became an extensive industry. But cheese and butter production also increased and consumption of these items spread in time to the poorest.

Diet and living conditions generally underwent steady improvement. "Wages gradually rose during the Middle Ages; in the fourteenth and fifteenth centuries the working-classes were better off and could more often enjoy wheaten bread, mutton, pork, and goats' flesh. The diet remained essentially the same throughout this period," says an outstanding scholar of medieval technology (R. J. Forbes, Food and Drink, in Vol. 2 of *A History of Technology* edited by Charles Singer *et al.* Oxford, 1956. pp. 103-146). The same was true of the peasants; according to the same authority, many "fifteenth-century sources tell of the gradual improvement of the peasants' diet." (*ibid.*, p. 126) A significant medieval new food was the making of macaroni, vermicelli, etc., which "seems to have originated at the court of Naples toward the end of the Middle Ages," and consisted of careful preparation of desiccated dough of cereal or rice flour, thus permitting the safe preservation of cereals.

Another medieval innovation was the widespread use of hops to add flavor to beer and secure its preservation. Perhaps for the same reasons that most governments prohibited tobacco and public drinking of coffee and tea, Henry VIII banned hops for beer. However, his son Edward VI withdrew the ban. The early Middle Ages also saw the discovery of alcohol distillation apparently by Italian alchemists or apothecaries in whose hands the art remained for some time. Distilled alcohol came later to be prepared in monasteries as a solvent for herbs and spices, and later came to be employed in the production of liqueurs, perfumes, and medicines. Early alcoholic drinks such as brandy were first prepared from wine, but by the fourteenth century came to be made from the fermentation of cereals. Strict laws against drunkenness, and the heavy taxation of alcoholic drinks, date from the thirteenth century.

Few are the areas of technical skill which stood still in the Middle Ages or failed to make significant progress. The tanning of leather is perhaps the only trade in which little progress was made. The textile industry, on the other hand, saw considerable changes. The manufacture of cloth was well subdivided among a large number of skills, and fell, therefore, under the control of many guilds. There were the carders who combed and cleaned the wool, the spinners who produced the threads, the weavers who made the cloth, the fullers who finished the cloth, and finally the dyers. With craft specialization came mechanization, which made its debut in fulling. In this task of "finishing" the cloth, it is beaten or treaded in water filled with fullers earth so that the material is felted and thickened and the gaps between fibers obliterated. In antiquity, as described by Pliny, the cloth was beaten with clubs. But already in the eleventh century, fulling-mills were known in Europe; they became widespread by the thirteenth. They were operated by waterwheels which raised and let fall two large wooden hammers upon the wet cloth.

Weaving underwent some mechanization. In the twelfth century foot-controlled treadles were introduced which permitted speeded up production of rich designs and varied weave. Simultaneously, the horizontal frame of the loom made its appearance, which facilitated the weaving process. Spinning, too, underwent changes. The use of the spindle with its whorl was an ancient, though fairly sophisticated invention. Gradually, however, the spinning wheel came into fashion, although like most inventions apparently against strong odds, since the first reference to it is a regulation of the Drapers' Guild of Speyer, in 1298, which prohibits the use of yarn for the warp if spun on a spindle wheel. Available illustrations from that date on show the growth of complexity and efficiency of that clever mechanical device. Similarly, the cropping machine used to shear off surface fibers after raising them so as to give a soft finish to the material, was prohibited in England in 1495; the "gig mill" employed in raising the fibers, was proscribed by an act of 1551. But in spite of constant antagonism to the novelty of mechanization, already during the early sixteenth century, about 250 years before the coming of the steam engine, Europe saw "the firm establishment of the factory system." (R. Patterson. Spinning and Weaving. Vol. III, *History of Technology.* 1957)

There were shops with as many as two hundred looms in one large room. In another, "an hundred women merrily were carding hard with joyful cheer," while in a third, two hundred women spun all day. In time there took place an accelerated intensification of the process. Just as knowledge is autocatalytic and, as a rule, consistently expanding, so is technology. Artisans, craftsmen and investors are participants in an activity that is as conducive to growth and inventiveness as much as the process of inquiry in natural philosophy.

The early part of the fourteenth century saw the invention of gunpowder, which consisted at first of a mixture of finely divided carbon and saltpetre, or potassium nitrate, to which later sulfur was added. This brought in its trail the development of cast iron, which became the chief item of medieval metallurgy. Early in the fifteenth century cast iron cannons, or "bombards", were in common usage, and the demand for them induced mass production. The drawplate for the making of iron wire had already been invented in the tenth century, but by the fifteenth many objects of common usage reached markets in large numbers, such as, small urns, scythes, needles, horseshoes, knives, and the like. The mass use of cannon by armed forces led to thought of interchangeability of parts and their standardization.

We must not overlook the whole array of instruments that may be regarded with certainty as distinct medieval contributions. Among these instruments are the crank and connecting rod, both of which led to the development of continuous rotary motion, the fly wheel and governor, the treadle, the overhead sapling-spring, the bow-spring, the spinning wheel, complex geared planetaria as well as astrolabes, weight-driven clocks (13th century) to which numerous tricky and entertaining automata were appended, then clocks with coiled springs, stack freed, and fusee, (15th century) and some other inventions of high caliber. Concludes Lynn White: "By the latter part of the fifteenth century, Europe was equipped not only with sources of power far more diversified than those known to any previous culture, but also with an arsenal of technical means for grasping, guiding, and utilizing such energies which was immeasurably more varied and skilful than any people of the past had possessed, or than was known to any contemporary society of the Old World or the New. The expansion of Europe from 1492 onward was based in great measure upon Europe's high consumption of energy, with consequent productivity, economic weight, and military might.... Considering the generally slow tempo of human history, this revolution of machine design occurred with startling rapidity. Indeed, the four centuries following Leonardo, that is, until electrical energy demanded a supplementary set of devices, were less technologically engaged in discovering basic principles than in elaborating and refining those established during the four centuries before Leonardo." (*Medieval Technology and Social Change.* Oxford University Press. 1962, p. 128)

Our knowledge of mining, metallurgy, the chemical and glass industries in the Middle Ages is in a most fortunate state by virtue of the great classic *De Re Metallica* by the Saxon physician George Agricola, first published in 1556, and in our own century masterfully translated into English and fully annotated by Herbert Hoover and Mrs. Hoover. The original text is supplied with numerous informative woodcuts that tell their detailed pictorial story of the tools, machines and methods employed. One is impressed above all with the widespread use of machinery such as seven kinds of suction pumps, the use of water power, flywheels, and treadmills turned by horses and even goats. Of special interest, for example, is a series of pumps placed at different depths with the lower one feeding the one above it, all operated so that "a wheel fifteen feet high raises the piston-rods of all these pumps at the same time and causes them to drop together. The wheel is made to revolve by paddles, turned by the force of a stream which has been diverted to the mountain." (From Georgius Agricola's *De Re Metallica,* p. 184) Advanced techniques for drainage, hoisting, and ventillation were employed, as can be seen from the beautiful woodcuts with which the text is amply supplied. There were few processes indeed in the mining industry to which water power was not applied. We see it used in the crushing of rock, jigging, sieving, and roasting, for example. Prior to the sixteenth century "the price of iron had been fairly stable, though wages and the price of raw materials rose steadily; but with the general rise in prices during the sixteenth century, iron rapidly became much dearer." (Hist. of Tech., Vol. III, p. 30. Article on *Metallurgy and Assaying* by C. S. Smith and R. J. Forbes) The rise in iron furnaces in which charcoal was still employed to reduce the ore, brought about a scarcity in wood and the search for a new fuel. The only addition to ancient metallurgy was zinc, discovered and mined in the sixteenth century. It was used to improve the quality of brass, an alloy of copper and zinc, known since pre-Christian antiquity in the form of ores, but now worked as a pure material.

Considerable progress was made in the art of glassmaking. Clear, crystal, and properly controlled colored glass came from the numerous plants of Venice and other cities of Northern Italy, where also late in the thirteenth century eyeglasses origniated. That people were grateful for some innovations, is seen from the text of a sermon by a certain Friar Giordano of Pisa, who declared in 1306 at Florence: "It is not yet twenty years since there was found the art of making eye-glasses, which make for good vision, one of the best arts and most necessary that the world has."

Little need be said about progress in the architectural and building crafts since both Romanesque and Gothic cathedrals testify to their high achievements. Another area in which much engineering skill and inventiveness were exhibited, was the building of dykes and sluices, as in Holland, and in canal locks, as developed mostly in northern Italy. The art of canal and bridge-building moved ahead at a steady pace, as did skill at pile-driving and the building of coffer-dams, which are enclosed compartments in a body of water. They are kept watertight by firm walls around a space from which the water has been pumped out, and in which supports or foundations for bridges can then be built. Drainage canals were improved, and so were navigational river and canal networks in many parts of Europe.

By the thirteenth century significant numbers of ships plied the western Mediterranean from the ports of Venice, Genoa, and Pisa. These had two masts with lateen, or triangular, sails. With the beginning of the fourteenth century, the northern type boat began to prevail in the Mediterranean; these had a single mast, a square sail and stern-post rudder. Next came the three-masted, round merchantmen, or carracks, which made their appearance about two generations before Columbus' famous voyage. These are the trading-galleys in which usually five men, and often as many as eight men rowed with one oar when human propulsion was required. The boats were usually heavily armed. The flat-bottomed, one-deck vessels, known as galleys, gave way to the galleon, which was broad-beamed, three or four-decked, round-bottomed, constructed with turretlike fortifications at both bow and stern, and with cannon along the gunwales. Such ships were capable of long voyages since they could be loaded with heavy provisions as well as cargo. Nevertheless, it must not be overlooked that the Victoria, Magellan's only ship out of five to survive his journey in circumnavigating the globe, was only 85 tons, though at that time ships of 600 tons were becoming common. From some time in the twelfth century, the employment of the magnetic needle as compass, rendered navigation bolder and securer, especially so since most navigators came to employ astrolabes for the determination of latitudes, hour-glasses for accurate timing, and scale-drawn charts for locating positions. Declination of the compass needle, or deviation from true north, was well known.

While vellum and parchment were the principle materials for writing in the early Middle Ages, they became in time replaced by paper, which Europe first obtained from the Moslem world, early in the twelfth century. The subsequent century saw a report by Marco Polo about the printing of paper money in the Mongol empire, and a later report of biblical pictures from block prints. By the middle of the fifteenth century we suddenly become aware of the invention of printer's ink (lampblack in linseed-oil varnish), the printing press, movable type and the means of casting type in metal, or die-casting, first practiced by Johann Gutenberg at Mainz. The manufacture of paper had begun much earlier, and by the time printing was formally introduced, quite a few innovations had already entered the process of its manufacture.

Throughout all this period, roughly up to the seventeenth century, when stirred up medieval science began to expand in the culture of the West, the practical activities of man in the arts and crafts, proceeded along their respective courses at relatively uninterrupted rates, slow at times, and faster at others. This process occurred without the benefit of so-called pure science, or the thoughts and speculations of the natural philosophers. Each field of pursuit, the practical and philosophical, wended its own way, as if unaware of the possibility that anything could be gained by the fusion of their activities. That each was fertile in novelty, is of interest in that it reveals the potential creativity of man in any activity in which he indulges. Moreover, the rate of growth is not the same in all activities, nor is it uniform in time. A given innovation, such as the invention of movable type, may bring in its trail many possible challenges, discoveries and inventions, while others of similar merit or intrinsic cleverness, may lie idle for some time before they stir up other innovations. The latter is not common, but we may cite the tanning of leather as one craft which has remained unchanged for centuries. Similarly in our own times, car manufacturing is extremely mechanized, while the construction of houses is far less so, except for the excavation of foundations and some secondary activities such as the riveting of beams. Yet, it often transpires that after a prolonged period of little change, some new addition may act as a breakthrough and release a flood of novelty in its trail. In its general outline this process seems to parallel the mode of progress in pure science as well.

2. Characteristically Medieval Instruments

There are a few scientific instruments that are uniquely medieval. Among these may be cited the Cross-staff, or Jacob's staff, first described by the Provençal Jewish mathematician, Levi ben Gerson, in 1342. Like most other ancient and medieval instruments, it was used primarily to measure the altitude of a celestial body. In its simplest form it consists of a short rod placed at a measured distance from the eye so that its ends coincide with the distance to be measured. In principle it can be done by covering a given distance, say, of the sky with the fingers of the hand and the arm outstretched. Clearly the nearer the fingers are held, the larger is the distance covered. Or one might also say that the larger the angle subtended at the pupil from a given object sighted, the larger that object will be taken to be.

The instrument with the movable arm, BC, upon it, is held so that end A is close to the eye. It was essentially a ship's instrument. Three cross pieces were commonly used: The shortest for angles up to 30°, longer pieces for angles between 30° and 60°; the longest for angles between 60° and 90°. The staff, the rod on which CB rides, had three scales of altitude corresponding to the distances of each of the three crosses, i.e. cross pieces. The small vertical rod BC is moved along the longer rod AD to point E in which position it just covers the length FG. We thus have two similar triangles in which $FX/AX = BE/AE$; $\therefore$ $FX = BE \cdot AX/AE$. (Figure 11.2)

The Cross Staff

Figure 11.1

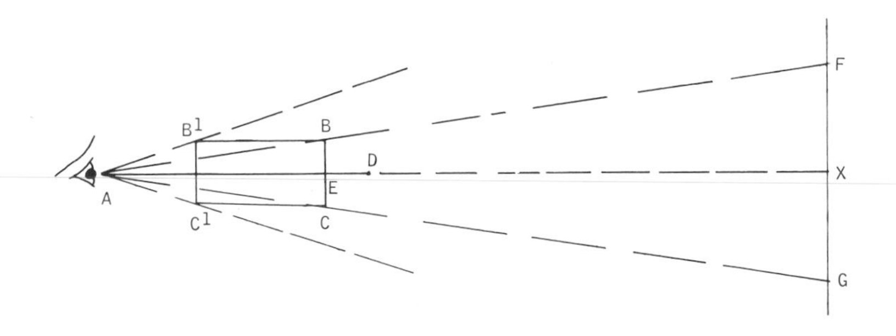

Figure 11.2

Considering AX as constant, since it is the distance to the sky, FX is measured by the known ration BE/EA which is the tangent of the angle at A. Some form of this instrument was used by Hindu and Moslem sailors. The staff AD is graduated with values of the tangents, or better still, the corresponding angles. Trigonometric functions were not used, however, until after 1600 A. D. Until then all calculations were made by geometric methods of similar triangles and the Pythagorean Theorem. Since different crosspieces were used, the staff carried several scales.

The most popular instruments of the late Middle Ages were various forms of the quadrant. These were mainly of two types: The fixed sight, or meridian type, and the more serviceable azimuthal type. They were used in surveying, navigation, and in connection with artillery; at sea the portable azimuthal type was used. These were quadrants supplied with an alidade, or a movable rod, for sighting. They consisted of a square provided with an arc: It could be held horizontally to take readings of azimuths when necessary, and usually contained compasses.

In Figure 11.3 the sights are fixed; a plumbline hangs down to indicate the angle of the star's or sun's altitude. The meridian type has movable sights. The instrument can be used horizontally to measure azimuths. (Figure 11.4)

An interesting modification of Jacob's staff is the backstaff of John Davis in which the observer measures the elevation of the sun by standing with his back to it, and sights upon the line of the horizon. He then moves the sliding arc carrying the sight so as to see the horizon through it together with the tip of the shadow of the sun cast by the upper rod. The sum of the two angles subtended at the horizon point will then give him the angle of the sun's elevation.

In the torquetum of Regiomontanus, first introduced in the thirteenth century, an interesting and clever simplification is presented. The base of the instrument consists of two hinged plates, A and B, that can be arranged at any desired angle to each other. The lower plate A is held in the plane of the table, which is the horizon centered with the plane of the meridian across its center. The upper plate, B, is inclined so as to be in the plane of the equator. The angle between them is therefore the complement of the latitude. (Figure 11.5)

Figure 11.3 Figure 11.4 Figure 11.5

The third plate, C, is permanently placed in the plane of the ecliptic, hence at an angle of $23\frac{1}{2}°$ to B, and can be rotated on a central pivot. Upon the plane of the ecliptic is pivoted a vertical plane D with an alidade upon it, E. In this manner, all celestial readings are directly referred to the ecliptic. The alidade is provided with a protractor and also carries a plumbline. Thus, the reading of data is rendered simple and measurements are obtained directly.

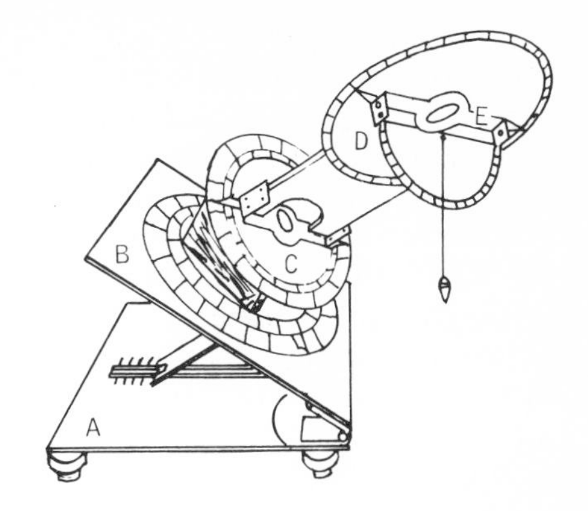

Figure 11.6

Most characteristic of the Middle Ages, however, are two instruments that enjoyed wide popularity. The first is the sun dial, and the second the planimetric astrolabe. Sun dials, seen today mostly as lawn or garden ornaments, were highly popular as the only functioning clocks during the Middle Ages. The vertical gnomon (Chapter II, Section 2) has probably been known to the ancients since before the inception of recorded history. From the beginning of the Christian era, men of learning began inclining the gnomon so as to render it parallel to the earth's axis, by placing it in the plane of the local meridian so as to have it point to the celestial pole, near the north star. We know that throughout the year the sun moves about 1° per day from west to east along the ecliptic, and finds itself for six months above and for a similar period below the celestial equator. We also know that each day the sun will move with the rotation of the whole sky along a circle parallel to the equator, that is, along a parallel circle of latitude marked upon the sky. Therefore, as the gnomon is made to point to the heavenly pole, it will be parallel to the earth's axis. The sun in its daily path will then of necessity describe something of a semicircle around the gnomon, and so will correspondingly the gnomon's shadow on the plane which supports it, called the dial plate.

We have seen that it was customary throughout antiquity and the early Middle Ages to measure time by unequal hours, by dividing the daily interval of time from sunup to sundown into twelve equal parts. This, yielded long hours in the summer and short ones in winter. With the advance of the Middle Ages the utilization of equal hours, or as they were called, equinoctial hours (since they prevailed during the two equinoctial days) became ever more popular, and sundials underwent important improvements. In time, the common, or garden sundial, became the most widespread of the many possible devices of telling time by the sun. It is still accurate and valuable today.

The garden sundial is described as horizontal. It consists of two components: a vertical gnomon and a plate placed horizontally. The gnomon casts the shadow which falls upon the plate which has lines and numbers on it to indicate the hour of the day. It is this plate which must be placed horizontally and gives the dial its name. Since the gnomon has the inclination of its edge determined by the latitude of the place, so as to render the edge parallel to the earth's axis, the distribution of diverse sundials on the northern hemisphere will be as shown in the illustration.

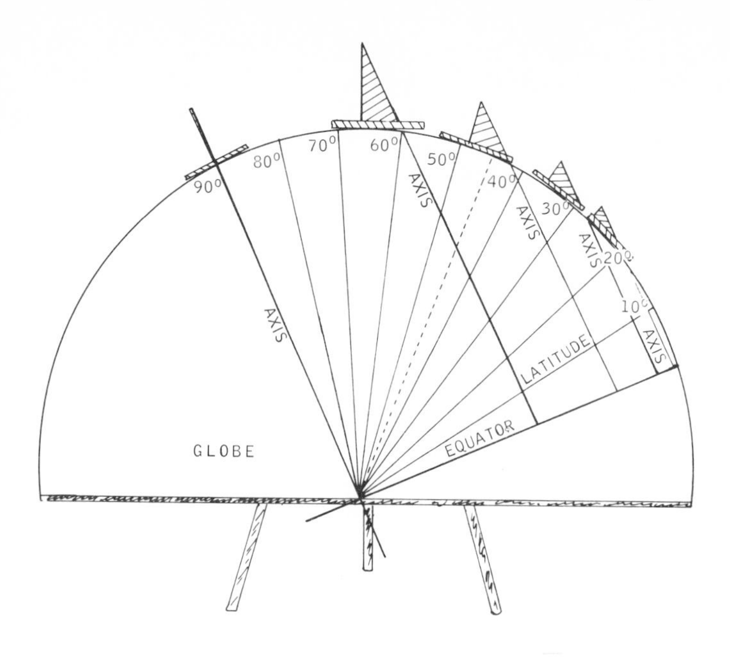

Figure 11.7

The dial at left with vertical gnomon is intended for the North Pole; the next one is for latitude 60°, next latitude 45°, 32° and 18°.

Let us consider the building of a sundial and the principles underlying its construction. To begin with, consider the ideal situation. At the earth's north pole the simplest horizontal sundial would prevail and it would yield the simplest and most direct results. The gnomon would be a vertical rod and the dial would be a circle upon which on any day between March 22 and September 22 when the sun is at all visible, his shadow would each hour move clockwise 15°. The reason for this regularity is that the sun moves in a regular circle wherever he is in the zodiac, completing it in 24 hours in a plane at all times parallel to the horizon. Since a circle has 360°, then in the interval of one hour, the shadow will move 15°.

Let us consider how the corresponding motion of the sun will influence the motion of a shadow of a gnomon anywhere else on earth between the north pole and the equator. The sun travels along the ecliptic, which is its path in the middle of the band of zodiacal constellations, which are taken to extend eight degrees north and eight south of that midline. Six months of the year the sun will be on its path above the celestial equator, and six months below. But wherever it is, it will describe *daily* a circle parallel to the equator. It will also change its position daily by 1°, but as the celestial sphere makes *its daily revolution,* the sun will revolve with it in a plane parallel to the equator. For computation's sake we may therefore assume the sun to be on the celestial equator at all times. It must therefore follow that its shadow will move equal amounts and trace equal hours on the horizontal dial. In reality, the sun is on the celestial equator only twice a year, on March 21 and September 22, the equinoxes. The lengths of the solar day vary, and so do the

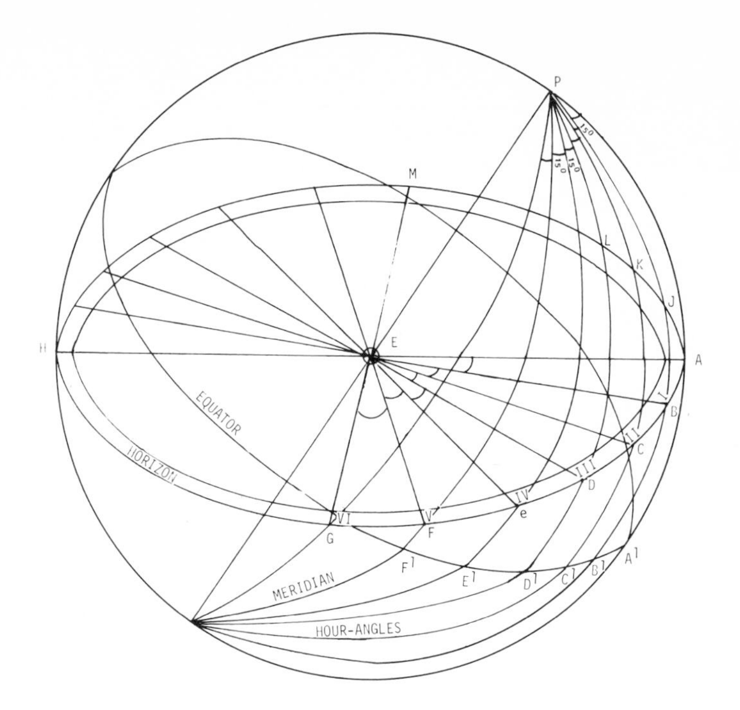

Figure 11.8

lengths of the diurnal motion of the sun for different horizons north and south of the equator. The sun's motion actually observed is the "apparent motion," or "apparent time," shown on the sundial. The theoretical motion of the sun, as if he were on the equator, is called the "mean sun" and constitutes an ideal situation. The mean sun's motion is uniform and so is the mean day's length. When the sun is actually on the meridian at any given place, we have local apparent noon. The true sun, meaning the sun's actual place on the ecliptic, will cross the local meridian mostly either before of after the mean sun.

The celestial sphere is divided lengthwise for convenience into meridianal lines 15° apart, which lines designate hour-angles. The Equation of Time gives us the angular amount in hour angle distance by which the "mean sun's" crossing of the local meridian differs from the "true sun's" crossing, that actually observed. The "mean sun," is taken to be situated on the equator, and will traverse upon it equal arcs per hour, so that $A^1B^1 = B^1C^1 = C^1D^1 = D^1E^1$, etc. The meridians crossing these points will cut off corresponding segments AB, BC, CD, DE, etc. on the dial, meaning on the horizontal circular plate. These segments are not equal, since AB for example is closer in length to A^1B^1 than F^1G^1 is to FG, on account of the inclination of the equator to the horizon. As a result, the angles which these horizontal arcs subtend at their center E, on the horizon below the zenith, will also be unequal. On the other hand, all the angles at P, made by the hour-angle lines, are 15° each. The task for the dial maker at any particular horizon of latitude, is therefore primarily to transfer the ideal, equal, hourly arc of the "mean sun's" path on the equator, to the actual arc of the "apparent" or "true sun's" path at the given locality. This is achieved by a clever though simple geometrical, trigonometrical step as shown in the diagram.

This diagram outlines the geometrical logic employed in finding the actual angles on the horizontal plate. The circle AGHM represents the local horizon with its zenith overhead and the north star at P. The arc AP represents the latitude of the place since it is the angle of elevation of the polar star. Moreover, the angle PAE is a spherical right angle. This renders any other point on the horizon circle amenable to simple treatment in terms of the Pythagorean theorem.

In addition to the horizon circle, we also have here the celestial equator and a grid of meridional lines of great circles, all of which are perpendicular to the plane of the equator. These meridional lines form hour circles and are 15° apart, the arcs A^1B^1, B^1C^1, C^1D^1, etc., which are equal. On the other hand, the segments cut off by these meridianal lines on the horizon circle are unequal, as are necessarily the angles these segments subtend at E. It is therefore required to deduce the numerical values of these horizontal arc segments, and-or their angular values at E, from the known parameters of the hourly arcs and angles of the equator. This calculation is readily negotiated, as follows.

1. Consider the horizon angle AEB.
   tan AEB = AB/AE;
2. But considering the angle which arc AB subtends at P, we have,
   tan APB = AB/AP; ∴ AB = tan 15° · AP;
3. But AP = sin angle of latitude, since sin PEA = AP/AE; AE = EP = radius.
   Assuming radius = 1, ∴ sin latitude = AP
   ∴ AB = tan 15° · sin latitude (2, above)
4. Returning to 1, above: tan AEB = AB/1 = AB = tan 15° · sin latitude.

From tables of geometrical functions we obtain value for tan 15° and multiply it by sin of angle of latitude of place. Product is tan AEB, which gives us the angle, AEB. This then is the angle we measure off on our horizontal dial for the motion of the sun's shadow from 12 noon to 1:00 p. m. We start with noon since our gnomon lies then in the plane PAE.

5. In two hours from noon the angle of the hypothetical mean sun will have moved on the celestial equator = 30°, or on arc A^1C^1. We must adhere to an arc extending from PA to PC rather than from PB to PC, because only PA is perpendicular to the horizon circle, while PB, PC, PD etc. are not. Hence on similar grounds, tan AEC = tan arc AC, tan AED = tan arc AD; tan AEe = tan arc AE, etc. Consequently,

tan AB = tan 15° · sin latitude
tan AC = tan 30° · sin latitude
tan AD = tan 45° · sin latitude
tan AE = tan 60° · sin latitude
tan AF = tan 75° · sin latitude
tan AG = tan 90° · sin latitude.

6. Point E is the point from which the hour lines radiate and the point which is the vertex of the vertical triangle; *but this triangle is the Gnomon.*

The edge of this gnomon (the hypotenuse) makes an angle equal to the angle of latitude with the plane of the dial. This edge is called the style, and is parallel to the earth's axis and must point to the north star in all sundials, as can be seen in Figure 11.7.

7. After choosing a point E on the dial where the vertex of the style is placed, a line is drawn through it, perpendicular to the line EA or plane EPA, or the plane of the gnomon. This is line MEG, or the line designating the hours 6 A. M. (M) and 6 P. M. (G).

8. Continuations of lines EB, EC, ED, etc. give morning hours before 6 A. M. in quadrant HM.

9. Measuring off equivalent angles to the left of EA will give the horizon angles for the corresponding ante-meridian hours. (A. M.) Thus AJ = AB; KL = CD, etc. The continuations of lines joining them to E, into the HG quadrant, will give the hours after 6, post-meridiem (P. M.).

Two more points remain to be considered: one, the correction for local longitude; and two, the correction resulting from the Equation of Time. Consider the first correction.

Our globe is marked off by lines of longitude which are great circles containing the earth's axis in their planes. They extend from the prime or zero meridian, passing through Greenwich, England, a suburb of London, to the east and to the west of it. For convenience they are placed every 15°, so that each corresponds to an hour's difference from Greenwich, those to the east later, those to the west, earlier. Thus New York, lying near the 75° longitude, will be close to 75/15 = 5 hours earlier than London. The lines of longitude are thus made to divide the earth's surface into time zones, each segment of 15° differing by one hour from the segments adjoining it to the right or left.

The creation of time zones gives identical time to localities which at the equator will be as far as 1,000 miles apart, but less than that the further north or south we go. Neighboring localities having identical standard time by convention, can have significantly different real local times, if located away from equator. Eastern Standard Time, for instance, prevails in the region including Boston and Detroit. Yet, Boston will have its moment of noon more than 50 minutes before Detroit since the meridianal plane of Boston will be in line with the sun that much earlier, the earth rotating from west to east. Our standard time zones in the United States are roughly so arranged that they extend to the right and left of their corresponding key meridian of longitude. To obtain the actual, or true local time, it is necessary to know the local longitude and correct for it by adding to or subtracting from the standard, which is the time of the actual meridian. Minneapolis, for example, is in the Central Standard Zone, but about 3.3° west of the 90° meridian. This means that its local true time will be 3.3/15 of an hour earlier than central standard, or watch time. Since 15° = one hour and 1° = 4 minutes of time, Minneapolis local time will be 4 x 3.3 = 13.2 minutes earlier than Central Standard. Thus if C. S. T., or watch time shows 2:30 P. M., correct local time will be 2:16.8 P. M. Conversely, localities east of the 90th meridian in the same zone will be obliged to add corresponding intervals to 2:30 in order to obtain their actual, true local time.

The second correction is somewhat more intricate. Observe that the corrected local time above is actually *local apparent solar time* as compared to watch time, which is mean solar time based upon, as we saw, the convenient but fictitious average, or mean sun moving uniformly in the sky. The real sun, however, does not move uniformly for two reasons. First, our day is reckoned, from noon to noon, or from midnight to midnight, hence by the position of a point on the earth with regard to its alignment with the sun. However, the earth moves in its orbit as we note its rotation with respect to the sun. But, since the earth's motion in its annual orbit is uneven due to the orbit's elliptical shape, being slow in summer at aphelion and fast in winter at perihelion, the measurement of daily lengths of orbit must also be unequal. In January the earth moves actually 1.019° per day and in early July 0.953°. So much for the first cause of inequality of the day, or of the observed solar path.

The second cause is the obliquity of the earth's axis to its plane of revolution, which phenomenon leads to some special circumstances. Because of this angle of 23.5°, the sun as seen from the earth will appear half the year above the celestial equator and half the year below it. The sun's orbit against the stars thus tilts downward in the fall and inclines upward in the spring. Instead of moving around the sky along its path eastward against the stars in uniform arcs, the inclination of the path renders the sun to be seen at varying rates, sometimes ahead of the mean and sometimes behind it. These differences are accounted for by the Equation of Time. (This Equation differs from one year to the next by a few seconds, but after each leap year returns to what it was four years prior. The differences occur in cycles of four years.)

The Equation of Time corrects for both factors, the deviations from the mean caused by the earth's differences in velocity, and by the inclination of the earth's axis to its plane of revolution. The following curve gives the corrections for the year. Thus from December 26 to April 15 the apparent or dial sun is slow and to get standard time, varying numbers of minutes have to be added. From April 16 to June 14, the apparent sun is fast and minutes have to be subtracted. From June 15 to September 2 the apparent sun is again fast and from September 3 to December 25 again slow.

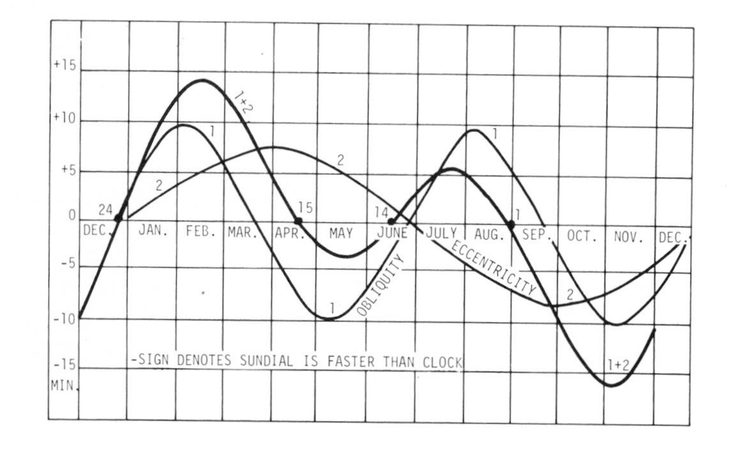

Figure 11.9

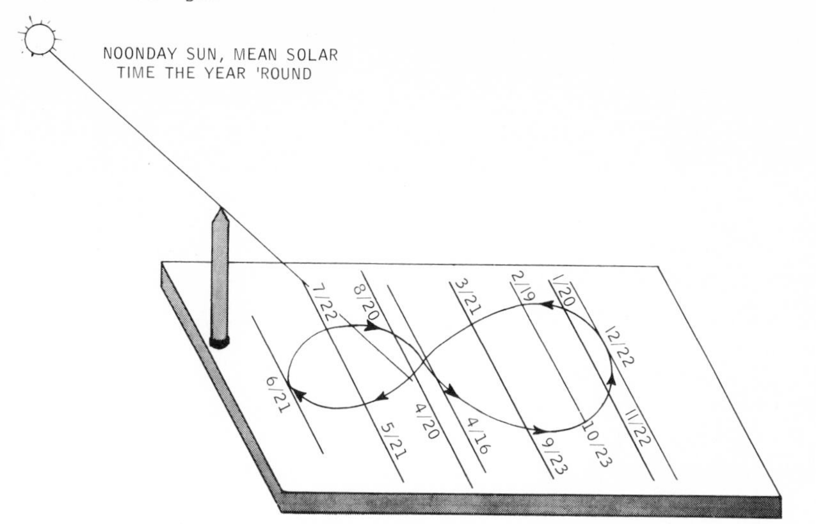

Figure 11.10

The Equation of Time can best be demonstrated by allowing a narrow beam of sunlight to come through a tiny hole placed in a shutter over a window facing true south. The beam of sunlight will then fall on the floor every exact moment of local noon. It will be seen that only on June 14, September 1, December 24, and April 15, will the sun be on the true local meridian. On all other days at noon, the sun will be either to the right or left of that line. This figure, known as the Analemma, shows precisely when the locally apparent sun is ahead of watch time and when behind. Standard time assumes the sun at noon to be daily on the midline, i. e., on the meridian of the appropriate time zone.

It is therefore necessary, by way of summary, to point out that a sundial needs two corrections: one, the correction for local longitude vis-a-vis the longitude selected for the time zone of the locality; and two, the correction of the Equation of Time based on the effect of the two factors cited. The longitude correction is a constant, while the Equation of Time varies from day to day.

Another instrument which reached wide popularity during the Middle Ages was the planimetric astrolabe. The term astrolabe (astrolobon, star-taker) was applied, prior to the coming of the telescope, to practically every instrument employed in the measurement of positions of celestial bodies. It is best, however, to use the term for the two instruments described by Ptolemy, the armillary and the planimetric. The former has already been explained. The latter, as indicated by its name, refers to a plane projection and appears in the form shown here. (Figure 11.11, A & B) It is based on the principle of stereographic projection, first described in Ptolemy's Planispherium and probably known for several centuries before him. The term stereographic projection refers to the art of mapping or projecting of spherical surfaces upon a plane, or flat surface. The basic phenomenon is best demonstrated in Figure 11.12.

In this illustration the observer's eye is the focal point of observation and the entire pictorial presentation rests upon this foundation. For practical purposes the inhabitants of the northern hemisphere require, spread before them upon the table, a flat projection of the northern skies obtained in the

Figure 11.11A

Figure 11.11B

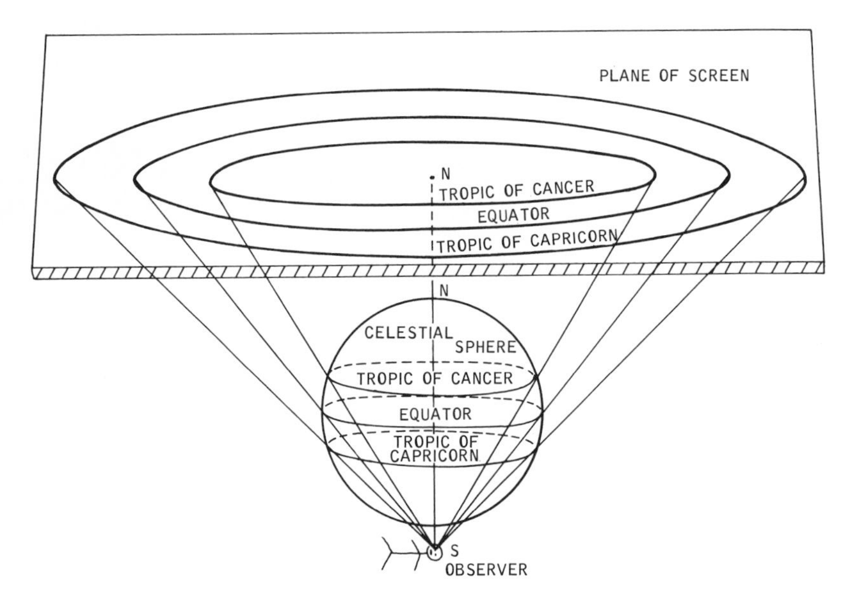

Figure 11.12

manner shown above. It is seen projected flat, by the observer's eye at the south pole of the celestial sphere, and looking upward towards the heavens' northern pole.

As can be seen from the illustration, it is best to place the screen upon which it is desired to have the projection, somewhere up above the sphere. Such a plane will conveniently have upon it the three major landmarks of the celestial sphere: the circle of the Tropic of Capicorn, of the Equator, and the

Tropic of Cancer. Objects closer to the eye subtend a larger angle of vision and will be seen as larger, while more remote shapes will appear smaller since they necessarily subtend smaller angles. A plane projection of the northern sky will have these three concentric circles as major landmarks. All circles on the sphere are circles on the plane of projection.

The planimetric astrolabe consists basically of two plates. The inner plate represents the horizon of any particular locality, characterized by its latitude, and the outer, the sky marked by some conspicuous stars in their correct positions and revolving about the celestial pole. This sky plate contains the projected zodiacal circle which, being situated in the sky at an angle to the celestial pole, will not appear in stereographic projection as a homocentric circle, but as eccentric to the pole. (Figure 11.13) The first plate, representing the particular local horizon, is held stationary within a hollowed out space of the holder-frame called the mother. The instrument is provided with several brass plates, or tympans, one for each desired latitude, for each famed city. These plates fit into the mother by having a cleft which is made to fit into a notch in the mother. The latter is provided with a ringlike raised edge which encircles the inserted plate.

At the center of the plate is a hole that permits the plate's insertion into the mother's projecting pin at its center. With the two plates in place, one is provided with the stereographic projection of the horizon, already described (Chapter III), which is engraved upon the plate, as well as a stereographic outline of the sky with its three major homocentric circles. In addition, each horizon plate also contains a network of lines of azimuth and altitude, much as our geographic maps contain a grid of latitude and longitude. The plate grid representing a horizon that is circular and presented as such, differs from a geographic map in that it has its azimuth and altitude grid in the form of circular arcs, stereographically projected and serving the same objectives.

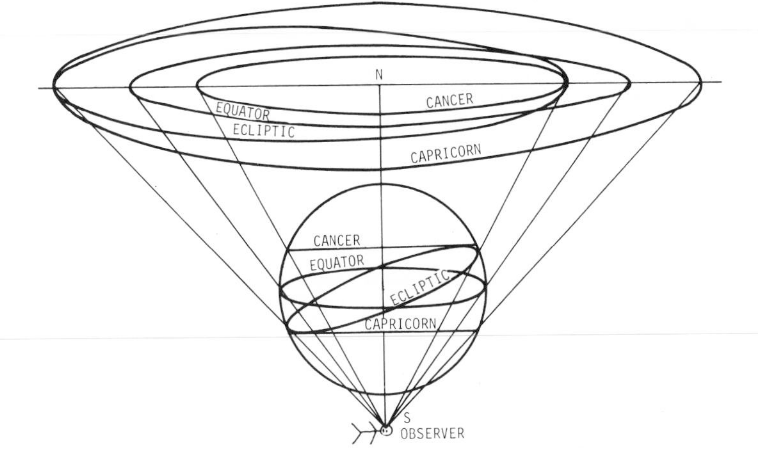

Figure 11.13

The outer plate which represents the stereographic projection of the northern sky, is referred to as the spider-web. It bears that name because it has many segments cut out of it so as to permit adequate views of the underlying horizon plate beneath it. Its netlike structure is sufficient to convey an outline of the sky as it appears at any given moment over the particular horizon. This weblike plate bears upon it the circle of the zodiac lying eccentrically about the north star and the locations of the more conspicuous stars. The two plates, the underlying horizon plate with its lines of azimuth and latitudes, and the overlying spider-web of the northern sky with its zodiacal ring and scattered stars, combine to yield a composite of the celestial vault in relation to any given horizon at any specific time, with each star in its proper, determined position. On the outer ring of the mother are engraved the degrees of a circle, the twelve signs of the zodiac, and the twenty-four hours of the day.

On the back of the mother there are marked two crosslines, the vertical representing the meridian, the south-north line, and the horizontal, the east-west line. (Figure 11.14) Its rim is also divided into degrees, the signs of the zodiac, the names of the months, and the days of the year. The back also has a movable pointer or sight, the alidade, which has two vertical plates at both ends. These have tiny openings in them so that they can be employed to sight the sun. When the sun's beam passes through both holes and its focused image can be seen on a card held behind the lower hole, it is certain that this rule is in line with the sun. Its arrowed end indicates on the rim of the instrument the sun's altitude in the eastern, southern, or western sky. Knowing the date, one then places the sun on the front spider-web plate in the right spot of the zodiac for the given day. Assume the date to be July 30. The sun will then be 8 degrees in Leo. This spot is then marked off on the spider-web plate, the sky, and rotated so as to be on the corresponding spot of the plate of the local horizon where the sun belongs. The two plates together then yield the exact picture of the sky above the local horizon. This is so because the sun has been placed first in its true position of the zodiac by virtue of the date, and in its true place on the local sky with respect to the given horizon, by virtue of its measured altitude. The sun being in its precise location, all the fixed stars are located as well, as if clearly seen by a local observer in spite of the daylight.

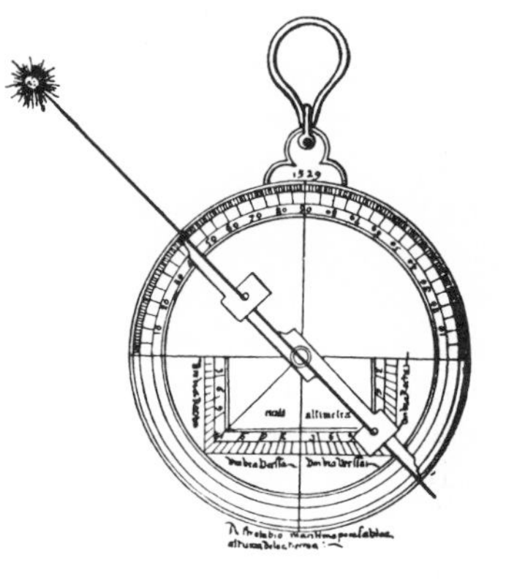

Figure 11.14

The back of the mother has engraved upon its outer rim the signs of the zodiac, the months and days of the year and the degrees of a circle, in successive concentric rings. It also has marked off the major holidays. In addition, it has a table of lengths of horizontal shadows of gnomons of given height, or what we would designate today by the tangents of the angle of the sun's elevation. These values are marked in the two adjoining right angles engraved below the horizontal line through the center and called the shadow square. The horizontal arm of each right angle is called umbra recta, straight shadow, and the vertical the umbra versa or converse shadow. The umbra recta corresponds to the shadow cast on the ground by a vertical rod, while the umbra versa corresponds to the shadow cast on a vertical wall by a horizontal rod perpendicular to the wall.

According to Chaucer's *Treatise on the Astrolabe,* the instrument can perform the following functions: 1) To find the degree in which the sun is day by day, according to its orbit. Knowing the date one sees on the rim of the back the degree of the sun in its proper sign. 2) To find the altitude of the sun, or of any other celestial body, at any time. 3) "To know every time of the day by the light of the sun; every time of the night by the fixed stars; and also to know by night and by day the degree of any sign that ascends on the east horizon, which is commonly called the ascendent or else horoscope." By knowing the date, then shooting the altitude of sun or star, one juxtaposes the proper positions against the horizon plate. Automatically one can then read off on the rim the respective hour. In addition, the East line will show the particular degree of a given sign of the zodiac crossing the horizon at the point of its intersection with the East-West line. This marks the point of ascendent, of great significance in reading one's horoscope. 4) "To determine the beginning of the dawn and the end of the evening, which are called the two twilights." Knowing the degree of the sun from the date, the point opposite it, by 180°, is the nadir. If one sets the given point of the nadir in the west 18° of altitude below the horizon (the refraction of light by the atmosphere causes light from the sun to reach us while it is still 18° below the horizon), the opposite point of the label, the indicator, will point to the hour of the sun's rising. Conversely, with the nadir of the sun's proper position 18° below the East line, the opposite end of the label will be on the true degree of the sun, and on the rim of the mother its pointer will show the hour of the end of the evening. 5) Finally, the arc of the day can be found, or the so-called artificial day, or the period from the sun's rising until it goes to rest. The degree of the sun is set upon the intersection of your horizon with the East line. Lay the label upon it and note its pointer on the rim. Next, turn the spiderweb plate until the degree of your sun is on the intersection of the horizon line with the west line, and note the pointer's position on the rim. The arc between these two points marks the number of hours of daylight on that particular day, or the time any particular star dwells upon the earth from your horizon's point of vantage.

This is a partial list of the functions rendered by this instrument which had many modifications and often carried additional data inscribed upon it, serving as partial almanac as well as working apparatus. It invariably was cleverly wrought, artistically finished and adorned.

This instrument was much modified and in simplified form gained diverse practical uses in navigation for sighting the polestar and midday sun, and in surveying. Only the back of the mother was used because it carried the alidade, or label, the shadow-square and the circles of degrees and dates. It ranked on ships only second in popularity to the Jacob's staff and did not fall into disuse until replaced by the sextant in the eighteenth century.

XII The Transition to Modern Science

1. Copernicus and Kepler in Astronomy: Also Galileo

When a scientific theory maintains itself for many centuries in a scientifically active culture, then that theory must possess many intrinsic merits. If it is not possible to deceive all the people all the time, it is certainly not possible to delude all the scientists for many centuries, unless their minds participate in the delusion. Wide acceptance rests on strong grounds in the realm of science, because scientists are in the habit of questioning, testing, and verifying every belief. Persistence of a theory must therefore mean that it withstood the customary tests and found a harmonious niche within the prevailing belief structure.

We have seen that the Copernican Theory was a mathematical, geometrical device aimed at demonstrating that a hypothesis rejected by all masters could effectively explain all the data, yield a harmonious, and gratifying scheme of the solar system, and render superfluous some Ptolemaic Theorems that seemed unsound and unnatural. We have also seen that while the Ptolemaic scheme was held in highest regard by the small group of mathematicians familiar with it, its common image among scholars was a modified Aristotelian system supplied with a physical rationale, acceptable to the medieval view of science. This was rooted in Aristotelian physics which had many gaps and weaknesses of which some scholars were fully aware. We shall now consider the consequences of the Copernican innovation.

Before half a century elapsed after the death of Copernicus, Kepler's fancy felt strongly attracted to the new theory, and his thoughts were directed toward answering the many questions it stirred in his mind. If the planets revolve around the sun, why are they spaced from the sun at the particular distances at which one fins them? Why not at different distances? What forces keep the planets in their unique orbits? Why are these orbits elliptical? In several of his books Kepler reminds the reader that the revered Tycho Brahe had conclusively demonstrated that there are in reality no spheres, since comets cut across them as if they did not exist. Having rejected the scheme of Ptolemy, and being obliged to abandon the belief in spheres, Kepler was somehow led to seek a credible, physical mechanism for his new faith. And he was both brilliant enough and fortunate enough to find an answer to each of the questions he raised. In doing so he singlehandedly put the Copernican theory on a firm pedestal, which Newton, later in the seventeenth century, converted into a sound foundation.

Kepler's answers to the above questions came in several steps. His first book *Cosmic Mystery,* published in 1596, indicates its objective by its very sub-title: "A Forerunner to Cosmographical Treatises, containing the Cosmic Mystery of the admirable proportions between the Heavenly Orbits and the true and proper reasons for their Number, Magnitudes and Periodic Motions." The gist of this work is as follows: There are, as Plato suggested and Euclid first proved, only five perfect solids, that is, polyhedrons, bodies of many faces, all of which are equal in each solid, respectively. And if the faces are equal, their sides are equal. These solids are the tetrahedron with four equilateral triangles, the cube with six squares, the octahedron with eight equilateral triangles, the dodecahedron with twelve pentagons, and the icosahedron with twenty equilateral triangles. All these bodies are of course symmetrical and can have spheres inscribed within them and circumscribed around them, so that in the first instance all faces touch the sphere and in the second, the encircling sphere touches every vertex of the enclosed solid. Kepler was struck by the notion that there exist only as many perfect solids as there are intervals between planets, beginning with the Mercury-Venus interval. In his perspicacious study of Kepler in *The Sleepwalkers,* Arthur Koestler looks into this matter so adequately and interestingly, that little more need be said here about the role of this work in Kepler's future contributions and the onset of modern science, in general.

As summarized by Lloyd W. Taylor in his *Physics, the Pioneer Science,* "the sequence (in The Cosmic Mystery) ran as follows, beginning at the exterior. If a cube is inscribed in the sphere representing the orbit of Saturn (at that time the outermost known planet), the sphere of Jupiter will just fit within the cube. If a tetrahedron be inscribed in Jupiter's sphere, the sphere of Mars will fit within the tetrahedron, and so on through dodecahedron, icosahedron, and octahedron, the sphere inscribed within each in turn being proportional in size to the orbit of the earth, Venus and Mercury, respectively" (New York, 1941, p. 153). The spheres represent the planetary orbits, and the ratios of their diameters are determined by the dimensions of the five perfect solids placed within them in the given sequence. The latter has no binding rule such as, number of faces. The only requirement is their being perfect solids.

In every line of activity pursued by Kepler, we see the influence of the Copernican scheme, in itself the most dramatic evidence for the constructive impact of the new theory. True, Kepler's labors on the Cosmic Mystery proved fruitless, but not so the question itself and the stimulation it gave its author. Both the question and its consequences were of momentous value to the future of science. Mystic, Pythagorean dreamer, Christian fanatic, but above all, lynx-eyed lover of nature that Kepler was, he never ceased peering into nature's wondrous mysteries, and never ceased speculating about the laws and regularities that could represent her conduct. Believing he had explained why there could be only six planets, and how their distances were ordered, he proceeded to the next logical set of questions, namely, the shapes of their orbits, the differences in their orbital velocities, the overt relationship between a planet's distance from the sun and its orbital velocity and its time of revolution, all of which puzzles were answered in his subsequent books. The first two were answered in his *Astronomia Nova* (1609) and the third in his *Harmonices Mundi* (1619).

In pursuit of his productive dreams and calculations, Kepler came to venture much further afield. In his mind, the stimulating potentialities of the Copernican theory knew no bounds. His Astronomia Nova bore the full title: "A New Astronomy Based on Causation or A Physics of the Sky derived from the Investigations of the Motions of the Star Mars Founded on Observations of the Noble Tycho Brahe." The problem of causation or the elaboration of a new physical machinery that could well account for the model he fashioned out of Copernican beginnings, stimulated his mind with oppressive force and provoked it to the maximum creativity. As usual, honest to perfection, Kepler wrote his friend and benefactor, Herwart von Hohenburg, the Catholic Chancellor of Bavaria, philosopher and friend of science and the arts: "My aim is to show that the heavenly machine is not a kind of divine, live being, but a kind of clockwork, (and he who believes that a clock has soul, attributes The Maker's glory to the work), insofar as nearly all motions of the clock are caused by a simple weight. And I also show how these physical causes are to be given numerical and geometrical expression." (Gesammelte Werke, Vol. XV, p. 145, 1605) And in the book he is referring to, his Astronomia Nova, he does indeed do what all astronomers had hoped for, namely, find a workable physical mechanism for the celestial system of the planets in their motions. Ptolemy did not have such a mechanical model, but his system possessed appealing mathematical beauty. Aristotle supplied a model to the scheme of Eudoxus, but even before the days of Kepler, souls and intelligences ceased to please as principles of motion. With the appearance of Kepler, the abstract, loose Copernican scheme began to acquire mechanical relationships out of which a feasible model could be constructed.

"If we want to get closer to the truth", Kepler says in the second section of his Cosmic Mystery, "and establish some correspondence in the proportions, [between the distances and velocities of the planets] then we must choose between these two assumptions: either the souls II which move the planets are the less active the farther the planet is removed from the sun, or there exists only one moving soul III in the centre of all the orbits, that is the sun, which drives the planets the more vigorously the closer the planet is, but whose force is quasi-exhausted when acting on the outer planets because of the long distance and the weakening of the force which it entails." In his Notes, he comments on this passage: "II. That such souls do not exist I have proved in my Astronomia Nova. III. If we substitute for the word 'soul' the word 'force' then we get just the principle which underlies my physics of the skies in the Astronomia Nova... For once I firmly believed that the motive force of a planet was soul... Yet as I reflected that this cause of motion diminishes in proportion to distance, just as the light of the sun diminishes in proportion to distance from the sun, I came to the conclusion that this force must be something substantial---'substantial' not in the literal sense but... in the same manner as we say that light is something substantial, meaning by this an unsubstantial entity emanating from a substantial body." (Quoted by Koestler, p. 258-59)

The concept of force, so real yet bothersome, was coming-into-being within the mind of Kepler as he was launched on his path of discovery by the Copernican theory. All new theories do their work in this fashion, often regardless of their intrinsic merit or destined duration. By so functioning they fully justify their existence even if they turn out not to be as we say, "true". A theory that stays long unmodified or unchallenged, as did the Ptolemaic for the few centuries of the medieval scientific renaissance prior to Copernicus, ceases to be either useful or stimulating. And the Ptolemaic remained unchallenged for two reasons. First, it was not in functional use because it did not lend itself to a physical schematization, and was kept for ritualistic or display purposes only. Secondly, no new idea appeared on the horizon until the work of Copernicus. And were it not for Kepler and his line of thought, the Copernican theory would have lingered on the same sacred shelf as Ptolemy's, with no progress recorded. It was Kepler through whom history spoke for the direct advancement of the Copernican foundation. Galileo did indeed make the unique and fundamental contribution in opening up the floodgates of telescopic observation with its first initial bolts, but their concrete fruits for the growth of Copernicanism lay still in the offing. Kepler's contributions were immediate.

In his search for a physical mechanism Kepler came across William Gilbert's stimulating work *De Magnete* (On Magnetism) which appeared in 1600. It is a fascinating book which initiated a revived interest in magnetism and set it off upon its successful course. On Kepler its effect was dramatic. If the earth is a magnet, the planets are no doubt magnets as well, and the sun is the largest magnet of them all. Sunspots demonstrate that the sun rotates, and its rotation is clearly responsible for all the planetary revolutions. "He was delighted to find a spring for his clock, a magnetic force within the sun that could satisfactorily hold the planets in their orbits, and on the assumption that the sun itself rotates, have the planets revolve around it. To him this idea was a great spiritual triumph even though it failed to combine in one thought his three loves--God, mechanism and mathematics. The latter was missing in this picture since the mathematical expression of the forces that kept the planets in motion and limited that motion to the particular orbital paths, eluded him. But then, he was much consoled by the numerous mathematical expressions he did extract from the bewildering phenomena, such as, his law of equal areas, based on his conclusion that velocities in planetary orbits were inversely proportional to distance from their central or focal point, of an excentric path, the relation of periods of revolution to distances from the sun, the law relating distances from the sun according to the properties of the five regular solids, etc." (Mark Graubard, *Astrology's Demise and its Bearing on the Decline and Death of Beliefs.* Osiris, Vol XIII, 1958, p. 226)

In his Cosmic Mystery he states that the velocity of a planet in its orbit is inversely proportional to its distance from the sun, a relationship that Newton replaced, as we know, with the inverse square law, but one which comes to mind at first glance. Ptolemy too had thought he saw this relationship in the motion of the epicycle centers on their respective deferents. But with Kepler this relationship assumes special significance. To him it meant that the seat of force must be localized in the sun, from which locus it must radiate with diminishing strength in all directions. Therefore, the elliptical orbits of the planets oblige them to move faster over certain areas of their paths and slower at other times. This must be so because they are closer to the seat of the force, the sun, when they are fast, and further from it when they move slowly.

It all became more lucid, more appealing and more compelling, with Gilbert's theory that the earth is a magnet. Anyone who has seen a magnetic needle rotate on its pivot due to the motion of another magnet, can readily understand Kepler's elation with his idea that all planetary motion is of magnetic origin.

Because he sees the world differently, he begins to evolve different concepts of force and motion. No longer are the Aristotelian conceptions satisfactory, nor Aristotle's and even Copernicus' ideas of motion, which anchored the planets to solid spheres. To all ancient and medieval naturalists, motion in empty space without a physical mover, was inconceivable. Kepler knows from Tycho's work on comets that there are no solid spheres, and his mind begins to picture the planets moving freely through space, impelled by a force that emanates from the sun in a manner akin to light. The earth, in a similar fashion, causes the moon to revolve around her. Motive power is not unique with the sun, but is characteristic of all masses. This again constitutes a novel thought. And so the whole set of physical problems entailing motion, attraction, force, weight, fall and inertia, begins to impinge heavily on his mind and to mark the beginning of ideological transition involving many concepts. This stirring will revolutionize science, resonate in a few other creative minds and lead finally, through the Newtonian synthesis, into the horizons of modern science.

"And if anyone asks me what I envision in the body of the sun that radiates forth as a motive force, I will tell him to press forward and look deeply into the analogous case of the magnet. The power of the magnet resides in its body, grows with its bulk and diminishes with the diminution of it. In the sun, similarly, the motive force seems to be so powerful as to render it reasonable to believe that its body is the densest in the entire universe... Moreover, the magnet does not attract with all its parts but possesses rectilinear filaments or fibers (seats of the motive power) extending in length in such a manner that an iron wire placed between its heads is not pulled but directed and placed parallel to its fibers... The example of the magnet is certainly very beautiful and accords so well with reality that it takes little enough to consider it as if correct...

"The conclusion seems therefore quite plausible since the Earth moves the Moon through a motive force, and is itself a magnetic body, and since the Sun moves the planets in a similar fashion through the force it emits. The Sun is similarly a magnetic body." (Johannes Kepler, *Gesammelte Werke,* Vol III, Astronomia Nova., Ed. Max Caspar, München, 1937, pp. 242-246, Caput, XXXIV)

But Kepler never postulated a theory without giving it geometrical justification, or without attempting to put it upon a foundation of geometrical proof. He therefore postulates a magnetic force within the planet which interacts with the magnetic force of the sun in a manner to yield the elliptical orbit he requires.

Assume EGFH to be the epicycle of the planet Mars with its magnetic axis along the line FE$\perp$to diameter GH which lies parallel to the line of apsides, or line joining the sun with the aphelion (above) and perihelion (below). Assume pole E attracted to the sun and pole F repelled. The magnetic axis maintains its position constant in space. When the center of the epicycle is at C, it can be seen that the planet will then not show any tendency to be either attracted or repelled by the magnetic power of the sun, since angle ACE = ACF, and the attractive and repulsive forces are then equal. When the epicycle center is at D and more so at K, the forces of attraction and repulsion between the sun's magnetic axis and that of the planet come into play and an excentric or oval orbit must result. Working out the full details of the geometrical situation, Kepler comes to the conclusion that "in all cases the attractive force will be as the sine of the true anomaly," the latter being the angle at the Sun, A, made by the planet as it revolves from C to D to K, hence △ CAD, DAK, etc. The attractive force gains as the planet advances in its orbit, being zero in the C position and at a maximum in the K position. And if it is attracted in the descending arc CDKI, it will necessarily be repelled in the complementary, or ascending half to the right. "So far, indeed, did Kepler carry his speculating on this part of the subject, as to attempt to deduce the time of a solar rotation from the period of a planet's revolution; and, having observed that the ratio of the semi-diameter of the sun to the semi-diameter of the orbit of Mercury was nearly the same as the semi-diameter of the earth to the semi-diameter of the lunar orbit, he supposed that the ratio of the revolutions to the rotations might also be the same; and he thence deduced this consequence, that the time of a solar rotation consisted of nearly three days." (Robert Small. *An Account of the Astronomical Discoveries of Kepler,* Univ. of Wisconsin Press, 1963, p. 216)

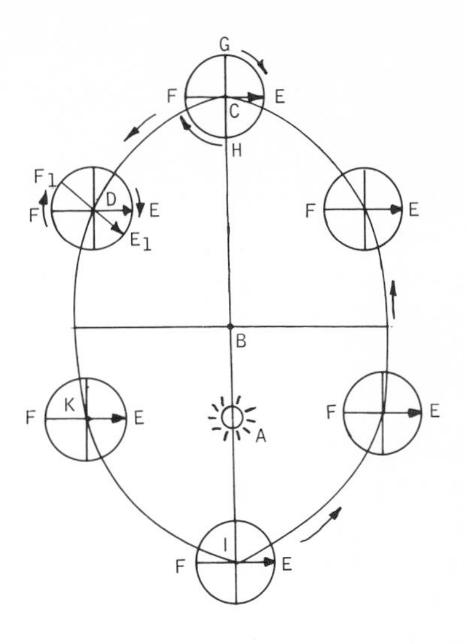

Figure 12.1

And since the above conclusions did not agree with the data, because "all observations testify that the libration itself, produced by either of these forces, is not as the sine of the true anomaly, but as the versed sine of the excentric anomaly," it is clear that the planets have no need for souls or intelligences to move them but of some mechanical force. Kepler then proceeds to postulate and calculate until the data and theory are fully brought in accord, which is characteristic of his method throughout. In the course of his calculations he finds that his forces cannot be harmonized with the supposed path of a planet in its epicycle. He has no hesitation about abandoning the epicycle and postulating a libration of the planet so that "though it did not move in the circumference, the libration was determined as if it had moved in it..." (Small, p. 218) At every step of each speculation, he struggles with all his mathematical and imaginative powers to supply both geometrical proof and physical reality to all his original conceptions. He does not always succeed, but in his utter frankness invariably admits it. After struggling to have his solar magnetic force explain simultaneously both the planet's circular motion along the epicycle and the circular motion of the center of the epicycle itself, he finally concludes: "But then, I find it impossible to conceive how all this could be realized in nature." (Astronomia Nova, p. 254) In this manner, he is gradually led to reject epicycles, introduce the oval path, and finally the ellipse. Through this process of groping from new springboards to new efforts, hits and misses grow side by side in his fertile brain, teeming with the seed of unbounded fancy and speculation. But such is the nature of genius that the harvest is ample under all circumstances, and the rewards beyond estimation, regardless of weeds, which are in Kepler's case full of charm. It is thus that a breakthrough is often achieved in science. The revolution in astronomy after centuries of becalmed standstill, was made by Johann Kepler from a springboard supplied by Copernicus.

A few words need be said about Galileo's contribution to the new astronomy, which began with Copernicus. In spite of the large number of medieval ideas one finds in the text of Copernicus' great work, and in spite of the mysticism and fancy in Kepler's, novelty was on the make. Its advent adumbrated changes in both the foundation and superstructure of science. The contribution of Galileo was unique and in a way extraneous to the work of the two giants named. His initial contribution was his *Starry Messenger,* the account of his construction of a telescope and his brief use of it to such telling effects. He opened up new vistas which fitted so harmoniously and inspiringly with the new vision initiated by Copernicus. His delivery to the reborn science the value of a new instrument was destined to be as potent a turning point in its future course as much as the Copernican Theory. It is for this reason alone that Galileo rightly deserves his membership in the trio that steered the course of man's search for celestial knowledge into the broad highway we see it pursue today.

But Galileo performed another great service. He laid the foundation for solving the great riddle of motion and force which made it possible not only to understand and use experimentally these two concepts which had tormented the minds of all sages for two thousand years before him, but by doing so, opened up the gates for the mind of Newton to apply the true meaning of these two concepts to an understanding of the motions of all bodies on earth and in heaven. And that again led in turn to still vaster horizons of knowledge.

2. Aristotle and Galileo in Physics

A breakthrough similar to the one wrought by Copernicus and Kepler, was attained at about the same time in the concepts of motion and force (kinematics and dynamics) almost singlehandedly by Galileo. We have already seen that the concepts of force and motion baffled the ancient and medieval mind, and literally defied clarification. As stated earlier, the entire subject of motion seemed to Aristotle to be basic to all physics. This was a sign of brilliance, because the subject of motion does indeed constitute the watershed of physical thought. If Galileo deserves all honors due him for selecting motion for a frontal attack in establishing the two new sciences, Aristotle deserves similar credit for singling out the problem of motion and for struggling with it to the best of human competence at the time.

Let us summarize Aristotle's view of the problem and warn the reader from the start to abandon the commonly encountered notion that his outlook was speculative, authoritarian, childish, naive, not based on facts, and what not. Only people unmoved by the intricacies of the problem as a whole, can speak thus. The problem of motion--velocity, acceleration, force, free fall, projectile motion, deceleration, angular momentum, and finally energy--constitutes one of the most complex and most intriguing challenges of science ever encountered by man. Because the study of mechanics has been overshadowed in recent years by the fascinating vistas of nuclear physics and its ramifications, and because it had been prior to that largely illuminated by the brilliant approaches of such men as Galileo, Newton, Huygens, Leibniz, Descartes and others, have its intrinsic difficulties paled or been reduced to the obvious. But with relativity, the problem of motion staged a comeback to prove its major significance.

The prime characteristic of Aristotelian physics as developed in his books on physical science, his *Physics, On the Heavens, Meteorology,* and *Generation and Corruption,* and in part also in his *Metaphysics,* is the fact that it is a coherent, and consistent theory which presents a complete scheme of the workings of the universe. Significantly, the scheme is firmly rooted in experience and although it indulges in generalizations, hypotheses, fantastic speculations and explanations - it would not be a theoretical construction without all these - it is powerfully anchored to verifiable reality, fore and aft. In fact, as has been brilliantly brought out by Alexander Koyré in his *Galilean Studies* (Paris, 1939) and by Ernest Cassirer in his essay, *Galileo's Platonism* (New York, 1944. Essays in Homage to George Sarton, Ed. M. F. Ashley-Montagu) it was the strength of that bond to reality that was the crux of the shortcomings of the Aristotelian scheme and the cause of its downfall. Its chief weakness lay in its adherence to common sense data, to unadulterated experience, in its reluctance to bow to fruitful abstractions, hence to mathematics, which may lure the mind away from the secure but limited senses, but only to come back enlightened, the better to handle the very realm it allegedly deserted.

Let us review the web of beliefs which composed Aristotelian physics. The nature of matter and its properties were taken care of by the four elements: Earth, water, air and fire. The properties of hot, cold, wet and dry served a laudable purpose in medicine, as the works of Hippocrates and Galen amply prove. In the physical realm, too, these concepts managed to account for a number of chemical and physical interactions. The four elements also accounted for the observed facts of density.

Consider next the question of motion. It is a fact that heavy bodies fall downward to the ground and not upward. When we see a heavy object move upward against gravity we know it is a deception, and we say it is unnatural. Similarly, if we saw a flame falling downward, or water form a layer beneath floating rock, we would describe these phenomena as unnatural. The Aristotelian use of that distinction is fully justified and merely represents a "natural" psychic response in man to regard as "natural" and "normal" that which he sees in nature, and as unnatural or abnormal that which is contrary to the usual.

That the rate of fall of bodies is related to the medium in which the fall occurs, was a clever and relevant observation. The discernment of air as a medium was a worthy feat. That light bodies, such as, feathers, fall more slowly in air than do compact solids, was an established fact. It was also a fact that only animals possessed the capacity for voluntary motion. Inanimate bodies lacked that capacity but possessed the potentiality for either natural motion, such as, fall, or forced, "violent", motion, which was equivalent to a disturbance of their natural state of rest. The latter point played a key role in the scheme of things. It was a basic credo of the Aristotelian belief-web that rest was natural for an object on earth. For a body to be moved, pushed, pulled or hurled was unnatural; it constituted force or violent motion, and was invariably associated with resistance. Except then for animal motion and natural motion, all motion had to be violent, that is, caused by a mover, and such motion could be effected by contact only. In the heavens, celestial bodies were attached to spheres which served as their bearers; these spheres were moved by the prime mover, the outermost sphere. Aristotle then goes to some trouble to establish the notion that a prime mover must not itself have any motion since that would require an external force to account for it; besides, "there is nothing more powerful so as to move it."

As Koyré points out in his rich *Galilean Studies* and his brilliant summary, *Galileo and Plato* (The Roots of Modern Science, Eds. P. P. Wiener and A. Noland, New York 1957, p. 155), Aristotle's "conception of 'natural place' is based on a purely static conception of order. Indeed, if everything were 'in order', everything would be in its natural place, and, of course, would remain and stay there forever. Why should it depart from it? On the contrary, it would offer a resistance to any attempt to expel it therefrom. This expulsion could be effected only by exerting some kind of violence, and the body would seek to come back, if, and when, owing to such a violence, it found itself out of 'its' place. Thus every movement implies some kind of cosmic disorder, a disturbance of the world-equilibrium." Because of this attitude toward the 'natural' represented by rest, motion was a pathological condition due either to a disorder, or to an effort at halting disorder. Movement is necessarily a "transitory state," rest is normal and natural. Movement is natural for the heavens, for the eternal and ethereal, but not for the sub-lunar world. In the heavens, movement spells becoming or potentiality, while on earth it spells disturbance. At this point Aristotle resorts to some complex metaphysical acrobatics to put that distinction on a firm footing. The universe moves about a fixed immovable point, its center, the center of the earth toward which all motion thrives. All such motion is natural. In the whole earth, apart from particulars which may be disturbances, movement is induced or caused by the celestial motions. But so complex is the heavenly influence that while the heavenly motions are "continuous, uniform and perpetual," the sublunar are irregular. Besides, motion "is a process, a flux, a becoming, in and by which things constitute, actualize and accomplish themselves." (p. 157)

These arguments constitute only one of the difficulties which Aristotle faced. He had others which were practical and direct. If there is no motion without a mover, and if all motion must cease when the cause is removed, how explain the motion of projectiles or the case of a wheel rotated on its axis by a strong turn, so that its motion persists long after the hand is removed. Aristotle grapples critically with both questions. An arrow flung from the bow, concludes Aristotle, may be said to cleave the air from the onset of its flight, pressing with its forward end against the air, just as a boat, propelled by oars, presses with its bow against the water. This forward pressure on the medium is explained by some, says Aristotle, as causing it to flow along the sides and gather behind the boat, or arrow, to propel the missiles forward, the arrow by the air, the boat by the water. It is "a series of movements contiguous to one another. This is why such motion occurs in air and water, and some thinkers call it 'mutual replacement'." Aristotle does not favor this explanation, but suggests that the air is moved by the original mover (or force), and simultaneously becomes in turn a mover, which explanation is no further elaborated by him (*Physics,* Book VIII, Ch. 10, Edition of W. D. Ross, Oxford, 1936) but by his commentator, Simplicius. The second question, of the persistent motion of a wheel on an axle, remained without a clear-cut answer.

But although Aristotle relegated motion on earth to the abnormal, he nevertheless examined it with much caution and insight. First, a body acted upon in violent motion will move with a velocity proportional to the force acting upon it, provided the resistance of the medium remained constant. Again, this is straight common sense observation. Second, uniform motion means persistent contact with a constant force acting directly on the body. Again, this is as general a phenomenon of simple, unadulterated sense experience. Third, the velocity of fall was taken by Aristotle to be proportional to the weight of the falling object, to its nature, to its motive power which varies with weight and resistance of the body itself, hence to its density. Aristotle is not quite specific on this point. He is specific, however, about the dependence of velocity upon the ratio of the motive power to the resistance of the medium. The concept of rest as a natural state in the sublunar sphere, that is, on earth, or in the space encompassed by the orb of the moon, brought in its trail a ready-made explanation of acceleration and deceleration. An object displaced from its natural position of rest by any force, showed deceleration. Such retardation of initial motion was an expression of its tendency to return to its position of normalcy. An object acted upon by a force so as to return to a more normal position from a more or less abnormal one, such as, a stone rolling off a mountain top, showed acceleration, or facilitation by nature for its re-establishment of normalcy. There still remained the problem of the medium which in Aristotle's thinking played a major role in all motion.

Bodies falling within different media exhibited different velocities, which could be due to nothing else but the varying resistances of the media. A stone fell in air faster than it sank in water, and in water faster than in honey, oil, or mud. The generalization was made by Aristotle rather casually and with no elaborate mathematical treatment or testing, that the velocity of fall was inversely proportional to the resistance of the medium. From this generalization it followed at once that within a space which contained no medium at all, within a void, the rate of fall of all objects would be infinite, since a constant over zero is infinity. Any motion necessarily requires time, reasoned Aristotle; infinite or instantaneous motion is an impossibility. Besides, no vacuum is ever encountered in nature, and is certainly not tolerated when it is about to form, both factual enough truths. Moreover, since instantaneous motion is impossible, a void is impossible, and even God could not make one. This conclusion shocked the religious sensitivity of theologians of the early Middle Ages, before the love of science sent its tentacles deep enough into the culture; in 1277 a council meeting in Paris declared many Aristotelian theses heretical, singling out this one among others. Aristotle's statement of the relationship of fall within a medium may be represented as V=P/M in which V=velocity of fall, P=the gravitational trend to the center of the earth which is also the center of the universe, a characteristic of all matter, and M= resistance of medium.

That Aristotle's solution to the puzzle of motion was not satisfactory, became apparent soon enough. Aristotle's *Physics* had numerous commentators who kept the basic issues alive, and frequently disagreed with him, idolized though he was. The most famous of these was Simplicius (sixth century A. D.) whose comments are themselves of great value, but who also quotes many critical passages from others whose books are now lost. Another author of a famous *Commentary On The Physics,* a contemporary of Simplicius', was John Philoponus who was the first to reject both explanations cited by Aristotle, that the air pressed at the front comes around to push from behind, called *antiperistasis,* and the one Aristotle favored, that the moved air became a mover presumably all over, in bucket-brigade manner. The latter explanation implies, says he, that the "air moves with a more rapid motion than the natural (downward) of the missile, thus pushing the missile on while remaining always in contact with it until the motive force originally impressed on this portion of the air is dissipated." (Marshall Clagett, *The Science of Mechanics in the Middle Ages,* Madison, Wisconsin, 1959, p. 509)

Philoponus advances his own explanation after arguing from experiments that a stone placed delicately on top of a stick cannot be pushed by moving air. He then says, "*Rather is it necessary to assume that some incorporeal motive force is imparted by the projector to the projectile,* and that the air set in motion contributes either nothing at all or else very little to this motion of the projectile." Presumably the impressed force "continues the movement of the body until it is spent by the resistance to movement presented by the weight of the body and perhaps the resistance of the air." This being so, "it is quite evident that if one imparts motion 'contrary to nature' or forced motion to an arrow or a stone, the same degree of motion will be produced much more readily in a void than in a plenum. And there will be no need of any agency external to the projector..."

On the subject of free fall, Philoponus has the following to offer: "Clearly then, it is the natural weight of bodies, one having a greater and another a lesser downward tendency, that causes differences in motion. For that which has a greater downfall tendency divides the medium better... To what other cause shall we ascribe this fact than that which has greater weight, has by its own nature, a greater downward tendency, even if the motion is not through a plenum?... If you let fall from the same height two weights of which one is many times as heavy as the other you will see that the ratio of the times required for the motion does not depend on the ratio of the weights, but that the difference in time is a very small one." (Cohen & Drabkin, Source Book, pp. 217-220)

When the scientific renaissance swept Europe and reached its first crest in the 13th century, it was Aristotle that was at first favored, and many scholars probably remained unfamiliar with Philoponus. Roger Bacon and Thomas Aquinas were supporters of the Aristotelian view. But in line with the great Islamic authorities, Avicenna, Abul-Barakat, Alpetragius, Averroës, and others, the European authors soon also began to exhibit strong interest in the shortcomings and contradictions of the Aristotelian view, and paid close heed to the several alternative explanations that came from a variety of authors. What is significant is that the subject was never allowed to rest, remained a constant challenge, and was discussed, weighed and argued by almost every author on physical science.

By the fourteenth century, however, Western culture brought forth its own conceptions of projectile motion that may come under the general name of "impetus theory." The dominant exponent of this theory is Jean Buridan who was for many years rector of the University of Paris (1300-?), and is regarded in a symbolic manner as the founder of the Paris school in that line of thought. As usual for the period, his ideas are expounded in treatises which are commentaries on Aristotle's physical works. The theory states that a projectile, set in motion by a projector, receives in the act a motive force, or an impetus, which "varies, on the one hand, as the velocity of the projectile (initially and immediately introduced), and as the quantity of matter of the body in movement, on the other hand... A dense and heavy body receives more of that impetus and more intensely, just as iron can receive more calidity than wood or water of the same quantity... This is also the reason why it is more difficult to bring to rest a large smith's mill which is moving swiftly than a small one, evidently because in the large one, other things being equal, there is more impetus... The impetus is a quality naturally present and predisposed for moving a body in which it is impressed, just as it is said that a quality impressed in iron by the magnet moves the iron to the magnet... The impetus would last indefinitely if it were not distinguished by a contrary resistance or by an inclination to a contrary motion..." As applied to the smith's mill which continues in rotation after the applied force is halted, Buridan says: "And perhaps if the mill would last forever without some diminution or alteration of it, and there were no resistance corrupting the impetus, the mill would be moved perpetually by that impetus." The impetus is not the same as the motion. He extneds the concept to the heavens as well. "It does not appear necessary to posit intelligences of this kind, because it could be answered that God, when he created the world, moved each of the celestial orbs as He pleased, and in moving them impressed in them inpetuses which moved them without his having to move them any more... And these impetuses which he impressed in the celestial bodies were not decreased or corrupted afterwards because there was no inclination of the celestial bodies for other movements. Nor was there resistance which would be corruptive or repressive of that impetus." (Clagett, p. 322)

Buridan rejects the "antiperistasis" argument in motion, "because of many experiences," all of which are valid. The argument that the projector moves the air near the projectile, and that "the first air moves the projectile into the second air, and the second into the third air, and so on", is also dismissed with cogent examples. Then there is the matter of acceleration. "From this theory also appears the cause of why the natural motion of a heavy body downward is continually accelerated. For from the beginning only the gravity was moving it. Therefore, it moved more slowly, but in moving it impressed in the heavy body an impetus. This impetus, now (acting) together with its gravity, moves it. Therefore, the motion becomes faster; and by the amount it is faster, so the impetus becomes more intense. Therefore the movement evidently becomes continually faster... One who wishes to jump a long distance drops back a way in order to run faster..." Another aspect of impetus is seen when "a cither cord which, put under strong tension and percussion, remains a long time in a certain vibration from which its sound continues a notable time." (Buridan, *Questions on the Physics,* in Clagett, pp. 532-538)

Buridan also evaluates prevailing theories on the causes of acceleration, dismissing them all, and presents his own. "From the beginning the heavier body is moved by its natural gravity only; hence it is moved slowly. Afterwards it is moved by that same gravity and by the impetus acquired at the same time; consequently, it is moved more swiftly... Thus the heavy body is moved by its natural gravity and by that greater impetus simultaneously and so it will again be moved faster; and thus it will always and continually be accelerated to the end." (Clagett, pp. 551-2)

The matter of free fall is treated by Buridan in his commentary on Aristotle's *On the Heavens*. Although many modern writers speak with definiteness of the Aristotelian views, the fact remains that most of his views were generally vague in Aristotle's mind. Far clearer is his great sixth century commentator, Simplicius, who states that "Aristotle holds that as bodies approach the whole mass of their own element (*i.e.* earth), they acquire a greater force therefrom and recover their form more perfectly; and thus it is by reason of an increase of weight that earth moves more swiftly when it is near the center." He then quotes from a lost work of Hipparchus that "in the case of earth thrown upward it is the projecting force that is the cause of the upward motion, so long as the projecting force overpowers the downward tendency of the projectile, and that to the extent that this projecting force predominates, the object moves more swiftly upwards; then as this force is diminished (1) the upward motion proceeds, but no longer at the same rate, (2) the body moves downward under the influence of its own internal impulse, even though the original projecting force lingers in some measure, and (3) as this force continues to diminish the object moves downward more swiftly, and most swiftly when this force is entirely lost... On the subject of weight, too, Hipparchus contradicts Aristotle, for he holds that bodies are heavier the further removed they are from their natural place." On the other hand, Alexander, a third century commentator, disagrees with Hipparchus on both issues, says Simplicius. He also cites Strato the Physicist, who lived six centuries before him, and who defined acceleration as "a movement such that equal spaces are traversed in succeeding periods of less time, *e.g.* to say, at continually greater speed." As water pours down from a roof, it is seen to be continuous at the top but is discontinuous as it approaches the ground. "This would never happen unless the water traversed each successive space more swiftly." Furthermore, the greater the height from which a stone is dropped the greater its impact on the ground, which is due to the accelerated speed. A 13th century author, Jordanus de Nemore, already had defined acceleration correctly as a movement in which "in equal periods of time greater and greater space is traversed, *i.e.* in equal periods of time the speed is greater." (Clagett, p. 548)

Another French commentator, Nicole Oresme takes a position similar to Buridan's on many aspects of motion. As Clagett points out, he even suggests that if an accelerating body fell through a tunnel piercing the center of the earth, it would be carried beyond it, then back again, thus oscillating "about the center of earth at gradually decreasing distances until it finally came to rest." (p. 553) But if an accelerated body were permitted to proceed to infinity, "infinite velocity would accordingly follow." A "continually accelerated" body is one in which "an addition of velocity takes place by equal parts, or equivalently", that is, "in the second hour twice as quickly, and the third three times as quickly, etc." Albert of Saxony, a Parisian contemporary of Oresme, a disciple of Buridan and a commentator on Aristotle who supports the impetus theory, gives support to "the view so popular since the time of Strato, Alexander of Aphrodisias, and others, namely, that the speed increases in direct proportion to the distance of fall, and this increase is arithmetic rather than geometric." (p. 555) As we shall see, this error was maintained by Galileo in his younger days, and constituted a serious hindrance to a successful solution of the problem of fall.

During the 14th century, by curious coincidence, there arose another center of intellectual vitality on the same topics at the University of Oxford, mustering several conspicuous scholars, namely Thomas Bradwardine, William Heytesbury, Richard Swineshead, and John Dumbleton. Like their Parisian contemporaries, there English logicians were well trained in mathematics, mostly geometry, and collectively made significant contributions. Bradwardine's treatise, *Proportions of Velocities in Movements,* considers the general phenomenon of a growth in intensity of any quality, a problem already treated by Duns Scotus and other scholastic writers. The general conclusion reached was that qualitative increase and diminution is negotiated by quantitative differences, hence by addition and subtraction of degrees of intensity. The problem of gradation in velocity was treated in a subtle, mathematical, manner. It was shown to be one of proportionality, rendered familiar in its original form in Euclid's Elements, but it also entailed a few points of considerable delicacy.

Another issue brought to the fore by the Merton College (Oxford) mechanicians, as they were called, was the realization of the distinction between kinematics and dynamics, an issue already raised in the writings of the Moslem scholars, Averroës and Avempace, and elucidated by the Oxford schoolman, William Ockham, as a difference "between the condition of 'being in motion', and the condition of being moved." (E. A. Moody, *Ockham and Aegidius of Rome.* Franciscan Studies, vol. 9, 1949, p. 437) Bradwardine puts the issues in clearer perspective in his analysis of the "proportion of velocities in movements in relationship to the *forces* of the movers and the things moved", and in treating of velocities "in respect to the magnitudes of the thing moved and of the *space traversed.*" Not only does he consider the two concepts as distinct, but he seeks to relate them by a law. Similarly, Swineshead states in his treatise: "It ought to be investigated diligently as to how velocity in any motion is measured, both with respect to cause and with respect to effect." The first, he believes can be measured "by the proportion of the motive force to the resisting force." Of the second, "it should be known that of local motions some are uniform, some nonuniform." In his *Treatise on Local Motion* he says: "In regard to the measure of its velocity, (we say that it is measured) by the maximum line which the most rapidly moving point in such a velocity would describe in (some) time." As Clagett points out, the Oxford mechanicians even elaborated a vocabulary employed by Galileo three centuries hence.

One of the great achievements of the Merton School is the concept of instantaneous velocity. The basic issue was to distinguish "between the measure of the intensity of a quality and its quantitative extension in some

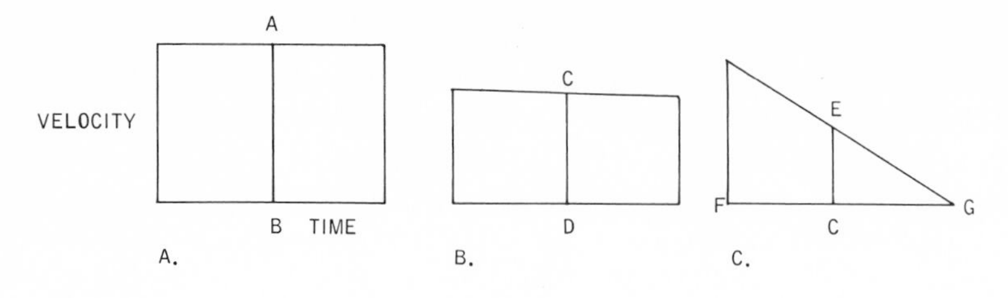

Figure 12.2

subject... rather like the common distinction between intensity of heat (temperature) and quantity of heat", (calories) or the similar relation between total weight and density (p. 212). Another distinction discerned was between "extensive" force, or power, and "intensive" force, pressure. There was also awareness of "quality of motion" expressed in "swiftness and slowness", and "quantity of motion" in which, for example, resistances are expressed quantitatively.

Another great step forward by this school was the idea of representing in geometrical form many aspects of mechanics. They employed rectangles of identical altitudes to represent velocities in uniform movement, with the bases of different lengths representing time, and the resulting areas representing the spaces traversed. The heights of the verticals at any point, say AB, and CD, respectively, would then represent the instantaneous velocities at moments B and D. A quantitative difference would be shown by the difference in lengths of AB and CD, for example. (Figure 12.2)

In uniform, negative acceleration, the velocity diminishes, or as they put it, the "quality" of the velocity diminishes, and "varies as the instantaneous velocity EC (in Figure 12.2C) varies from instant to instant." The concept of velocity at any moment in a system of varying velocity, led directly into a measure of uniform velocity in terms of average, or rather medial velocity, which means the velocity at the middle instant of the duration of the acceleration. Thus in above diagram C, EC is the medial velocity when FC=CG. It was this that was referred to as the *Merton Theorem,* and was soon applied to free fall by a Spanish-Parisian scholastic, Domingo de Soto. The Merton Theorem states that for free fall, $S=\frac{1}{2}V_f t$, where S=the distance traversed, V_f=the final velocity, and t=the time of acceleration, which relationship is of course the same as that also discovered by Galileo three centuries later, but by him verified with clever experimentation. Its dawn at Merton was no doubt the first germination of the seed planted by Aristotle's Physics in brilliant minds which became fertilized by intervening commentaries and scholastic discussions.

As a final achievement of pre-Galilean mechanics, should be cited the invention of the graphic system of representing quality and quantity of velocities. This gained in clarity and use with the extension of the influence of the Merton mechanicians into France, where Oresme had employed the same basic geometrical device, though greatly improved. The method entered Italy, where a number of authors helped strengthen and spread the new ideas. Concludes Clagett: "I think it can hardly be doubted that Galileo obtained both the theorem and the essentials of its proof from the medieval Oxford-Paris tradition, although the exact sources he used are not known." (p. 346)

Progress was difficult because motion constituted one of the greatest challenges that ever lured and bedevilled the human mind. A vast spectrum of the keenest intellects wrestled with the problem and failed, which alone testifies to its toughness. Many came close on one sector of the front but missed on a few others. Many approached it philosophically and mathematically and were keen observers of reality as well, but never thought of a concrete way of, or considering it irrelevent or improper shied away from, applying any aspect of their reasoning to experimental tests. Some great hits were scored, nonetheless, from Strato to the Merton School, each of which helped weaken the grip of the old, and added some stone to the edifice of the new. The final victory came with Galileo, who staged the kind of breakthrough, the impact of which was felt in every sector of the far-flung front. The ideas he employed were in the air. Even the idea of rolling a ball down an inclined plane so as to render the successive distances, hence acceleration, measurable, had previously been applied on numerous occasions. Yet, the novelty he added was precisely what mankind's search was after, and constituted the stroke that hit the triggering mechanism to open up the gates for the onward rush of ideas.

Even the recorded labors of Galileo show the intrinsic refractoriness of the problem. His own struggle with the concepts was grimmer and longer-lasting than Jacob's battle with the angel. His earliest known work on the subject in his *On Motion* (De Motu), written in 1589 when Galileo was twenty-five years old. We encounter here most of the old beliefs and few of the new ones which the author himself will introduce 40 years later, just before his death. The very second chapter asserts that "things that move naturally move to their proper places... Every day we observe with our senses that the places of the heavy are those which are closer to the center of the universe, and the places of the light those which are farther distant. Therefore we have no reason to doubt that such places have been determined for them by nature... I have found that nature chose the existing arrangement with complete justice and consummate wisdom." (Madison, 1960. p. 15) Earth of equal weight to water, occupies less space and is nearer the center. Heavy matter will tend downward, while "light bodies will move upward by their lightness." In addition, "we must consider not merely the lightness or heaviness of the moving bodies, but also the heaviness or lightness of the medium through which the motion takes place. For if water were not lighter than stone, a stone would not sink in water." Galileo then sets out "to prove that bodies equally heavy with the water itself, if let down into the water, are completely submerged, but then move either downward or upward. Secondly, we shall show that bodies lighter than water not only do not sink in the water, but are not even completely submerged. Thirdly we shall prove that bodies heavier than water necessarily move downward." (p. 17) The relation between heavy and light bodies in media of different specific gravities, by which he really defines light and heavy, is then compared to the principle of the balance. In general, Galileo is strongly under the influence of "the superhuman Archimedes, whose name I never mention without a feeling of awe." (p. 67)

Galileo next demonstrates that "since motion proceeds from heaviness and lightness, speed or slowness must necessarily proceed from the same cause. That is, from the greater heaviness of the moving body there results a greater speed of the motion, namely, downward motion, which comes about from the heaviness of the body, and from a lesser heaviness [of the body], a slowness of that same motion. On the other hand, from a greater lightness of the moving body will result a greater speed in that motion which comes about from the lightness of the body, namely, upward motion." (p. 25) Similarly, "The body moves downward more swiftly in that medium in which it is heavier, than in another in which it is less heavy; and it moves upward more swiftly in that medium in which it is lighter, than in another in which it is less light." (p. 25)

Consider bodies of same material in the same medium. According to Aristotle, says Galileo, "a large piece of gold moves more swiftly than a small piece." That this is ridiculous, "is clearer than daylight." There is no need to cite examples. "For what we seek are the causes of effects, and these causes are not given to us by experience, we shall set forth our own view, and its confirmation will mean the collapse of Aristotle's view. We say then that bodies of the same kind... though they may differ in size, still move with the same speed, and a larger stone does not fall more swiftly than a smaller." (p. 27) Similarly, "a very large piece of wood can float on water, no less than a small piece." Aristotle, of course, did not know Archimedes, and Galileo did. Once the heaviness or lightness of substances are spoken of in terms of specific gravity, these Archimedean conclusions follow quite reasonably, and are relevantly introduced. In arguing against Aristotle, Galileo cites no experiments performed, but gives only logical arguments. He concludes: "Let us then consider it sufficiently corroborated that there is no reason why bodies of the same material should move [in natural motion] with unequal velocities, but every reason why they should move with equal velocity." (p. 30) Those who defend Aristotle "must do some toiling and sweating before they can show that the velocity of (a body a thousand times as large as another of the same material) is a thousand times that of the other." Similarly, in the case of bodies of different densities in the same medium, the ratio of their velocities "in opposition to Aristotle's view... is not equal to the ratio of their weights."

E. A. Moody points out, (*Galileo and Avempace, in Roots of Scientific Thought,* edited by P. P. Weiner and A. Noland, N. Y. 1957) that Galileo introduces here into his reasoning a novel approach which Archimedes had not advanced. Galileo speaks of forces responsible for fall, and above all, of velocities of fall. Archimedes was concerned only with statics, equilibrium, and counterbalancing. Galileo next proceeds to disagree with Aristotle on a major issue.

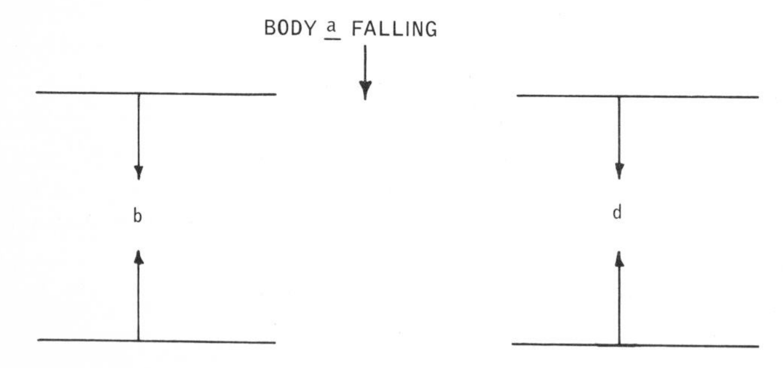

Figure 12.3

According to Aristotle "the medium which is denser interferes with motion more." If body a falls through a denser medium b, say water, and a less dense medium d, air, then "a will move through d more swiftly than through b in proportion as air is less dense than water." (Figure 12.3) By means of examples (demonstrations) Galileo proves again that Aristotle's scheme is inconsistent and impossible. Aristotle's notion of time of a in b/time of a in d = density of b/density of d which means that velocities vary inversely as densities:

$$\frac{\text{Vel. of a in b}}{\text{Vel. of a in d}} = \frac{\text{density of d}}{\text{density of b}}$$

Galileo then goes to much trouble to prove that "in the case of the same body falling in different media, the ratio of the speeds of the motions is the same as the ratio of the amounts by which the weight of the body exceeds the weights [of an equal volume] of the respective media." (p. 36) This means that in conception,

$$\frac{\text{Vel. in b}}{\text{Vel. in d}} = \frac{\text{weight - b}}{\text{weight - d}} = \frac{\text{density of a - density of b}}{\text{density of a - density of d}}$$

using the term density and specific gravity interchangeably. In a generalized form then V=P-M; the velocity in any medium equals the density, or specific gravity of the mobile object, minus the density, or specific gravity of the medium. The same reasoning applies to upward motion in which velocities are determined by the density of medium minus density of mobile object.

But Galileo is dedicated to the proposition of expressing these relationships, as he says, "in physical terms." He notes that wood submerged in water "moves upward with just as much force as is necessary to submerge it forcibly in the water." (p. 38) This, he points out almost with joy, gives us the clue to the meaning of force which we have been seeking from the start. The upward push then is a measure of that force, and equals the difference of the corresponding densities. "One can see this same thing in the weights of a scale... The weight on this side moves down with a force measured by the amount by which the weight on the other side is less than it." (p. 39) For bodies of "different material... equal in size, the ratio of the speeds of their [natural downward] motions is the same as the ratio of their weights... in the medium in which the motion is to take place." In a medium of air or of fire, bodies will have different weights. Thus, weight is the force responsible for motion and a measure of velocities in different media.

In full realization that his conclusions on motion and the hidden cause of motion differ from Aristotle's, Galileo proceeds to extend that difference into motion in a void. Considering velocities of objects to vary inversely as the densities of their media, Aristotle puts the cause in the medium itself, in tacit thought. Galileo, on the other hand, regards the medium as a modifying factor only, interacting with the initial force within the weight of the body. Aristotle had reasoned that in a void, velocity of motion must be infinite since density of medium is zero, which would require that velocity be instantaneous, a contradiction that renders the conclusion impossible. He therefore denied the existence of a void, a denial that was verified by experience at every step.

But Galileo shows Aristotle's reasoning to be faulty. He is enabled to do so by the different set of ideas in his own mind. He goes to considerable efforts to prove that his use of the ratio of the resistance of a given medium to that of the void, which is zero, yielding infinity as an answer, is misapplied by Aristotle and leads to impossible results, while his way of stating the case in mathematical terms avoids the pitfall. This may well have been the spring-board for Galileo's later victory in taking the first successful step toward a mathematical language for some aspects of motion. At the moment, he is merely led to the conclusion that "the body will move in a void in the same way as in a plenum... The difference between the weight of the body and weight of the void will be the whole weight of the body. And therefore the speed of its motion [in the void] will depend on its own total weight." Moreover, between the weight of a body in air and its weight of zero in a void, "an unlimited number of intermediate weights may exist"; hence it cannot be said that "a void is a medium infinitely lighter than every plenum; therefore motion in it will be infinitely swifter than in a plenum; therefore such motion will be instantaneous", as Aristotle says. The fact is, speed in a void is great but not instantaneous, and in it every body displays its "proper and natural weight." At the beginning of one paragraph Galileo asserts "that learned men, even Peripateties, have recognized that Aristotle's view on this subject was mistaken", but at its termination he claims that "no one up to now has ventured to deny this relation." As the translator points out (p. 49) this latter charge is not quite correct, since Philoponus, whom Galileo cites, had indeed denied it, and so have others.

Galileo then launches a strong criticism of Aristotle's foggy notions of the specific gravity concept, which could not have been as well understood before Archimedes as after him. "His arguments have no force, no learning, no elegance or attractiveness", says he of Aristotle's declaration that earth possesses absolute heaviness and fire absolute lightness, and that "a large amount of fire rises more swiftly than a small amount and a large amount of earth falls more swiftly." Aristotle's defenses are "childish arguments" and "inept attempts at subtleties." Surely, earth is lighter than metals, these lighter than mercury, and there may be media lighter than air or even fire, which though the lightest known, must still have some weight. Fire moves upward simply because air is heavier and fire moves in air. Only in a void can the true weights of heavy bodies be obtained, and the same holds for velocities.

Galileo then discusses a problem which, "has not been taken up by any philosophers, so far as I know", that of a body moving down planes inclined to the horizontal at various angles. The discussion is detailed and lucid, but had in fact been discussed by others before him. It leads to no definite results or physical insights of the kind he will manifest in his later *Discourses on Two New Sciences*, of 1638. He concludes, for example, that given two inclined planes, "line AD will be to AC... as the speed on AC is to the speed on AD."

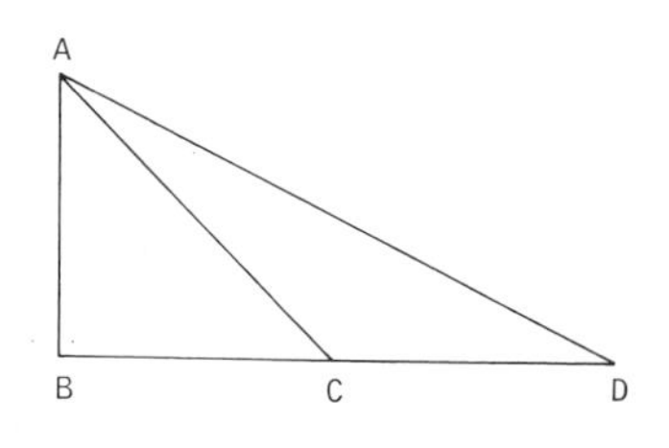

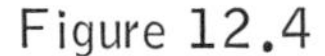
Figure 12.4

Galileo next takes Aristotle to task rather harshly for his failure to employ geometry, in which, says Galileo, he "was little versed" and "ignorant... even of the most elementary principles of this science." Again "the divine

Archimedes" shows many of Aristotle's statements in geometry to be false, and it is a poor excuse to say that Archimedes came years after him because, "he should not have made the rash assertion," that no straight line can be equal to a curved one.

After examining under what conditions circular motion is natural and when it is forced, Galileo dives in earnest into the subject, "By What Agency Projectiles Are Moved," a vital part of his thinking. He is firmly convinced that a body set in motion receives "an impressed motive force" which "is continuously diminished in the projectile", otherwise there would prevail uniform velocity, which is an absurdity. He shows with his customary logic that Aristotle's theory that prjectile motion is brought about by the initial air in contact with the moving body which sets contiguous regions in motion one after the other, each propelling the projectile, must be entirely untenable. To do so he employs the analogy of a boat moving in water, and concludes with, "and they are not ashamed to utter such childishness." (p. 77) An arrow can be fired against the wind, hence with the air moving in the direction opposite to its motion; similarly, a boat can be rowed upstream. Also, a cannon ejecting heavy and light missiles will fling the former larger distances than the latter, and a sphere attached in the middle of an axle can be made to rotate by hoisting the thin axle.

Galileo draws a close analogy between the impressed motive force and heat. Both can be transferred by flow, and both diminish in time. He thus has an entirely different conception, a different scheme, a different mode of visualization of the way in which things happen. One might comment parenthetically that in such cases it is both unfair and futile to revile another and different scheme of things as fallacious, childish, inconsistent and what not. Two schemes that differ perform different tasks and have different logics, so to say. All one can do is choose between them. Extolling one and belittling the other by claiming truth and consistency for my scheme and falsehood and childishness for that of the opponent, is quite human but hardly useful. Galileo has taken the impetus idea to heart as an abstract something, most valuable to comprehension. He finds another analogy to bolster his courage, a "more beautiful example", in a hammer that strikes a bell and causes it to ring until its sound slowly dies. The hammer strikes a small area, yet the entire bell can be felt to vibrate. The impressed motive power in a projectile acts similarly. "But this force, since it is lightness, will indeed render the body in motion light by inhering in it... That is naturally light which moves upward naturally." (pp. 80-81) Similarly, a stone is very light when it floats on mercury and will resist forceful submerging.

A light body moves easily while in contact with the mover, "but on being released by the mover, it retains for only a short time the impetus it received." Lead retains an impressed force longer than a feather. Air will be easily moved, being light, but will not at all retain any impetus received. Nor is the argument given by the Aristotelians sound, that a pebble thrown in water causes motion in an ever widening circle. The ripply water can be shown by a straw to bob up and down on wavelets, but not to move. The water rises and falls because it offers resistance to rising, while air offers none, and neither would water in the middle of its depth. Many false opinions have a way of persisting. Thus, some believe that coins appear larger in water, for instance.

Now this is false. "I finally had recourse to experiment and found that a denarius coin at rest in deep water did not al all appear larger (than actual size) but rather appeared smaller." (p. 83) People were led into error, he says, by noting that a plum usually put in a conoid vessel of water, appeared enlarged.

Galileo then demonstrates, by reasoning of course, that "the force, impressed by the projector, is continuously diminished in the projectile." This fact is responsible for the acceleration of a body in free fall. "According to my custom", he first proves Aristotle and all others wrong, and then proceeds with his own idea. The natural downward motion proceeds from weight. "For a heavy body to be able to be moved upward by force", there must be applied to it "an impressed motive force... greater than the resisting weight." This upward force, which he calls lightness, wears out as the body moves upward, until it is "reduced to parity with the weight of the body." This marks the highest point of the upward flight of a body, when it "will be neither heavy nor light." (p. 89) After this, the body begins to fall because the impressed force "continues to decrease." At the beginning of the fall the body moves slowly because it still has in it considerable lightness, or impressed upward force. But as this force continues to diminish, "the weight of the body, being offset by diminishing resistance, is increased, and the body moves faster and faster. This is what I consider to be the true cause of the acceleration of motion", which, he subsequently learned, were the views of Alexander and Hipparchus, cited in the commentary of Simplicius. These were full of errors which his theory corrects, he asserts. Clearly then, at the highest point of upward thrust, the body is as if at rest. "For even when no force impelling the stone upward had been impressed on it, and it falls from the hand, it leaves with an (upward) force impressed on it equal to its own weight." (p. 91) And natural motion, or fall, is therefore slow at the start and fastest at the end. It is all a matter of the interaction of lightness, the impressed force from upward thrust or from place of rest, and the weight which is the cause of the downward force. Hence Aristotle was clearly wrong when he asserted that after an upward thrust, an object is at rest at the point of highest ascent, just prior to starting on its descent. "For the motion in which the stone changes from accidental lightness to heaviness is one and continuous, as when iron moves (*i. e.* changes) from heat to coldness. Therefore the stone will not be able to remain at rest." (p. 99)

The previous point, as well as the following, are belabored with many arguments. Aristotle is wrong again in his belief that "natural motion is continuously accelerated until the body reaches its proper place, but also that, if the motion could continue without limit, the weight of the body and the speed of its motion would be increased without limit." (p. 100) This is not so. To begin with, a light object in falling moves slowly at first, then "maintains a uniform motion." This is so, because like heavy objects, they start with an impressed upward force which is small in light bodies, larger in heavy ones. This force is used up quickly in the light ones, and they therefore attain uniform motion sooner than the heavy ones. Heavy bodies reach uniform motion much later, since they have more lightness to overcome. Being heavier, they move more quickly and fall a greater distance. Since not many really high places are available, "a stone let fall merely from the height of a tower", will not "be observed to be accelerated all the way to the ground", the distance being too short to use up its lightness. "Reason and experience" prove this to be so. Long enough distances would prove that they too attain a uniform, terminal velocity, which Galileo is later to establish on sound logic. If, as Aristotle believes, speed of fall accelerates indefinitely, then the weight should increase indefinitely, which is impossible, and "hard to understand for those who are experienced in mathematics." (p. 102) This he proves by assuming that "the slowness of the motion (upward force) can be continually diminished (with consequent increase of the speed), and yet never be completely destroyed."

A rather gnarled task is to prove why "indeed--and this surely seems remarkable--lighter bodies will fall more swiftly than heavier ones at the beginning of their motion." (p. 105) Aristotle, Averroës and others are wrong in believing that this is due to the fact that light bodies have much air in them, since velocity of natural motion is due only to weight, wherever that comes from. True, "wood moves more swiftly than lead in the beginning of its motion; but a little later the motion of the lead is so accelerated that it leaves the wood behind it. And if they are both let fall from a high tower, the lead moves far out in front. This is something I have often tested." (107)

These results can easily be explained: "Oh, how readily are true explanations derived from true principles!" And the explanation is that since falling bodies "begin their motion from a state of rest...with an impressed force in the opposite direction equal to their weight, then the bodies that are heavier will begin their motion charged with a greater contrary force." They are thus slower at the start. What is implied here is that when a body rests upon the table or lies on one's open hand, it is acted upon by an upward force, equal to its respective weight. Similarly when one "throws two objects, one a piece of wood and the other a piece of iron (or lead), straight upward," the heavy object will rise higher. Clearly, "the motive force inheres more strongly in the iron and is preserved there for a longer time than in the wood." (107) A pendulum made of either of two such balls will show that the one with the lead ball will swing longer than the other. This is so, because "it is clear that in all cases that all contrary qualities are preserved longer, the heavier, denser and more opposed to these qualities is the material on which they have been impressed." (108) Employing here again the heat analogy, Galileo says: "If wood and lead are heated so they are both equally hot to begin with, the heat will still be preserved longer in the lead, even though the greater coldness of the lead offers more opposition to heat than does the lesser coldness of the wood."

In the last chapter Galileo is again led astray into another false alley. With clever, typically Aristotelian and scholastic sophistication, he proves what may seem, he says, the opposite of what he had previously demonstrated. He had shown before with clever geometric proof, that "the same heavy body will descend vertically with greater force than on an inclined plane in proportion as the length of the descent on the incline is greater than the vertical fall." (65) This means that "the more acute the angle that the (inclined) plane, over which motion takes place, makes with the horizon, the more easily will a heavy body be able to be projected up that plane." (110) But now he sets out to prove, forgetting inclined planes for the moment, that bodies fired from a a cannon "will move over a longer path in the same straight line, according as the line of motion makes less acute angles with the horizon," and is closer to the vertical. The more a body opposes the blow that strikes it, the more impressed force it receives in return. To oppose the blow a body is about to receive, it has to be in motion, as experience proves. This is so, because "when a body at rest is struck with a great force, it moves before the entire force is impressed on it." When a body moves in the direction opposite to the blow, it catches all the force to be impressed on it; the heavier the body, the fuller is its reception of that force.

If the ball goes upward at an angle along a straight line, [bodies thrown up or at an angle were supposed to move along a straight line, then bend and move downward] it will turn downward more readily, the larger the angle with the horizontal. (Figure 12. 5) At a small angle, "the body can change over to the (new) motion (*i. e.* downward) without the complete disappearance of the impelling force." When the body goes straight up, it will not start moving down until all the impetus is used up; hence it will go higher.

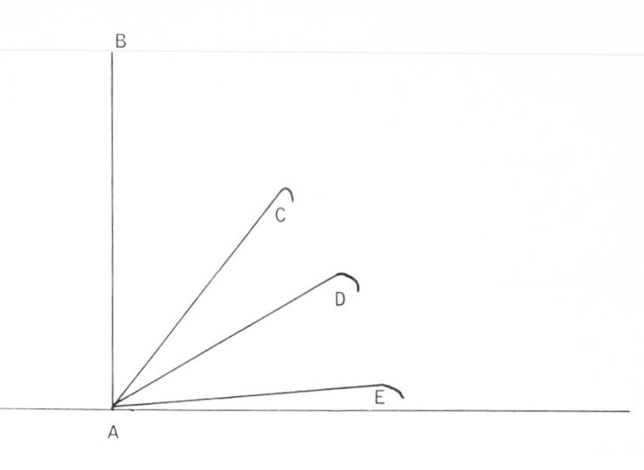

Figure 12.5

An examination of Galileo's reasoning in his De Motu, composed at Pisa where he presumably dropped the famous two balls from the Leaning Tower, is of the greatest moment to the understanding of science in the making, or science in the thinking. Observe, to begin with, the evidence for our repeated assertion that it is the height of folly to blame Aristotle or the Church for slow scientific progress in the Middle Ages. It was neither Aristotle that stopped it, nor was progress slow. No better evidence could conceivably be available for our statement that if a given theory maintained itself for almost twenty centuries, as did the Aristotelian theory of motion, (340 B. C. to 1640 A. D.), then one can only conclude that such a theory possessed intrinsically an equivalent amount of difficulty. Obviously, the theory of motion was crammed with insuperable difficulties, insuperable, that is, until the years of Galileo's old age, when he composed his *Discourses Concerning Two New Sciences* (1638). It is in this work that he finds the correct, experimentally verified, and conceptually lucid notion of uniform acceleration, distance traversed under its reign, average and instantaneous velocities, force, gravity, uniform motion in a right line, inertia, the role of the pendulum in stimulating thought about force, momentum, and gravity and a few further ideas. These were not all elaborated by him, but were singled out in suggestive outline. Many of the ideas he employs, clarifies and renders into mathematical workability, had in part or in total been worked upon by several medieval predecessors with whom he was no doubt acquainted. It was Galileo, nonetheless, who singlehandedly exploited and clarified the available ideas to produce a composite that laid the foundation for the effective modern science of motion.

He is fully aware of it in the masterpiece of his maturest years, the *Discourses.* (translated as *Dialogues Concerning Two New Sciences* by Henry

Crew and Alfonso De Salvio. Northwestern University, 1946) He begins the Third Day with: "My purpose is to set forth a very new science dealing with a very ancient subject. There is, in nature, perhaps nothing older than motion, concerning which the books written by philosophers are neither few nor small; nevertheless I have discovered by experiment some properties of it which are worth knowing and which have not hitherto been either observed or demonstrated. Some superficial observations have been made... So far as I know, no one had yet pointed out that the distances traversed during equal intervals of time, by a body falling from rest, stand to one another in the same ratio as the odd numbers beginning with unity." (p. 147) The rest is history.

Very little of the beauty and clarity he achieves in this work can be discerned in his De Motu. Galileo's skill in logic is there, but it is no different from that displayed by the usual, brilliant, Aristotelian scholar of the times. Galileo's basic assumptions are still largely medieval, and his approach is almost entirely in that spirit. His persistent disagreement with Aristotle is significant. From one point of vantage it is no different from the usual scholastic procedure of exercising one's mental powers by disagreeing with the master. But there is more to that in Galileo's disagreement. It is obvious that he has abstracted the concept of force, or energy, it is impossible to tell which, and that he shows general displeasure at the mode of approach adopted in Aristotelian physics, judging by the frequency with which he cites Archimedes and clearly honors him far above Aristotle in all relevant matters. This alone would show that Galileo had seen a new light. A new germ had found its way into his system and rendered his mind restless with disaffection and search, so that if agile and creative enough, it may well strike out on a new road. And Galileo's mind proved itself in possession of all that was required for finding that essential opening that was destined to lead him and many others out of the tormenting dilemma they were in. He and others before him, knew well enough that the Aristotelian scheme was unsatisfactory. Quite a few new ideas had been advanced, and Galileo employs them as if they were original with him, although they were not so. His rebellion and his frequently needless sharpnesses are personal. Original with him are his clever explanations. In his De Motu they are often no more reasonable than the ones he attacks so harshly. Do all passionate controversies appear so, in perspective?

Yet, the moral is inescapable. If a mind such as Galileo's can be seen to wrestle so pathetically with these problems, frequently to contradict himself, and generally speaking, have his ideas struggle like a mighty creature trapped in a hopeless net, there is only one conclusion to be drawn from it all, and that is, that the entire subject was superhumanly difficult even for the greatest minds. And yet, some decades later, this same Galileo came through with answers to most of the issues that baffled him in his De Motu, answers which made progress not only possible, but inevitable. As if to further stress the difficulties, it should be noted that even in his great final account, his *Dialogues Concerning Two New Sciences* of 1638, Galileo points out (*ibid.* p. 160-1) that he too had believed for many years that a falling body acquired velocities that increased with distance traversed. He soon came to realize this was wrong, and that velocity varied directly with time of fall. As Clagett notes, in a letter to Sarpi in 1604, 15 years after composing the De Motu,

Galileo still maintained the erroneous view, although he had already discovered the contradictory principle-that the distance was directly proportional to time squared. (*Science of Mechanics in the Middle Ages.* p. 580) Such then is the nature of progress. The mind struggles in the quest for new ideas but must of necessity work with quite a number of old ones as its foundation, scaffold, and brick and mortar. New ones do emerge in some minds, and they come slowly, one at a time. The mind at work may not at all see the contradiction which stands out so glaringly for us. The term contradiction may merely be an outsider's notion, not the insider's, and as such, apparently not even communicable.

3. The Revolution Galileo Wrought

We are now in a position to evaluate the two major revolutions which have marked the path of science so far, the Aristotelian, and the Galilean, or early modern. Although it would seem we limit ourselves to physical sciences, it will be clear, it is hoped, that the conclusions have universal application to the human mind at work in the pursuit of scientific knowledge generally.

Aristotelian physics was not the primitive chaos which served as a starting point for creation. It was in itself a tremendous achievement in that it performed nobly and beautifully what a scientific theory should perform. It unified and coordinated related phenomena in the field of nature, it postulated the necessary concepts, and harmonized them with observed data, it created an overall model for loose facts, which without it would be meaningless to the observer. By erecting a consistent and complex structure of concepts and hypotheses, it stimulated both observation and criticism, leading to thought and further testing of data. The Aristotelian achievement stands out most impressively if we compare it to the rich but scattered crop of ideas and philosophies of nature expounded by many of his predecessors, all of whom were shining meteors on the Greek firmament of science, yet essentially serving only as fertilizers or forerunners of Aristotle's great synthesis.

And now let us look closely at the general features of Aristotle's method, of the characteristic mode of his approach to his material and to the task he set for himself. Aristotelian physics was basically direct, unsophisticated experience. The medieval division of philosophy into two camps, realism and nominalism, was both sound and perceptive. Plato stood for realism, which meant at the time that only by abstraction is mankind in a position to comprehend reality. Only generalized ideas truly represent objects, since experience, which deals with the endless diversity of individuality, is misleading. The very nature of diversity and the vicissitudes of chance make it so. You may encounter round and square tables, three and six-legged ones, broken and wobbly ones, and carefully note the qualities of each and adjust your behavior to the demands each makes upon you. But thinking about the table, its function in the house, its identity as a marketable item, its production and sale, and the like, cannot proceed to advantage until the idea correctly representing that object in general, has been fashioned in the mind and duly catalogued. That idea is the true working reality, and all individual mishaps, fancies, accidents and variants, can occur as they may without affecting the hard-won true reality, the idea of the table.

The school of Aristotle took the opposite view. Aristotle stood for realism directly understood through sensory intervention, an attitude called nominalism, in contradistinction to Platonism. It was based on experience, on immediacy, on verifiable phenomenalism, on abstention from wandering into the treacherous morasses of the expanses of the mind with its labyrinthine alleys and the imaginative allure of fancy lurking in each one of them. Hence Aristotelianism stood for verifiable science, for facts, for hard-won knowledge based on specific, communicable and verifiable experience. Platonism stood for abstract philosophizing, romantic philosophic visions, the unsoiled beauty of mathematics, the ideal society, and even pure religion, poetry and mysticism, rendered philosophically presentable in appropriate decor.

Plato truly loved the mathematical approach to science, while Aristotle sincerely distrusted it. As Koyré points out in his "Galileo and Plato," (*ibid.* 147-175) in which this point was originally developed, Galileo after his return to Pisa as professor, must have been fully aware of the book on Plato and Aristotle issued by his friend and colleague, Jacopo Mazzoni, in which is written: "It is well known that Plato believed that mathematics was quite particularly appropriate for physical investigations, which was the reason why he himself had many times recourse to it for the explanation of physical mysteries. But Aristotle held a quite different view and he explained the errors of Plato by his too great attachment to mathematics." Which must not be interpreted to mean that Aristotle had no regard for mathematics. He merely did not think that it was relevant to the problems of physics as he envisioned them, as they manifested themselves in nature. There are people today, for example, who hold mathematics in high regard but do not believe that psychological problems of love, complexes, loyalty, ethics, repressions or hope, can be handled by mathematics, or even by statistics. They may think that the approach should be through thought, comprehension, feeling, keener observation, more detailed self-analysis, and better reporting. Aristotle's attitude to physics was essentially no different. As Koyré points out, Aristotle would certainly not have objected to a mathematical representation of the motions of the heavenly bodies. These were celestial, perfect, and beyond generation and corruption. But physical events on earth proclaimed to him that the application of mathematical abstraction would only remove the observer from the workings of nature and from the true tasks of a scientist, which is patient adherence to detailed observation, the true description of individual events, of natural phenomena, and of sensory reality. Astronomy can well make use of geometrization and can in fact not do without it. Physics demands the very contrary approach, dealing as it does with the very essence of complex and diverse terrestrial doings.

Galileo was one of the few people who broke with nominalism, and being no dedicated Platonist but a devoted student of mechanics, realized the need for breaking the bonds of servitude to the immediacy of sense perceptions, the tyranny of direct experiences which nominalism demanded. To begin with, the nominalists' approach to nature was never really quite what they claimed it to be. That approach invariably required quite a few concepts, abstractions and mathematical operations. This is best demonstrated by Aristotle's book on *Physics* which is full of abstract considerations, argumentations and to us clearly pointless and irrelevant Quixotian flourishes. Although Aristotle's base was orthodoxly experiential, he could, as a scientist, no more than any other thinking being, avoid singling out problems and relationships beyond the sense-data. The scientist must go beyond the apparent and the felt, and into the realm of speculation. But fate willed it that Aristotle's axioms and concepts did not permit fruitful advances.

Galileo, on the other hand, succeeded in selecting some bold and novel abstractions which Aristotelianism feared and avoided, and in its experiential and consistent scheme of things, believed to see no real need for. Others had tried Galileo's approach but somehow failed to bring it to fruition. Galileo used the terms and tricks of these pioneering predecessors of his, consciously or unconsciously, struggled and agrued, but somehow in the end emerged victorious. Some ideas which he hit upon, he clarified with complete success; others, such as force, inertia, and gravitational action, remained incomplete but spiked with germinating powers, so that they could hardly be kept from sprouting.

Thus, in a manner of speaking, Plato won the day, although Aristotle was not completely discarded. Reality was still honored; sensory, direct, experiential, observational reality remained enthroned as the final authority, but not quite in Aristotle's initial sense of experiences. This was essentially the revolution Galileo wrought. Galileo was fully conscious of the conflict and alludes to the Plato versus Aristotle dichotomy on several occasions in his Discourses, allying himself explicitly with Platonism. (*Ibid.* p. 172) He spurred the science of mechanics to great heights and to great activity in the laboratory, in which nature was manipulated with skill and cunning so as to display many of her aspects, charms and wrinkles to the avid senses of her skilled and anxious observers.

We may extend the same concept of revolution to the Copernican theory. It was the practical man with trust in direct experience, the Aristotelian, who opposed the Copernican speculation that demanded of its sympathizers considerable imagination, faith, and a penchant for gambling with the abstract and unreal. Aristotle would no more surrender to this kind of logic than he surrendered to the atoms prancing in their void under the baton of Leucippus and Democritus, later dramatized in the heavy-footed yet in lissome poetry of Lucretius', *On The Nature of Things.* No sensible nominalist could respect these impish atomic figments, any more than he could respect the topsy turvy unseen and unverifiable rotation and revolution of the earth. But here again Plato won out, and the man of common sense took a bitter defeat. For consolation he could note that mathematical abstraction ruled more or less only as a constitutional monarch, subject to experimental suffrage. The court of last appeal was still experimentation, perhaps not as direct as in kinematics and dynamics, but the best under the circumstances. After all, astronomy was not as ready to hand as were colliding balls, falling objects, inclined planes, pistons, vector forces, and engines.

The term revolution is merely a euphemism. There was historic continuity, but there were crucial turning points as well. The same is true in any natural process. In geology, the battle over uniformitarianism and catastrophism led to the same kind of compromise. The process of continuity in no way excludes occasional catastrophies, which are events of long periodic cyclicity, but comprise part of the process of continuity at the same time.

Works Cited in Text

Agricola, Georgius. *De Re Metallica,* London,1912, Dover, N. Y., 1950.
Aristophanes. *The Clouds,* Oxford University Press, 1928.
Aristotle. *Metaphysics, Meteorology, On the Heavens, On the Soul, Politics,* Loeb Classical Library, Harvard University Press.
Aristotle. *History of Animals,* Oxford University Press, 1910.
Aristotle. *Physics,* Oxford University Press, 1910.
Athenaeus. *The Deipnosophists,* Loeb Classical Library, Harvard University Press, 7 vols.
von Basserman-Jordan, E. *Die Geschichte der Zeitmessung und der Uhren,* Berlin, 1920.
The *Bible.*
Brehaut, Ernest. *Isidore of Seville*, New York, 1912.
Caesar, C. Julius. *The Gallic Campaigns*, by Sidney G. Brady, Harrisburg, Pa., 1963.
Calley, E. R. and Richards, J. F. C. Theophrastus' *On Stones,* Ohio State University, Columbus, 1965.
Cassirer, Ernest. Galileo's Platonism, in *Essays in Homage to George Sarton,* New York, 1944.
Chaucer, Geoffrey. *Complete Works.*
Cicero. *On the Commonwealth,* University of Ohio Press, Columbus, Ohio, 1929.
Cicero. *On the Nature of the Gods,* University of Chicago Press, Chicago, Ill., 1950.
Clagett, Marshall. *The Science of Mechanics in the Middle Ages,* University of Wisconsin Press, Madison, Wisc., 1959.
Cohen, M. R. and I. E. Drabkin. *Source Book in Greek Science,* New York, 1948.
Coon, Carleton S. *The Story of Man,* New York, 1962.
Copernicus. *On the Revolution of the Heavenly Spheres,* Great Books Vol. XVI, Encyclopedia Britannica, Chicago,1952.
Crombie, A. C. *Medieval and Early Modern Science,* Garden City, New York, 1959, 2 vols.
Diels, H. *Antike Technik,* Leipzig und Berlin, 1924.
Dio Cassius. *Roman History,* 9 vols., Loeb Classical Library, Harvard University Press.
Diodorus of Sicily. *History,* Loeb Classical Library, Harvard University Press, 12 vols.
Drachmann, A. G. *Ktesibios, Philon, and Heron, A Study in Ancient Pneumatics,* Copenhagen, 1948.

Drachmann, A. G. *The Mechanical Technology of Greek and Roman Antiquity,* University of Wisconsin Press, Madison, Wis., 1963.
Dreyer, J. L. E. *A History of Astronomy, Planetary Systems,* Cambridge, 1953.
Dreyer, J. L. E. *Tycho Brahe,* New York, 1963.
Euclid. *Elements of Geometry,* 3 vols., Dover, N. Y.
Farrington, Benjamin. *Greek Science,* Pelican Books, 1949, 2 vols.
Fisher, L. and O. M. Miller. *World Maps and Globes,* New York, 1944.
Forbes, R. J. *Studies in Ancient Technology,* Leiden, 1964, 9 vols.
Frontinus, Sextus Julius. *The Aqueducts of Ancient Rome,* Loeb Classical Library, London, 1925.
Galen. *On the Natural Faculties,* Loeb Classical Library, Harvard University Press.
Galileo Galilei. *Dialogues Concerning Two New Sciences,* tr. by Henry Crew and Alfonso De Salvio, Northwestern University, 1946.
Galileo Galilei. *On Motion (De Motu),* University of Wisconsin Press, Madison, Wis., 1960.
Gellius, Aulus. *Attic Nights,* New York, 1928, 3 vols.
Gershenson, D. E. and D. A. Greenberg. *Anaxgoras and the Birth of the Scientific Method,* New York, 1964.
Gilbert, William. *On the Loadstone,* tr. P. Fleury Mottelay, New York, 1892.
Goodfield, June. "The Tunnel of Eupalinus," *Scientific American,* June, 1964, vol. 210.
Graubard, Mark. *Astrology's Demise,* Osiris, 1958, Vol. XIII, 226.
Heath, Sir Thomas. *Aristarchus of Samoa,* Oxford, 1913.
Heath, Sir Thomas. *Greek Astronomy,* London, 1932.
Heath, Sir Thomas. *The Works of Archimedes,* Dover Publications, New York.
Hero of Alexandria. *Pneumatics,* Bennet Woodcroft, Ed., London, 1851.
Herodotus. *The History of Herodotus,* New York, 1944.
Hesiod. *Work and Days,* London, 1932.
Hippocrates. *Collected Works,* Loeb Classical Library, Harvard University Press, 4 vols.
Isadore of Seville. *Traite' de la Nature,* Jacques Fontaine, ed., Bordeaux, 1960.
Jowett, B. *The Dialogues of Plato,* 2 vols., New York, 1937.
Kepler, Johann. *Gesammelte Werke,* Max Caspar, ed., Walther van Dyck, Munich,1937-1958, 18 vols.
Kirby, R. S., S. Withington, A. B. Darling and F. G. Kilgsur. *Engineering in History,* New York, 1956.
Koestler, Arthur. *The Sleepwalkers,* New York, 1959.
The *Koran.*
Koyré, Alexandre. *Etudes galilèennes*, 3 vols, Paris, 1939-40.
Koyré, Alexandre. *La Rèvolution Astronomique,* Paris, 1961.
Koyré, Alexandre. *Galileo and Plato in The Roots of Modern Science,* P. P. Wiener and A. Noland, Eds., New York, 1957.
Kubitschek, Wilhelm. *Grundriss der Antiken Zeitrechnung,* München, 1928.
Kuhn, Thomas S. *The Copernican Revolution,* Harvard University Press, 1923.
Langdon, S. *The Babylonian Epic of Creation,* Oxford University Press, 1923.
Langdon, S. *Tammuz and Ishtar,* Oxford, 1914.

Luckenbill, D. D. *Ancient Records of Assyria,* Chicago, 1926, 2 vols.
Lucretius. *Of the Nature of Things (De Natura Rerum),* tr. Wm. Ellery Leonard, New York, 1921.
Lucretius. *The Nature of the Universe,* Penguin Classics, Baltimore, Md., 1951.
Mach, E. *The Principles of Physical Optics,* Dover, New York.
McKeon, Richard, ed. *The Basic Works of Aristotle,* New York, 1941.
Moody, E. A. *Galileo and Avempace in Roots of Scientific Thought,* P. P. Wiener & A. Noland, eds., New York, 1957.
Moody, E. A. *Ockham and the Aegidius of Rome,* Franciscan Studies, Vol. 9, 1949.
Morison, Samuel Eliot. *Admiral of the Ocean Sea,* Time Edition, 2 vols.
Neugebauer, Otto E. *The Exact Sciences in Antiquity,* Harper Torchbook, 1962.
Neugebauer, Otto E. *Studies in the History of Science,* University of Pennsylvania Press, Philadelphia, 1941.
Nilsson, Martin P. *Primitive Time-Reckoning,* Lund, 1920.
Palter, R. M., ed. *Toward Modern Science,* 2 vols., New York, 1961.
Pannekoek, A. *A History of Astronomy,* New York, 1961.
Parker, R. A. and W. H. Dubberstein. *Babylonian Chronology,* Brown University Press, 1956.
Parker, Richard A. *The Calendars of Ancient Egypt,* University of Chicago Press, 1950.
Plato. *The Dialogues,* tr. by B. Jowett, New York, 1937, 2 vols.
Pliny. *Natural History,* Loeb Classical Library, Harvard University Press, 10 vols.
Plutarch. *The Lives of the Noble Grecians and Romans,* Loeb Classical Library, Harvard University Press, 11 vols.
Plutarch. *Moralia,* Loeb Classical Library, Harvard University Press, 12 vols.
Ptolemy. *The Almagest,* Encyclopedia Britannica, Great Books, vol. 16.
Ptolemy. *Tetrabiblos,* Loeb Classical Library, Harvard University Press, Cambridge, Mass.
Rawlinson, G. *The History of Herodotus,* New York, 1928, 1944.
Rosen, Edward. *Three Copernican Treatises,* Columbia University Press, New York, 1939.
Sayce, A. H. *Lectures on the Origin and Growth of Religion,* London, 1909.
Science. Journal of the American Association for the Advancement of Science.
Seneca. *Natural Questions, Physical Science in the Time of Nero,* London, 1910.
Sextus Empiricus. *Against the Professors,* Works, vol. IV, Loeb Classical Library, Harvard University Press.
Singer, Charles, et al., ed. *History of Technology,* Oxford University Press, 1958, 5 vols.
Small, Robert. *An Account of the Astronomical Discoveries of Kepler,* University of Wisconsin Press, Madison, 1963.
Stevenson, E. L. (trans.). *The Geography of Claudius Ptolemy,* New York, 1932.
Strabo. *The Geography of Strabo,* translated by H. L. Jones, Loeb Classical Library, Harvard University Press, 8 vols.
Taylor, Lloyd W. *Physics, The Pioneer Science,* New York, 1941.

Thompson, E. A. *A Roman Reformer and Inventor,* Oxford, 1952.
Thompson, R. Campbell. *The Reports of the Magicians and Astrologers of Nineveh and Babylon,* London, 1900, 2 vols.
Thorndike, Lynn. *The Sphere of Sacrobosco and its Commentators,* Chicago University Press, 1949.
Treatise on the Astrolabe, Oxford, Clarendon Press, 1894-1900, vol. 3.
Vallentin, Antonina. *Leonardo da Vinci,* New York, 1952.
Vergil, Maro Publius. *The Georgics,* London, 1931.
Vitruvius. *On Architecture,* Loeb Classical Library, Harvard University Press, Cambridge, Mass., 2 vols.
White, Lynn. *Medieval Technology and Social Change,* Oxford University Press, 1962.
Witzel, P. Maurus. *Perlen Sumerischer Poesie,* Fulda, 1925-1930.
Zimmern, Heinrich. *Das Babylonische Neujahrfest,* Leipzig, 1926.

Suggested Readings

Archer, P. *The Christian Calendar and the Gregorian Reform*, Fordham University Press, New York, 1941.

Aristotle. *Of Marvellous Things Heard*, *Mechanical Problems in Aristotle Minor Works*, Harvard University Press, 1955.

Aristotle. *Physica in the Basic Works of Aristotle,* Clarendon Press, Oxford, 1913.

Boll, F. J. and Bezold, C. *Sternglaube und Sterndeutung,* Leipzig, 1931.

Bolton, L. *Time Measurement*, New York, 1924.

Budge, E. A. W. *Babylonian Life and History,* London, 1925.

Bunburg, E. H. *A History of Ancient Geography*, New York, 1959.

Butterfield, H. *The Origins of Modern Science*, Macmillan, New York, 1957.

Carcopino, Jerome. *Daily Life in Ancient Rome*, Yale University Press, New Haven, Conn., 1940.

Cato, Marcus Porcus. *On Agriculture*, and Varro, Marcus Terentius *On Agriculture*, Harvard University Press, Cambridge, Mass., 1934.

Champdor, A. *Babylon*, New York, 1958.

Clagett, Marshall. *Greek Science in Antiquity*, Abelard-Schuman, Inc., New York, 1955.

Columella, Lucius Junius Moderatus. *On Agriculture*, 3 vols. Harvard University Press, Cambridge, Mass., 1941.

Conant, James Bryant. *On Understanding Science*, New Haven, Conn., 1947.

Cramer, F. H. *Astrology in Roman Law and Politics*, Philadelphia, 1952.

Crombie, A. C. *Medieval and Early Modern Science*, Doubleday Anchor Book, 2 vols, Garden City, N.Y., 1959.

De Camp, L. Sprague. *The Ancient Engineers*, Doubleday & Co., Garden City, N.Y.; 1963.

Duhem, P. *Le Systeme du Monde*, Paris, 1910.

Forbes, R. J. and Dijksterhuis. *A History of Science and Technology*, 2 vols., Penguin Books, Baltimore, Md., 1963.

Glanville, S. R. K. (Ed.). *The Legacy of Egypt*, Clarendon Press, Oxford, 1942.

Green, A. R. *Sundials*, Macmillan, New York, 1926.

von Grunebaum, G. E. *Medieval Islam*, University of Chicago Press, Chicago, 1966.

Haskins, C. H. *Studies in the History of Medieval Science*, Cambridge, Mass., 1924.

Heath, T. L. *A History of Greek Mathematics*, Oxford, 1921.

Heiberg, J. L. *Mathematics and Physical Science in Classical Antiquity*, London, 1922.

Henslow, T. G. W. *The Sundial Booke*, London, 1935.
Lloyd, Seton. *Ruined Cities of Iraq*, Oxford University Press and Humphrey Milford, Bombay, 1942-45.
MacNaughton, D. *A Scheme of Egyptian Chronology*, London, 1932.
Montet, Pierre. *Everyday Life in Egypt (in the days of Rameses the Great)*, St. Martin's Press, New York, 1958.
Needham, Joseph, Wang Ling and Price, Derek J. de Solla. *Heavenly Clockwork (The Great Astronomical Clock of Medieval China)*, Cambridge University Press, Cambridge, 1960.
Neuburger, Albert. *The Technical Arts and Sciences of the Ancients*, Macmillan Co. New York, 1930.
Olmstead, A. T. *History of the Persian Empire*, University of Chicago Press, Chicago, 1966.
Panth, Bhola D. *Consider the Calendar*, Columbia University Teachers College, New York, 1944.
Parsons, E. A. *The Alexandrian Library (Glory of Hellenic World)*, Hume Press, London, 1952.
Partington, J. R. *A History of Greek Fire and Gunpowder*, W. Heffer and Sons, Ltd., Cambridge, 1960.
Philip, Alexander. *The Calendar*, Cambridge University Press, Cambridge, 1921.
Price, Derek J. *The Equatorie of the Planetis*, Cambridge University Press, Cambridge, 1955.
Reinhardt, K. *Posidonius*, München, 1921.
Sambursky, S. *The Physical World of the Greeks*, London, 1956.
Sarton, George. *A History of Science*, 2 vols, Harvard University Press, Cambridge, Mass., 1952-59.
Sarton, George. *Introduction to the History of Science*, 3 vols, Williams and Wilkins Co., Baltimore, Md., 1927-48.
Stahl, William H. *Roman Science*, University of Wisconsin Press, Madison, 1962.
Steindorff, G. and Seele, K. C. *When Egypt Ruled the East*, University of Chicago Press, Chicago, 1966.
Thorndike, Lynn. *History of Magic and Experimental Science*, 8 vols, Columbia University Press, New York, 1928-58.
Usher, A. P. *A History of Mechanical Inventions*, Beacon Press, Boston, 1954.
Waerden, B. L. van der. *Science Awakening*, Tr. by A. Dresden, Groningen, 1954.
Watkins, H. *Time Counts: The Story of the Calendar*, N. Spearman, London, 1954.
Whittaker, T. *Macrobius; or Philosophy, Science and Letters in the Year 400*, Cambridge, 1923.
Wilson, John A. *The Ancient Culture of Egypt*, University of Chicago Press, Chicago, 1951.
Winter, H. J. J. *Eastern Science (An Outline of its Scope and Contribution)*, John Murray, London, 1952.
Zinner, E. *Die Ältesten Räderuhren*, Bamberg, 1939.

Index

DATE DUE